S0-AJL-733

Previously published volumes and issues of **Chronica Botanica:—**

Vols. 1–3 (1935–1937): **"An Annual Record of Pure and Applied Botany"** (an **International Annual Census of Plant Science Research**), each volume $10.50 (or, if available, bound in buckram, $12.00).

Vols. 4–7 (1938–1943): **"International Plant Science Newsmagazine,"** each volume $10.50:—

Vol. 4 (1938): Numbers 1, 2, 3, 4/5, & 6. — Vol. 5 (1939): Numbers 1, 2/3, & 4/6. — Vol. 6 (1940–1941): Numbers 1, 2, 3, 4, 5, 6, 7, 8, 9, 10, 11, 12, 13, 14, 15, 16, 17/18, & 19/20. — Vol. 7 (1942–1943): Numbers 1, 2, 3, 4, 5, 6, 7, & 8. — Separate issues of Vols. 4–7 are often no longer available (mainly as a result of losses in transit during World War II).

Vol. 8 seq. (1944–): **"International Collection of Studies in the Method and History of Biology and Agriculture,"** each volume on a standing order basis, *i.e.*, to members of the INT. PLANT SCIENCE PUBLICATIONS SOCIETY, $7.50:—

Vol. 8, No. 1 (1944): C. A. BROWNE: **Source Book of Agricultural Chemistry,** $6.00

Vol. 8, No. 2 (1944): C. S. RAFINESQUE: **A Life of Travels** (1836) — Foreword by E. D. MERRILL and Critical Index by F. W. PENNELL, $2.50

Vol. 8, No. 3 (1944): C. A. BROWNE: **Thomas Jefferson and the Scientific Trends of his Time,** $1.25

Vol. 8, No. 4 (1944): F. VERDOORN: **On the Aims and Methods of Biological History and Biography, with some notes . . . Index Botanicorum,** *separate copies no longer available*

Vol. 9, No. 1 (1945): H. A. JACK: **Biological Field Stations of the World,** $2.50

Vol. 9, No. 2/3 (1945): F. VERDOORN (ed.): **Chronica Botanica Calendar,** *separate copies no longer available*

Vol. 9, No. 4 (1945): W. B. CANNON and R. M. FIELD: **International Relations in Science — A Review of their Aims and Methods in the Past and in the Future,** *separate copies no longer available*

Vol. 9, No. 5/6 (1945): W. L. HOWARD: **Luther Burbank — A Victim of Hero Worship,** $3.75

Vol. 10, No. 1 (1946): A. DE SAINT-HILAIRE: **Esquisse de mes Voyages au Brésil et Paraguay** (1824) — with an introductory essay by A. E. JENKINS, $2.00

Vol. 10, No. 2 (1946): A. ARBER: **Goethe's Botany** — with a new transl. of the 'Metamorphosis of Plants' (1790), $2.00

Vol. 10, No. 3/4 (1946): E. D. MERRILL: **Merrilleana — Selected General Writings,** $4.00

Vol. 10, No. 5/6 (1947): D. R. WYMAN: **The Arboretums and Botanical Gardens of North America,** $1.50, *separate copies no longer available*

Vol. 11, No. 1 (1947): H. W. RICKETT: **The Royal Botanical Expedition to New Spain,** $2.50

Vol. 11, No. 2 (1947): V. C. ASMOUS: **Fontes Historiae Botanicae Rossicae,** $1.25

Vol. 11, No. 3 (1947): N. E. STEVENS: **Factors in Botanical Publication and other Essays,** $2.00

Vol. 11, No. 4 (1948): E. E. DETURK (ed.): **Freedom from Want — A Survey of the Possibilities of Meeting the World's Food Needs,** $2.00

Vol. 11, No. 5/6 (1949): H. S. REED: **Jan Ingenhousz, Plant Physiologist — with a History of the Discovery of Photosynthesis,** $3.00

Volume 11 was supplemented by **Biologia I** (a folio, four-page newsletter, six issues, still available at $1.25) which should be bound in a pocket in the back of Volume 11 (or of Vol. 11/12 if our regular binding cases are used).

Vol. 12, No. 1/2 (1950): J. LANJOUW et al.: **Botanical Nomenclature and Taxonomy — A Symposium,** $2.50

Vol. 12, No. 3 (1950): F. W. WENT: **The Earhart Plant Research Laboratory,** $1.00

Vol. 12, No. 4/6 (1951): F. VERDOORN (ed.): **Biologia II,** $4.75

Vol. 13, No. 1/6 (1951): N. I. VAVILOV: **The Origin, Variation, Immunity and Breeding of Cultivated Plants,** transl. by K. S. CHESTER, $7.50

Vol. 14, No. 1/2 (1951): J. E. GRAUSTEIN: **Nuttall's Travels into the Old Northwest** (1810), $3.00

Vol. 14, No. 3/4 (1953): G. H. M. LAWRENCE et al.: **Plant Genera, their Nature and Definition — A Symposium** — with an introd. on generic synopses by TH. JUST, $2.00

Vol. 14, No. 5/6 (1954): E. D. MERRILL: **The Botany of Cook's Voyage and its unexpected Significance in relation to Anthropology, Biogeography, and History,** *separately available only in a bound trade ed.*, $4.75

Vol. 15 (1954): I. W. BAILEY: **Contributions to Plant Anatomy,** buckram, $7.50

Vol. 16 (1955): T. H. GOODSPEED: **The Genus Nicotiana — Origins, Relationships and Evolution of its Species in the Light of their Distribution, Morphology, and Cytogenetics,** buckram, $12.50

Chronica Botanica, *An International Collection of Studies in the Method and History of Biology and Agriculture, edited by* Frans Verdoorn

• Volume 17 •

The EXPERIMENTAL CONTROL of PLANT GROWTH

The EXPERIMENTAL CONTROL of PLANT GROWTH

With special reference to the Earhart Plant Research Laboratory at the California Institute of Technology

by FRITS W. WENT

Professor of Plant Physiology, California Institute of Technology

With contributions by W. C. ASHBY, L. T. EVANS, A. W. GALSTON, H. HELLMERS, and WM. M. HIESEY

1957

WALTHAM, MASS., U.S.A.

Published by the Chronica Botanica Company

LIBRARY OF CONGRESS CATALOG CARD NUMBER: 57-10941

Authorized Agents:—

New York 3, N. Y. (U.S.A.): Hafner Publishing Co.—31 East 10th Street

San Francisco, Calif. (U.S.A.): J. W. Stacey, Inc.—551 Market Street

Toronto (Canada): Co-operative Book Centre of Canada, Ltd.—146 Wellington Street West

Mexico, D.F. (Mexico): Axel Moriel Sucrs.—San Juan de Letran 24–116; Ap. 2762

Caracas (Venezuela): Suma, S.A.—Sabana Grande, 102, "El Recreo"

Bogotá (Colombia): Libreria Buchholz.—Avenida Jimenez de Quesada

Lima (Peru): Libreria Internacional del Peru.—Casa Matriz. Boza 879; Casilla 1417

Santiago (Chile): Libreria Ivens.—Calle Moneda 822; Casilla 205

Rio de Janeiro (Brazil): Livraria Kosmos.—Rua do Rosario, 135–137; Caixa Postal 3481

São Paulo (Brazil): Livraria Civilização Brasileira.—Rua 15 de Novembro, 144

Buenos Aires (Argentina): Acme Agency, Soc. de Resp. Ltda.—Suipacha 58; Casilla de Correo 1136

London, W.C. 2 (England): Wm. Dawson and Sons, Ltd.—Cannon House, Macklin Street.—*Chief Agents for the British Commonwealth*

London, W. 1 (England): Wheldon & Wesley Ltd.—83/84 Berwick Street

Groningen (the Netherlands): N.V. Erven P. Noordhoff.—*Chief Agents for Continental Europe*

Stockholm (Sweden): Almqvist & Wiksell Bookstore.—Gamla Brogatan 26

Uppsala (Sweden): A.-B. Lundequistska Bokhandeln.—Drottninggatan 2

Copenhagen K (Denmark): Store Nordiske Videnskabsboghandel.—Rømersgade 27

Paris VI (France): Librairie P. Raymann & Cie.—17, Rue de Tournon

Hamburg 11 (Germany): Buch- und Zeitschriften-Union mbH.—Brauerstrasse 27

Leipzig, C 1 (Germany): Deutscher Buch-Export und -Import GmbH. (Koehler & Volckmar).

Berlin-Charlottenburg 2 (Germany): R. Friedländer & Sohn.—Knesebeckstrasse 15

Basel (Switzerland): Wepf & Co., Verlag.—Eisengasse 5

Wien I (Austria): Gerold & Co.—Graben 31

Moscow (U.S.S.R.): Mezhdunarodnaja Kniga.—Kuznetski Most 18

Torino (Italy): Rosenberg & Sellier.—Via Andrea Doria, 14

Madrid (Spain): Libreria J. Villegas.—Preciados, 33

Lisbon (Portugal): Livraria Sá da Costa.—Rua Garrett, 100–102

Athens (Greece): Messrs. Eleftheroudakis.—Constitution Square

Istanbul (Turkey): Librairie Hachette.—469 Istiklal Caddesi, Beyoglu

Ankara (Turkey): Librairie Hachette.—38–40 Bankalar Caddesi

Jerusalem (Israel): Messrs. Ludwig Mayer.—P.O. Box 1174

Cairo (Egypt): Lehnert & Landrock Succ.—44 Sherif Pasha Street; P.O. Box 1013

Cape Town (South Africa): Juta & Company, Ltd.—P.O. Box 30

Johannesburg (South Africa): Juta & Co. Ltd.—P.O. Box 1010

Tokyo (Japan): Maruzen Company, Ltd.—6 Tori-Nichome Nihonbashi; P.O. Box 605 Central

Taipei, Taiwan (China): The Southeast Book Company.—105 Po Ai Road

Agra (India): Banwari Lal Jain.—Moti Katra.—*Chief Agents for India*

New Delhi 1 (India): Oxford Book & Stationery Co.—Scindia House

Calcutta 16 (India): Oxford Book & Stationery Co.—17 Park Street

Bombay 7 (India): Popular Book Depot (Regd.).—Lamington Road

Karachi (Pakistan): Pak American Commercial, Inc.—Elphinstone Street, Saddar

Manila (Philippines): Philippine Education Co., Inc.—1104 Castillejos, Quiapo; P.O. Box 620

Djakarta (Indonesia): G. Kolff and Co.—Djalan Nusantara 13

Melbourne, C. 1 (Australia): N. H. Seward Pty., Ltd.—457 Bourke Street

Sydney (Australia): Angus & Robertson, Ltd.—89 Castlereagh Street; P.O. Box 1516 G.P.O.

Wellington (New Zealand): Technical Books, Ltd.—101–103 Vivian Street; P.O. Box 6318

Printed in the United States of America

Designed by Frans Verdoorn

PREFACE

The present book is mainly the story of a large-scale coöperative effort in the plant sciences. Therefore, the authorship only refers to the recording of this effort, and I appreciate the opportunity this preface gives me to thank openly so many persons for the vital part they played in the development and operation of the Clark Greenhouses and the Earhart Plant Research Laboratory, the Controlled Environment Facilities at the California Institute of Technology. Only through their collective efforts these have become a success, while they might have failed because of the lack of previous experience with a large-scale laboratory for environmental research with plants.

The general idea that in experiments with plants the environmental factors should be controlled goes back at least a century, but it was really the knowledge, experience, and intuitive insight of Dr. H. O. Eversole which led to the construction of the first air-conditioned greenhouses at the California Institute of Technology. For the first time, these Clark Greenhouses, the gift of Miss Lucy Mason Clark, enabled an experimental and exact study of climatic effects on mature plants.

The responses of plants in the Clark Greenhouses indicated the feasibility of a complete study of plant climatology, of ecological problems, and of many other subjects, provided an extensive set of greenhouses could be constructed, covering the whole range of growing conditions for plants. I am most grateful to Mr. H. B. Earhart and Dr. Robert A. Millikan for the trust they put in this project, which induced the Earhart Foundation to provide $407,000 for construction costs, and to the California Institute of Technology for underwriting the operating costs of the Earhart Plant Research Laboratory.

No one but myself can appreciate better what architect, engineer, contractor, and construction workers have contributed towards the realization of the ideas now incorporated in the Earhart Laboratory. Mr. Palmer Sabin, architect, Mr. William J. Kaupp, electrical engineer, and foremost, Mr. Arthur J. Hess, mechanical and air-conditioning engineer, designed the building and its complicated machinery. That we could occupy the building within one year after ground was broken is a tribute to the planning and hard work of the contractor, Mr. Ray Gerhart and his crew of workers.

It is impossible to mention all personnel which has made possible the operation of so complicated a research tool as the Earhart Laboratory since July 1949. Exceptions have to be made, in the first place, for Mr. G. P. Keyes, superintendent of the building since its inception. All visiting scientists will remember his kind and effective help in all matters. But his greatest achievement is that the laboratory runs smoothly at all times. The casual observer has no idea how much attention to details this requires and I want to thank Mr. Keyes here publicly for his never-failing devotion. Mr. J. Cunningham, assistant superintendent, is largely responsible for the high standard of the photographic work in the laboratory, as evidenced by the plates at the end of this book. The bookkeeping, which keeps track of all growing space, has become a fine art in the hands of Mr. A. Leeping. Among the gardeners, Mr. A. Miotto particularly should be thanked for his many years of painstaking help. Many of the elegant pieces of apparatus in the laboratory were designed and built by Mr. W. P. Thomson.

In the scientific direction of the Earhart Laboratory I am ably assisted by Dr. H. R. Highkin. His and Mr. Keyes' activities have made it possible for me to be absent from the Laboratory for extended visits to different parts of the world to observe growing conditions of plants in nature.

The maintenance department of the California Institute of Technology has always stood ready to service our equipment, day and night, weekdays, and Sundays. Although the contributions of the personnel of the Electrical and Mechanical Shops may not appear so prominently in the description of the Earhart Laboratory, they are vital, and I want to thank every one of them for their splendid coöperation.

All the preceding acknowledgements only concerned construction and operation of the Earhart Laboratory described in the first part of the book.

As far as the second and third parts of the book are concerned, I have to thank first of all my scientific assistants who have so ably and enthusiastically helped me in the numerous experiments, and who for longer or shorter periods have carried most of the burdens of the work: Mrs. Rachel M. Behnke, Mrs. Selina Bendix, Mrs. Ruth Corbett, Mrs. Marcella C. Juhrèn, Mrs. Helene F. Metzenberg, Miss Lillian Overland, and Miss Evelyn Pinsker.

A very large portion of the results in the laboratory is due to the work of visitors from other institutions who worked for an average of one year in the Earhart Laboratory. A few of them have written up their own research as chapters in this book and I want to thank Dr. W. C. Ashby, Dr. A. W. Galston, Dr. H. Hellmers, Dr. Wm. M. Hiesey, and Dr. Lloyd T. Evans for their contributions. The work of several other visitors has been mentioned at appropriate places, but definitely their contributions have not been given the proper emphasis for which I want to apologize. Many subjects and plants which have been investigated in the Earhart Laboratory are not even mentioned in the text, such as *Taraxacum kok-saghyz* investigated by Dr. W. de Ráfols, or carnations investigated by Dr. S. Monselise, or the extensive work with pines and other trees by Dr. P. Kramer, or the work on *Trifolium subterraneum* by Drs. C. R. Millikan and L. T. Evans. Details of this work are in the course of publication and will appear elsewhere.

Since this book is mainly a record of the operation of and the results obtained in the Clark Greenhouses and the Earhart Plant Research Laboratory, very little related work by others is included, and hardly any pertinent literature references are quoted, since this would have extended the book beyond reasonable limits. This one-sidedness has one advantage, however, in that all reported experimental results were obtained under the same general conditions and with the same degree of control over the environment. I am aware of only one book with a similar scope, in which a review of literature is given; this is R. O. Whyte's *Crop Production and Environment*.

Many friends have read parts or all of the manuscript and have helped in eliminating errors; among them I would like to mention Mr. G. P. Keyes, Mr. A. J. Hess, Dr. A. W. Galston, Dr. K. J. Mitchell, and Dr. L. Ballard. But in connection with the publishing of this book thanks go primarily to Dr. and Mrs. F. Verdoorn who have done so much to make it possible to include so much pictorial and factual material, making this book not only a digest of published articles, but also a record of much unpublished work. I have had much help in the preparation of this book from Mrs. R. M. Behnke and Miss L. Overland. For most of the drawings, I am indebted to Mrs. R. M. Behnke, Mrs. H. F. Metzenberg, Mr. G. P. Keyes, and Mrs. M. C. Juhrèn. The vignettes and head pieces were kindly drawn by Dr. Paul E. Pilet.

Most of the experimental material presented concerns work carried out prior to 1956. Results from 1956 and 1957 were added, only in a few cases, after most of the manuscript had been completed. Then, some changes were made in the laboratory after the completion of the manuscript. Since some of these may be of importance to those concerned with other phytotrons they are mentioned here briefly.

In 1956 the operation of the Earhart Laboratory was interrupted for the whole month of July. Only a limited amount of perennial plants was kept under insect-free conditions in a single greenhouse, but the rest of the building was opened to facilitate a number of major repairs, required after 7 years of uninterrupted operation. During this month the following repairs or improvements were made:

1) The roof and walls of the two Clark Greenhouses were torn down because during 17 years of operation the wooden frame work and rafters had rotted. They were replaced with two aluminum frame greenhouses of the same dimensions, but with glass sides, which are an advantage not only in eliminating shading by the walls but in allowing visitors to look into the greenhouses without having to change clothes. Thus far, none of the panes in the side walls have been broken.

2) The roof gutters of the main greenhouses were rebuilt and made leak-proof. This could never have been done during regular operations for the walls had to dry out for over a week.

3) An additional 75 h.p. compressor and two more chillers to cool the chilled water were installed, relegating the 60 h.p. compressor to stand-by operation. This not only insures uninterrupted operation, but the new compressor has greater capacity and is more efficient, providing sufficient cooling even on the hottest days.

4) The glass panes were all removed from the greenhouse roofs and were cleaned in hydrochloric acid to remove the calcium carbonate which had accumulated during the years.

5) All air-conditioners were overhauled, repainted, re-adjusted, and bearings and shafts replaced with stainless steel ones. This could have been done during the regular operation of the laboratory only by closing one of the greenhouses or light rooms at a time, after letting the machinery dry out for some time. This would have taken a long time, and now all these operations were performed in 31 days, a remarkable feat of organization and work performance.

On August 1, 1956 the whole building was sealed and refumigated and the next day it was in operation again, performing better than ever before.

Spring, 1957

F. W. Went

This book is dedicated to
Miss Lucy Mason Clark
Dr. Henry O. Eversole
and to the memory of
Mr. Harry B. Earhart
and Dr. Robert A. Millikan

Through their vision and support
control over the plant environment became practical
allowing large-scale experimentation.
Without their concerted efforts
the development of phytotrons
of such paramount importance
for the future of the plant sciences
would have been delayed
for a score of years.

The Clark Greenhouses
and the Earhart Plant Research Laboratory
have furnished the contents of this book
and the inspiration to the author.

F. W. WENT, son of Dr. F. A. F. C. WENT, the well-known Dutch professor of Botany at the University of Utrecht, was born in 1903. During his youth he lived next to the Botanical Garden and Botanical Institute of the University, in constant contact with plants and botanists, and this stimulating environment induced him to become a botanist himself. After receiving his Ph.D. degree at the University of Utrecht in 1927, on a thesis describing the role of the growth hormone in the Avena seedling, he went to Java, where he was connected with the famous Botanical Gardens at Buitenzorg (Bogor) for 5 years. In 1933 he went to the California Institute of Technology at Pasadena, where he is Professor of Plant Physiology. During his early years in California he worked on hormonal control of plant growth, as well as on root formation and other auxin-affected phenomena, but his research interests gradually turned to environmental influences on plant growth. The results of over 15 years of work in this field are summarized in the present volume. His other botanical interests lie in the fields of Ecology, especially of the tropical forest and the desert, and Evolution, which developed in the course of rather extensive travels, all over the world. His interests in Botanical Gardens are still evident as a member of the Board of Governors of the Los Angeles State and County Arboretum. He has lectured on his work in different parts of the world (twice as national Sigma Xi lecturer). Honorary doctor at the Université de Paris, Member of the National Academy of Sciences, Correspondent of the Koninklijke Nederlandse Akademie van Wetenschappen, Amsterdam, and of the Académie des Sciences, Paris. Author (with K. V. THIMANN) of *Phytohormones* (New York: Macmillan, 1937).

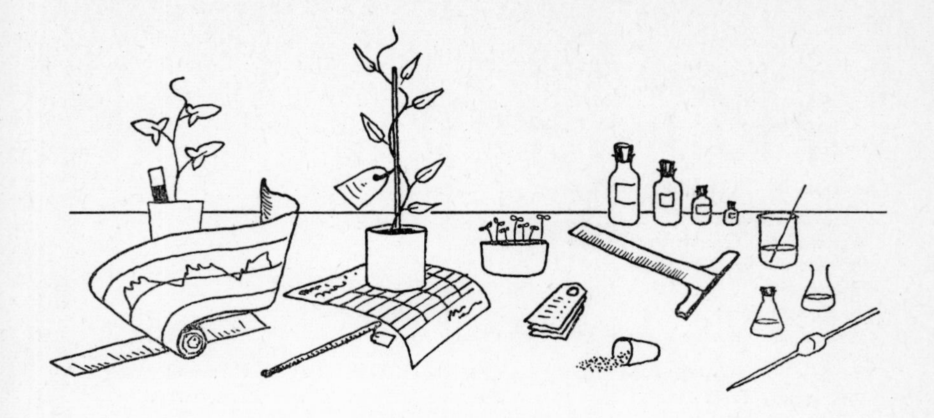

TABLE *of* CONTENTS

Part I: Construction and Operation of the Earhart Plant Research Laboratory:—

Part II: **Climatic Response of Individual Plants:—**

PART I

CONSTRUCTION and OPERATION of the EARHART PLANT RESEARCH LABORATORY

Introduction:— As will become clear from the results obtained, control of the environment is essential if significant results are to be obtained from experimentation with plants. Control of the environment was long recognized as essential in physics and chemistry, where temperature, radiation and other factors have been carefully adjusted in all experiments. When it came to experiments with mature plants, however, botanists have had to work with the uncontrolled aerial surroundings of plants grown in the open or in conventional greenhouses. Control is necessary not only while each experiment is carried out, but also during the raising of the experimental plants. For it is generally accepted that an organism is the product of its genetic constitution and its environment. Therefore, no matter how uniform plants are genotypically, they cannot be phenotypically uniform or reproducible, unless they have developed under strictly uniform conditions.

First the Clark greenhouse, and later the Earhart Plant Research Laboratory were constructed to fulfill the basic requirements of a reproducible environment in the growth of mature plants. Where such environmental factors as pests, diseases, soil and nutrition are being studied in great detail each has its own well-established methodology. The study of the effect of climate alone on plants is much less developed because control of the aerial surroundings presents great difficulties. The Earhart Plant Research Laboratory was designed to control climatic factors individually and jointly, enabling the culture of reproducible experimental material and also establishing a methodology for plant climatology. The complete control over growing conditions makes the laboratory also useful for the solution of many other botanical problems, where uniformity and environmental control are essential.

In the Earhart Plant Research Laboratory flexibility in the number of experimental conditions that can be administered is achieved with twenty separate air-conditioners which provide air of different temperatures and humidities, and through the possibilities of controlling the amount of light given to plants grown under these various temperature conditions. There are 54 separate chambers, comprising greenhouses and artificial light and dark rooms, in the laboratory, and as the plants are all grown on wheeled tables which can be moved between the 54 chambers, a large number of permutations and combinations of temperature, light, humidity, rain and wind treatments are possible. However, in spite of the fact that the possibilities are very broad, this flexibility must be achieved at the expense of sudden changes in environment instead of the gradual shift in temperature and light usually found in nature.

The Earhart Plant Research Laboratory is the culmination of several centuries of improvements in the control of the environment of plants. The simplest and oldest controls involved protective walls and shading structures by which the sun's radiation could be modified. The next steps were the conservatories or orangeries, in which plants in tubs could be kept frost-free through the winter. Active growth was impossible in these conservatories, for light could enter only through ordinary windows and the intensity was low during most of the day. During the seventeenth Century skylights were added, and the prototype of a greenhouse evolved. At the same time, more heat was supplied which enabled plants to grow actively during winter as well as summer. Stoves and ventilators provided a minimum control over the plant environment, limited to raising the temperature above that outside. Thus, tropical plants could be grown in temperate climates, and summer plants in winter.

During the next three centuries technical improvements in construction and heating arrangements were made but the role of the greenhouse, as a heated or hothouse, was not changed. Temperature control of greenhouses during summer proved to be almost impossible. At the Wisconsin, Ohio State and Cornell Universities a number of greenhouses were used during winter to grow plants at constant temperatures, the outside temperature during winter being low enough that by differential heating those greenhouses could be kept at temperatures not exceeding 15°C.

Only the introduction of air-conditioning made cooling as well as heating possible, which entailed complete temperature and humidity control. This was achieved for the first time twenty years ago, when Dr. L. C. Marshall and Dr. H. O. Eversole succeeded in constructing and operating air-conditioned greenhouses in which the temperature could be controlled throughout the year regardless of the amount of heat radiation coming from the sun. The principle which they established for such successful air-conditioning — a large volume of air being distributed equally through the greenhouse — was then used to construct the Clark greenhouse at the California Institute of Technology in 1938 (Went 1943*a*). After this had been in operation for several years, it became clear that air-conditioning of greenhouses offered a very important tool in the study of plant growth. On the basis of the experience gained in the Clark greenhouse, the Earhart Plant Research Laboratory was designed and built in 1948-49 (Went 1950).

With the advent of electric light at the end of the last century many new possibilities for controlled plant growth were introduced and have also been fully utilized in the artificial light rooms of the Earhart Laboratory. During the last six years, this has shown its value in providing many new technical developments which enable the botanist to study plants, unhampered by the vagaries of climate and preconceived ideas of growers.

Chapter 1

INTRODUCTION AND GENERAL PRINCIPLES OF AIR-CONDITIONING GREENHOUSES

Principles of Air-conditioning Greenhouses:— In order to make a greenhouse suitable for the growing of plants, we must first consider the main requirements of the plants themselves. A number of these have been discussed by Marshall *et al.* (1948). The following is a brief outline of these requirements for growth under optimal conditions:

1) The air temperatures during both day and night should be accurately controlled, according to the species that is to be grown. Different plants have very different temperature requirements, not only species but even varieties or races of the same plant differ in their optimal day and night temperature. For instance, the growth and flowering of peas, strawberries and stocks are mainly controlled by the temperature they receive in light. For such plants attention should be given to controlling the day temperature. On the other hand, plants such as tomatoes, potatoes, and chili peppers are principally limited by the temperature they receive in darkness. The day temperature is relatively unimportant within reasonable limits, and only night temperature need be carefully controlled. For all plants, it is essential that greenhouse temperatures not exceed certain limits, for any plant will die if exposed to temperatures exceeding the heat-tolerance of protoplasm. To our knowledge, optimal root temperature is slightly higher than the surrounding air temperature. However, it is not known whether this is a direct effect, or whether it is due to a concomitant increase in relative humidity of the air over the soil.

2) Light is essential for the growing of plants. A large number of plants seem to have an optimal light requirement which approaches the intensity of full daylight (5,000-10,000 foot-candle or 50,000-100,000 lux), whereas other plants can thrive at lower intensities. It must also be remembered that the length, as well as the intensity, of illumination controls the development of many plants. Therefore, daily darkening or lighting arrangements should be considered part of general greenhouse requirements.

3) In general, plants grow best when the relative humidity of the air is fairly high, somewhere in the range of 50-88 per cent.

4) Controlled ventilation of the greenhouse is essential for a number of reasons. In the first place, an adequate CO_2 supply must be maintained during day for mesophytic and most other plants, and during night for succulents. Renewal of the air will keep the CO_2 supply fairly constant, and do away with any toxic exhalations of plants, such as C_2H_4. However, a certain amount of air movement in the greenhouse is also necessary to give a sufficiently steep CO_2 gradient from air to leaf, and to prevent stratification.

With these requirements in mind, we can now consider the design of the ideal greenhouse. Let us first take up the question of temperature control. The more positive it is, the more uniform the resultant growth of plants in a greenhouse will be. Usually, temperature is controlled by regulating the amount of warm water or steam which is fed through the heating elements inside the greenhouse, thus producing a fairly even temperature through the greenhouse. This method is useful when the outside temperature is low, but when heat is no longer required in the greenhouse, the temperature becomes completely uncontrolled. Therefore, regulating greenhouse temperatures by heating elements is positive only in the absence of strong radiation while outside temperatures are well below those required. This heating is often regulated manually, especially in the greenhouses of Europe. This requires careful stoking to produce the amount of heat anticipated in connection with weather forecasts. It is interesting to note that among greenhouse growers in the United States there is greater awareness of the importance of controlling night temperature than in Europe; this is probably due to the more extensive use of thermostats in the United States.

Radiation:— During day another heat source comes into play, and this is radiation. On a perfectly clear day, the amount of radiation which reaches a horizontal surface at sea level is 80 gram calories per $cm.^2$ per hour, when the noon position of the sun is 90° above the horizon, 70 gr. $cal./cm.^2/hour$ at 60° and 40 gr. $cal./cm.^2/hour$ at 30°. Since these figures are not dependent upon latitude, this means that at noon on a sunny summer day almost as much total radiation reaches a greenhouse in the tropics as one at 40°-50° latitude. The glass in the greenhouse roof transmits about 90 per cent of all this radiation. Once inside, this 90 per cent is almost completely transformed into sensible heat and heat of evaporation which cannot be returned through the glass and, therefore, is trapped inside. The per cent of radiation used for evaporation depends on how wet the greenhouse is kept. We can assume that under conditions of average ventilation and normal greenhouse use, 50 per cent of all radiation falling on plants is used in evaporation. Of the rest, probably about 1 per cent or less is transformed into chemical energy by the photosynthetic process, and the other 49 per cent heats the absorbing surfaces. Depending on the degree to which a greenhouse is filled with plants, different percentages of radiation fall on non-plant surfaces in the greenhouse and are largely transformed into heat. Therefore, we can say that usually more than 50 per cent of all radiation falling on a greenhouse roof, inside this greenhouse is transformed into heat on the absorbing surfaces. This heat can then be transferred to the surrounding air, in which state it can be removed by ventilation. In the steady state, as much heat is removed by ventilation as is brought in by radiation. Therefore, we can calculate what the temperature rise will be for any given amount of radiation and rate of ventilation. In the Earhart Laboratory's greenhouses an air velocity of 6 m. per minute is maintained during day. This means 0.6 l. of air per minute passes over any $cm.^2$ of surface. The surface transforms about half of the total outside radiation into heat, and, therefore, produces at noon on a summer day about 0.6 $cal./min./cm.^2$ of surface. One calorie will heat 0.6 l. of air 5.3°C. Actually it was found that under those conditions the air leaving the greenhouse was 4° warmer than the incoming air. This shows that our assumptions about heat penetration and transformation are of the right order of magnitude. In addition, we have to take into account that in the Earhart greenhouses about 20 per cent of the total sun radiation is removed by absorption of infrared rays due to a screen of water which is constantly being passed over the glass roof.

These calculations explain why an unshaded and poorly ventilated greenhouse is insufferably hot in summer, and why air-conditioning, as well as heating, is a necessary part of the design of a modern greenhouse.

Plant temperatures will differ from air temperature, depending upon their transpiration and upon the rate of air movement, or rather upon the temperature gradient between plant and air. Therefore, uniform plant temperatures in a greenhouse can only be maintained when there is a uniform amount of constant-temperature air flowing past all surfaces sub-

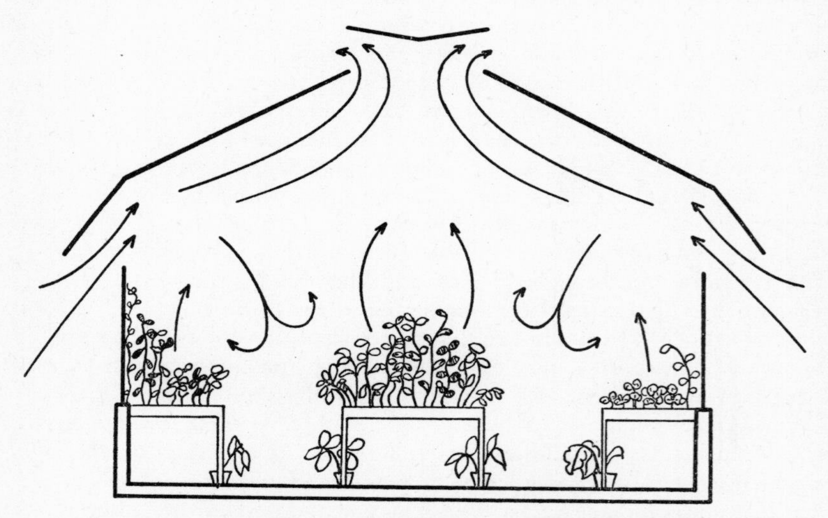

FIGURE 1.— Air circulation in standard type greenhouse with open ventilators. Observe irregular air supply of plants on benches.

jected to radiation. In a greenhouse with forced draft most plants can be grown in full sunlight any day of the year, without danger of "burning." This so-called "burning" of plants in unshaded greenhouses is due to one of two causes:

1) With insufficient ventilation the actual leaf or stem temperature may become so high that heat-death of the cells occurs. This can be prevented either by shading or increasing the rate of air flow.

2) When plants are kept in weak light, their sucrose content becomes very low. Then sudden exposure to full sunlight causes bleaching of the leaf pigments, and the leaves show burned areas between the veins. This type of burning can be prevented by slowly increasing the light to which the plant is exposed, until its sugar content becomes high enough, or by spraying a 10 per cent sucrose solution on the leaves one day prior to exposure to full sunlight (WENT 1944*b*).

An ordinary greenhouse with side and top ventilators will have a fairly large volume of air moving through it when the ventilators are open, and when there is a great deal of radiation. The greatest volume of air will move up close to the glass surface, and will mix with the warm air which rises from the plant surfaces. Probably less than half of the air leaving through the top ventilators has been near the plants, and thus has not contributed to their cooling. Therefore, the convection-ventilation in a greenhouse of traditional design is less than half as effective as the forced ventilation (*see* FIGURES 1 and 2) of a fully air-conditioned greenhouse. This means that the amount the plants are cooled is determined by the proportion of air actually moving past the plants, not the total volume of air passing through the ventilators. Therefore, the actual position of the

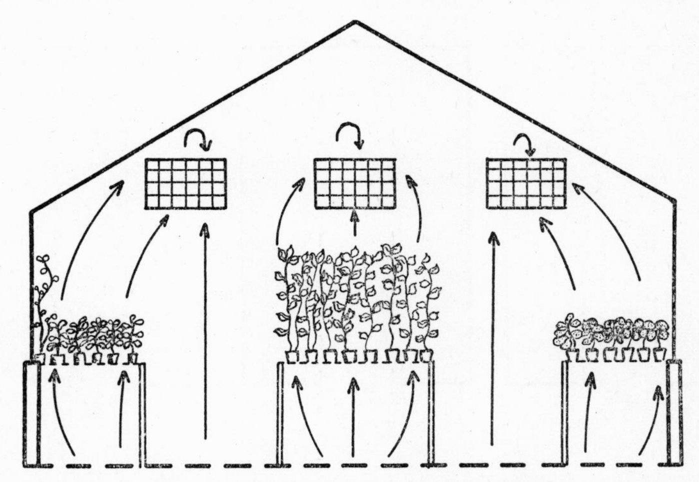

FIGURE 2.— Air circulation in fully air-conditioned greenhouse with air introduction through slotted floor, even air supply of plants on benches, and air removal through registers in walls.

side-ventilators in a regular greenhouse and of the air intake dampers in an air-conditioned greenhouse is of paramount importance in the matter of temperature control. In greenhouse design these matters have not as yet received the amount of attention warranted by their importance. For instance, the usual difference in size of plants grown in the center and on the edge of greenhouse benches is due to difference in temperature over the whole bench. Other considerations play an important part in the placement of ventilators in a greenhouse. Through them insects enter, and, in several cases, lack of ventilation is considered less serious than increased insect infestation.

It is possible to calculate from the size of the greenhouse and the temperature rise which can be tolerated over the outside temperature, how much air has to be blown into an air-conditioned greenhouse to protect the plants against the effects of overheating. In some cases, as in corn and tomato, day temperatures of well over 40° will not cause damage. In other plants, such as peas and *Lathyrus,* sustained day temperatures above 30° are lethal in the course of weeks or days. At noon on a hot summer day a 10 × 30 m. greenhouse transforms about 1.2 × 10^8 cal./min. of radiation into heat. All of this energy has to be removed through air circulation. If a 10°C rise in temperature can be tolerated, 600 $m.^3$ of air per min. will be needed from the outside to be distributed evenly throughout the greenhouse.

During the hottest time of day the relative humidity of the air is fairly low; therefore, the incoming air can be easily and cheaply cooled by water evaporation. If a sufficiently fine mist is produced in the air supply to the greenhouse, the droplets will evaporate before the air has

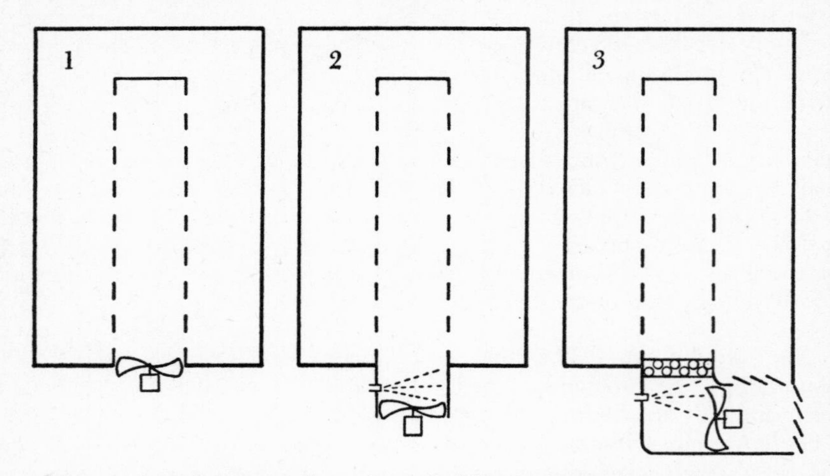

FIGURE 3.— Schematic floor plans of different types of greenhouses with central air duct, and with fan (1), fan plus humidifier (2), and fan, humidifier plus heating radiator (3), with possibility of recirculation of air.

reached the plants. At a relative humidity of 50 per cent, air of 30°C can be cooled to 22° by evaporating water only; at 30 per cent humidity, an air temperature of 40° can be reduced to 28°. The spray has to be produced near the entry of air into the greenhouse, if this evaporative cooling is to be effective. Sprays inside the greenhouse without sufficient ventilation will only temporarily lower the temperature, until the air is saturated with water vapor.

In all conventional, non-air-conditioned greenhouses, the rise in air temperature due to radiation is so great that only in cold weather can they be used without reduction in light intensity. In summer they are useless unless they are shaded. This is done either by: (*1*) roller shades, which are lowered each morning when the temperature inside reaches a predetermined limit, then raised again in the afternoon, or (2) whitewashing the glass in spring, an inflexible method which has only its cheapness to recommend it. Another method occasionally used is (3) putting cheesecloth screens under the glass. This traps all absorbed radiation inside the greenhouse, and thus largely defeats its purpose. An ideal method of shading would be (4) adjustable Venetian blinds which would regulate the amount of light entering the greenhouse, and should be operated automatically either with a photocell or a thermostat inside the greenhouse (or with both).

We must admit that temperature regulation through shading partly defeats the primary purpose of a greenhouse. From a purely logical standpoint, it is easy to see that the daytime temperature in the greenhouse can best be regulated by controlling the temperature of the entering air or by forced ventilation. Neither of these methods is necessarily very expensive. Diagrams 1, 2 and 3 of FIGURE 3 show the basic arrangements necessary for forced ventilation (1), ventilation with cooling by evaporation (2), and complete air-conditioning (3). Whereas in schemes 1 and 2 the air supply fan must run only as long as cooling is needed, in case 3 the fan runs continuously. More or less fresh air can be supplied by regulating dampers, and when heating is required, the outside air supply may be completely closed and the inside air re-circulated. By placing radiators in the supply duct, one can heat the greenhouse in a simple manner. The increased costs for construction of air-conditioning (3) are partly offset by the saving in heating elements throughout the greenhouse, and by elimination of most of the roof ventilators.

Air Circulation:— The two main problems in air-conditioning greenhouses are: (*1*) circulating a sufficient volume of air to remove radiation heat, and (2) distributing this air evenly through the whole greenhouse. The latter poses interesting engineering problems. Introduction of the air from above is undesirable, because the large air ducts which are required would interfere with the light. Besides, such downward air movement is in the opposite direction from the natural ventilation, which produces pronounced updrafts due to the heating of the air.

Introduction of the air through the side walls would result in uneven rates of air flow: the strong drafts produced near the ventilators do not mix immediately with the greenhouse air, but slow down further out, after they have mixed. The outcome of this type of ventilation is that the air gradually gets warmed from the side to the center, so that a temperature difference of a few degrees exists between side and center.

Theoretically, the best way to introduce air is from below. This is done in most air-conditioned greenhouses through diffusers placed at regular intervals under benches, blowing the air obliquely up the aisles, or through perforations in the floor. The latter arrangement is the best, provided the plants are not grown on solid benches, but in individual containers between which the air can rise. Benches made of metal lath are suitable. In the new greenhouse of the University of Liège the air enters through perforated steel plates in the floor; in the greenhouses of the Earhart Plant Research Laboratory a second floor of steel channel beams is placed 12-18 inches above the concrete floor of the greenhouse. The air-conditioner blows air into the space between the two floors. This air then passes through slots between the steel beams of the topmost floor, and rises evenly throughout the greenhouse (*see* FIGURE 2). The position of the return-air ducts is not very critical, but their capacity should be ample. They can be arranged along the sides of the greenhouse as far above the floor as practicable. For best results, the main air resistance in such an air-conditioning system should be in the injection of air into the greenhouse: the resistance in the return ducts should be less.

The peculiar properties of air must be taken into account in the design of the air-duct system and of the air inlets. In general, a moving air mass does not mix with an adjoining stationary air mass unless a speed differential of over 500 m. per minute exists. Therefore, if air is injected into the greenhouse at a speed of less than 500 m. per minute, it continues to move as a mass of the same diameter as the inlet opening, and in whatever direction the orifice points, until it is deflected by a solid surface. It will then continue to move with approximately the same dimensions, in the deflected direction. Thus, a sheet of air of 0.2 m. thickness which is blown across the floor of the greenhouse, will rise as a sheet of the same thickness upwards along the greenhouse walls and under the glass roof mixing very little with the rest of the greenhouse air. If we want mixing of the injected air we must use one of several methods. With the Venturi principle air is injected at such a rate that turbulence occurs between injected air and surrounding greenhouse air. We can also change the energy of flow of air into pressure, or encourage turbulence of the air by the installation of more fans inside the greenhouses. This control over air flow and pressure is not only of importance inside the greenhouse, but even more so in the air ducts carrying the air towards the greenhouse, and in the plenum under the floor of the greenhouse.

Very little work has been done in air-conditioned greenhouses as yet on the effects of varying degrees of relative humidity of the air on plants. Until further work makes it possible to draw more precise conclusions, it is safe to say that in most cases a relative humidity of 70 per cent should prove satisfactory; higher humidities are recommended in the case of very tender plants with weak root systems. Only in propagating houses should relative humidities of over 90 per cent be maintained.

The rate of air movement within the greenhouse is not only important to control the temperature, but it also controls the CO_2 supply to the plants. The rate of CO_2 uptake depends primarily on the concentration gradient of CO_2 from the air to the leaf. This can be made steeper, and consequently photosynthesis can be increased, by increasing the CO_2 concentration in the air, or by increasing the rate of air movement past the leaves (*cf.* Chapter 20, and FIGURE 57). Therefore, we can say that release of CO_2 in a greenhouse is only warranted when there is already an optimal rate of air movement inside the greenhouse, and when the light intensity is high enough for the utilization of the applied CO_2.

Greenhouses in cold climates are usually kept tightly closed during cold weather because of the high costs of heating. This means that relatively little CO_2 renewal in the greenhouse air is possible. Under such conditions a CO_2 source inside the greenhouse is imperative. It seems likely that the use of large quantities of manure, bean straw, or corn cobs as a dressing for the soil in greenhouses in winter is primarily important because they constitute a source of CO_2 as they gradually decompose. A rough calculation shows that half or all of the CO_2 present in the air can be supplied by decomposition of the organic matter added to the soil. The CO_2 present can be made more effective by moving the air at a considerable rate past the leaves. The optimal CO_2 concentration and the best rate of air movement will have to be determined in future research.

Light:— The light intensity in a greenhouse varies from hour to hour due to the change in elevation of the sun and clouds, and from day to day due to weather changes; from season to season due to the declination of the sun. Because of these variations, it is impossible to determine the optimal light intensity required by a particular plant, using natural daylight and different degrees of shading. We can find the best location for a plant in a greenhouse in this way, but that gives us only a constant proportion of a very variable entity. This probably explains why experimental results obtained with shading are different from those obtained with artificial light. Many of our crop plants require full sunlight (5,000-10,000 ft.-c.) for optimal growth, but photosynthesis in individual leaves is saturated at 1,000 ft.-c. This difference in saturating light intensity for a whole plant in the open, and an individual leaf in the laboratory can partially be explained by the fact that to obtain an intensity of 1,000 ft.-c. over a sufficiently long daily and monthly period, much higher top intensities are required. At lower light intensities photosynthesis and growth are much reduced, and most plants cannot grow below 100-200 ft.-c. In climates where a considerable number of days have light intensities below 200 ft.-c., special measures must be taken if plants are to be grown in a greenhouse. Here are three things that can be done:

1) Lower the temperature so that the plants use up less carbohydrate by respiration. Under these conditions growth is also reduced to practically zero. This method is very successful in tiding plants over a dark period.

2) Supplement insufficient daylight with artificial light. This method has quite a few disadvantages; for one, it is fairly expensive, and cumbersome. It is suggested that a fairly satisfactory way of using supplementary electric light would be to mount fluorescent tubes in between, and not above, the plants. Thus the light would radiate in all directions, and reflectors would be unnecessary. The fixtures could be mounted between the end boards of the benches. Since the fluorescent tubes remain fairly cool while burning, leaves are usually not injured even when they touch the lamp.

3) Spray the plants with a 10 per cent sugar solution. Some plants, such as tomatoes and lettuce, take up this sugar through their leaves in sufficient quantities to substitute at least partially for the insufficient photosynthesis.

Many investigators have found that warming the soil makes plants grow better. This is probably not the case when the growing conditions are optimal and the root medium is well aerated; bottom heat is apparently only important when the root system is poor. Positive effects of bottom heat were found in the following:

1) Pot or crock experiments, where the root system is rather severely restricted.
2) Hydroponics, in cases where the root system does not develop too well in the nutrient solution.
3) Cutting frames, where no roots have developed at all as yet.

It is possible that in all these cases the bottom heat only increases relative humidity in the root crown area or in the cutting frame itself. Further experiments will have to establish whether increased root temperature is important in itself. At present, there is not enough experimental evidence to advocate placing heating elements under the benches instead of in other places, particularly when the humidity is kept high in the greenhouse.

One of the most important considerations in the planning of a greenhouse is the scope of the plant materials to be grown in it. Most plants have different optimal growing conditions, but the optima for some may lie closely enough together so that they can be grown conveniently in the same greenhouse. Many plants, however, cannot possibly be grown together because under optimal conditions for the one the other dies. Commercial growers invariably keep only one or at most a few species or varieties in the same greenhouse, and have different greenhouses for different crops. University greenhouses with demonstration collections must have a large number of plants, and the different genera and species are grouped together regardless of their requirements. They are usually arranged according to taxonomic systems instead of on ecological and climatological bases. There are types of plants, however, that could be grown all together; all succulents, for instance, seem to require rather dry conditions, ventilation and low temperature during night. This is due to their acid metabolism which requires a CO_2 supply at low temperatures during darkness. Some orchids probably belong to this group, too, and might be grown profitably in a succulent house. Water plants can also grow well together in a special greenhouse. A general "orchid" house is impossible, though, because the main genera, *Odontoglossum, Cypripedium, Cattleya, Cymbidium* and *Phalaenopsis* have very different temperature requirements and climatic preferences. The same thing can be said about a "fern" house.

The ideal arrangement is to have a number of separate greenhouses kept at different temperatures. Then the ferns, orchids and other plants can be distributed over the different greenhouses according to their temperature requirements. In growing plants the right temperature means the difference between success and failure. It is possible, to some extent, to find within a single non-air-conditioned greenhouse places where temperature and light differ enough to encompass the optimal conditions of different plants, because of the uneven distribution and movement of the air, and differential shading from the sun.

The degree to which greenhouses are useful depends on the climate, the latitude, and the plants to be grown. On these factors are based the amount of temperature control required and the amount of supplementary illumination needed for growth. For instance, in southwestern America, the sunlight during winter is intense enough to allow most plants to grow as well in winter as in summer, so no artificial light is needed in the greenhouse. In northern areas, total radiation during the winter is much lower, and there are long stretches of cloudy, dark weather. Artificial lighting or sugar sprays are a necessity in these areas and have been used with moderate success (additional lighting: ROODENBURG 1952, VAN DER VEEN 1950; sugar sprays: VAN KOOT and VAN ANTWERPEN 1952).

The air-conditioning, or temperature control, is also dependent on the climate of the area and can be fairly simple if climatic details are taken into consideration. In northern climates, heating is of paramount importance during the winter, whereas in other localities, such as southern California, cooling during summer is a problem. In heating, the total amount of radiation must be taken into account — the length of day, the declination of the sun and the number of cloudy days. In cooling, all these factors plus the dew point of the outside air must be considered. Evaporative cooling can only bring the air temperature within a few degrees of the dew point, so this type of cooling is best in climates which are hot and dry. The temperature in greenhouses in localities where the summer months are hot and humid can be reduced somewhat by evaporative cooling, but refrigeration will be needed to maintain temperatures lower than the wet bulb.

When considering all aspects of air-conditioning and air circulation in greenhouses, the most important one is the volume of the greenhouse itself. The volume of the house decides how much air must be treated, and, therefore, how much machinery will be needed to maintain adequate temperature control.

There are several secondary advantages to air-conditioned greenhouses. By installing simple mechanical filters in the air intake, insects can be removed and thus the disadvantage of side ventilation, through which insects enter, can be overcome. More important is the possibility of installing activated carbon filters in the incoming air stream. These filters will remove all toxic air pollutants which are now present in the air of all our large cities, and which cause more or less severe damage to plants (WENT 1955*a* and Chapter 24).

The principles involved in air-conditioned greenhouses hold also for controlling temperature in artificially lighted rooms for growing plants. The problems are simpler here, however, because the radiation and heat loads are less when fluorescent lamps are used as a light source, and the heat load remains constant. In general, one can say that all sources of heat should be eliminated as much as possible. Therefore, fluorescent

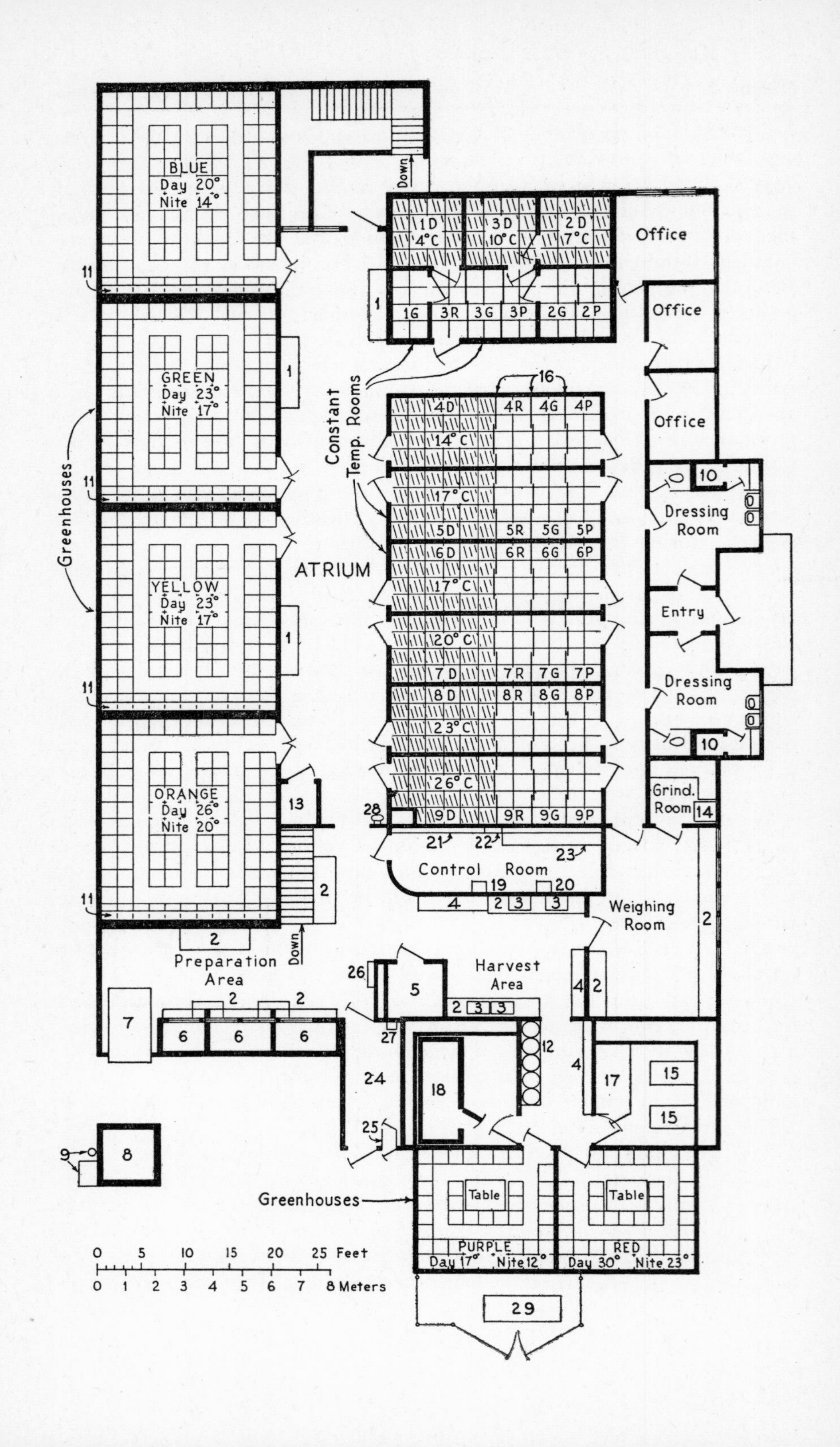
BLUE
Day 20°
Nite 14°
GREEN
Day 23°
Nite 17°
YELLOW
Day 23°
Nite 17°
ORANGE
Day 26°
Nite 20°
Greenhouses
ATRIUM
Constant Temp. Rooms
Down
1D 4°C
3D 10°C
2D 7°C
1G 3R 3G 3P 2G 2P
Office
Office
Office
4D 14°C
4R 4G 4P
17°C
5D 5R 5G 5P
6D 17°C
6R 6G 6P
20°C
7D 7R 7G 7P
8D 23°C
8R 8G 8P
26°C
9D 9R 9G 9P
Dressing Room
Entry
Dressing Room
Grind. Room
Control Room
Weighing Room
Preparation Area
Harvest Area
Table
Table
PURPLE
Day 17° Nite 12°
RED
Day 30° Nite 23°
Greenhouses
0 5 10 15 20 25 Feet
0 1 2 3 4 5 6 7 8 Meters

tubes should be used in preference to incandescent lamps, since with the same current consumption they produce about four times as much usable light, but only half as much heat. Almost half of the heat they produce remains in the ballasts, which can be placed outside the air-conditioned room.

With these general considerations in mind, dictated by physical, botanical and physiological facts, it becomes possible to plan and design efficient greenhouses and artificially lighted growth rooms.

Planning of the Earhart Plant Research Laboratory:— Results obtained in the Clark greenhouses made it clear to what extent research in air-conditioned greenhouses can aid in solving problems of basic plant physiology, ecology and plant climatology. In these greenhouses it was found that the applicability of air-conditioning lay in several directions:

1) It can provide constant and controllable conditions for the growing of plants. In this way reproducible plant material can be obtained, and experiments can be carried out under reproducible conditions.

2) Because each of the environmental factors can be controlled separately, the effect of these variables on plants can be individually investigated.

3) The effect of the sum total of the naturally occurring fluctuations in environment (which we call climate) can be measured, providing an experimental basis for plant climatology and ecology.

The size and complexity of the laboratory can be determined from the type of problems to be investigated and from the degree of air-conditioning to be incorporated. When the Earhart Plant Research Laboratory was designed, it was decided that all possible applications of air-conditioning would be tested to the degree that space and funds would permit.

The operation cost and effectiveness of air-conditioned greenhouses depends to a large extent on the local climatic conditions. From earlier experiments (WENT 1944*a*) it seemed likely that the relative humidity of the air had little effect on growth of plants. In dry climates, where the dew point or wet-bulb temperature always remains low, temperatures can be controlled by evaporative cooling, which uses the heat of evaporation of water to lower the air temperature. Since in Pasadena the wet-bulb temperature seldom reaches 20°C, and usually is lower, evaporative cooling could be used extensively in the Earhart Plant Research Laboratory. Therefore, it is possible during the day to keep greenhouse temperatures down to 23°C, using evaporative cooling only.

FIGURE 4 (*opposite*).— Ground floor plan of Earhart Plant Research Laboratory (the small squares in greenhouses and constant temperature rooms indicate the available truck spaces): 1, folding work table; 2, work table; 3, sink; 4, shelves; 5, elevator; 6, sand and gravel bins; 7, autoclave; 8, roof spray filter tank; 9, roof spray water treating equipment; 10, shower; 11, wall shelves; 12, nutrient stock solution tanks; 13, spraying chamber; 14, grinder; 15, drying ovens; 16, partitions with sliding doors; 17, 30° artificial light room; 18, walk-in cold box; 19, CO_2 analyzer; 20, temperature recorder; 21, air-conditioning control panel; 22, motor indicator panel; 23, time switch panel; 24, fumigation entrance; 25, fumigation box; 26, control panel for 24 & 25; 27, heater and fan; 28, drinking fountain; 29, emergency engine and generator.

During the winter in Pasadena temperatures below freezing seldom occur. This simplifies insulation problems, and makes it possible to use aluminum rafters for the greenhouse roof.

The most important decision in the planning of air-conditioned growing rooms for plants is the degree to which sunlight and/or artificial light should be used. Sunlight has the advantage of cheapness and high intensity, but it is highly variable and only available during the day. Besides, it necessitates very large air-conditioning installations because so much radiant heat has to be removed. Artificial light is expensive and in practical installations its intensity remains well below sunlight (2,000 ft.-c. in contrast with 10,000 ft.-c. for normal noon sunlight). However, its intensity is constant, it is available at any time of day or night, and it is far easier to control temperature and humidity in artificially lighted rooms. Since so little information was available as to how well most plants can develop in artificial light, the decision was rather arbitrary concerning the extent to which artificial light was to be used. Some radiation measurements were carried out for one year in Pasadena, which showed that when the maximally possible radiation during summer is set at 100 per cent, during the brightest week in summer 90 per cent, and during the darkest week in winter 29 per cent of this amount of light was received. This 29 per cent seemed sufficiently high to earmark 70 per cent of the growing space for sunlight and 30 per cent for artificial light. In other climates with more cloudiness and less light in winter, or at higher latitudes (Pasadena lies at 34° N. Lat.), other decisions may be made as far as the proportion between greenhouses and artificial light rooms is concerned. It is even possible that exclusively artificial light is indicated, especially with the newest improvements in fluorescent lighting (*e.g.*, high frequency current). In such cases one probably will yet want some limited greenhouse space for occasional comparison between artificial light and daylight.

The most important consideration in the planning of air-conditioned greenhouses is the type of problems which are to be investigated. In our case it was decided that main emphasis would be laid on study of the physiology of the normal plant with the exclusion of pest and disease problems. As experimental material herbaceous land plants were anticipated, and consequently room size and door height did not have to be adapted to trees or large shrubs. To achieve greatest flexibility, a large number of individual air-conditioning systems was envisaged; whenever possible the air from a conditioner was passed through lighted and dark rooms, so that at the same temperature and humidity a number of photoperiodic treatments could be given. By moving the plants between light and dark rooms and greenhouses, any combination of temperatures, humidities and light could be achieved.

Due to size of lot, building restrictions and existing structures (Clark greenhouses), the area available for the Earhart Laboratory was approximately 7,000 sq. ft. With a basement for machinery, main floor and the

Table 1: *Space distribution (in square feet) in the Earhart Plant Research Laboratory:—*

	Surface in sq. ft.	Totals
Plant growing space:—		
Greenhouses		
2 of 14 x 16′ (Clark Greenhouse)	448	
4 of 20 x 24′	1920	
	2368	
Artificially lighted rooms, constant temperature		
7 of 8 x 12′ (each divided into 3 compartments)	672	
5 of 8 x 8′ (each divided into 2 compartments)	320	
2 of 8 x 4′	64	
	1056	
Constant temperature dark rooms		
6 of 8 x 12′	576	
3 of 8 x 8′	192	
1 of 8 x 4′	32	
	800	
Constant temperature laboratories in basement 9 with about 40 sq. ft. working space	360	
Total controlled temperature growing space		4584
Temperature control facilities:—		
Control room and main switchboard	300	
Air conditioners	1600	
Heating (boiler room)	400	
Cooling (compressors, pumps, cold water storage)	600	
Air cleaning	400	
Auxiliary machinery (transformers, deionizer, Kathabar, motor generator, etc.)	700	
Total space for air conditioning		4000
Space required for the handling of plants:—		
Atrium (space for moving of trucks, photographing, analyzing results, etc.)	1000	
Potting and washing area	600	
Harvesting and weighing room	300	
Drying ovens, grinding room, spraying cabinet	200	
Sterilizing and fumigating	100	
Total plant handling facilities		2200
Offices and other staff facilities:—		
Offices	500	
Instrument makers' shop, wood working area	500	
Laboratory	400	
Photographic rooms	150	
Storage space	1000	
Dressing rooms	250	
Total auxiliary facilities		2800

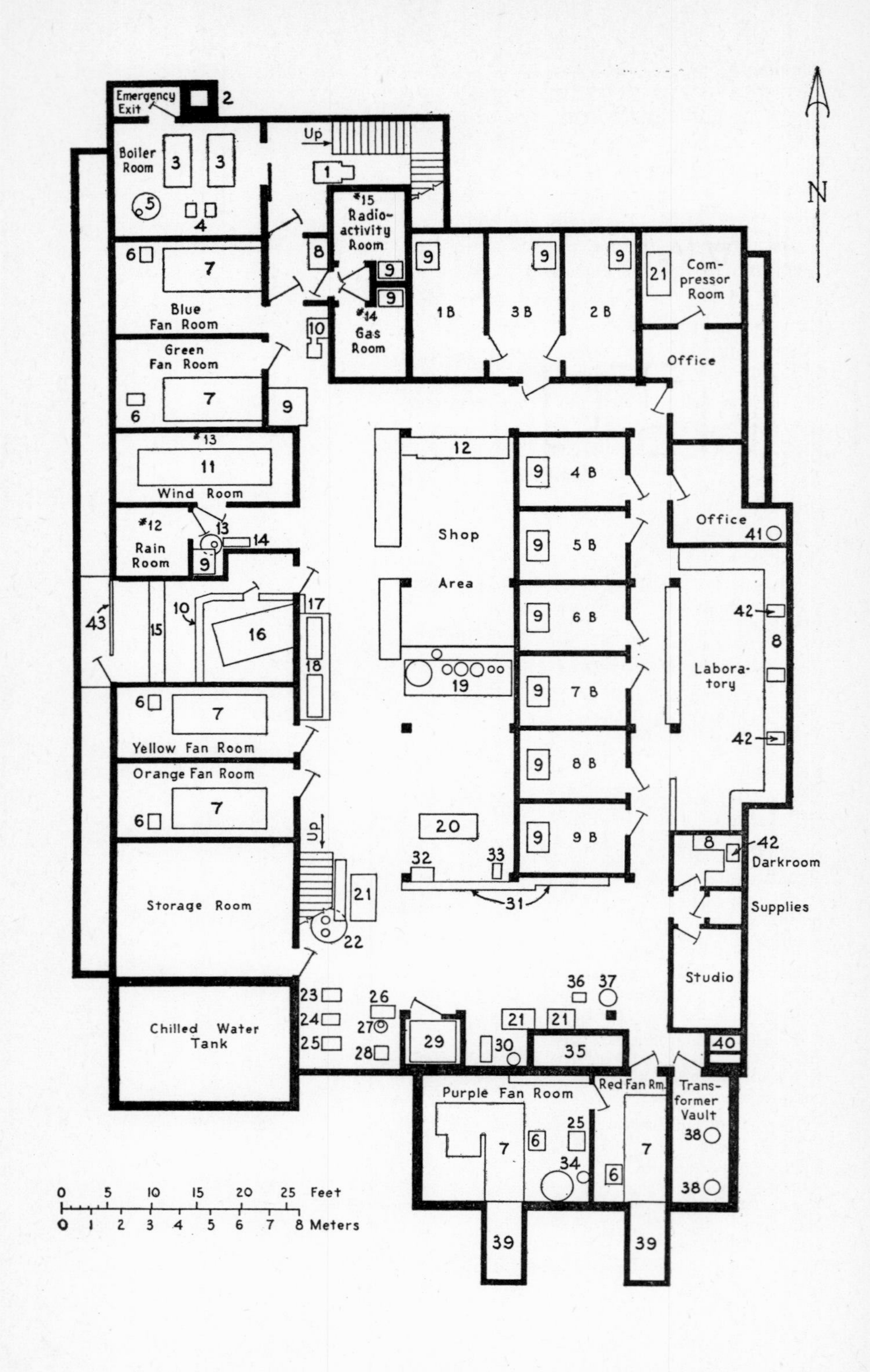
Emergency Exit
2
Boiler Room
3
3
5
4
Up
1
#15 Radio-activity Room
8
9
9
#14 Gas Room
10
6
7
Blue Fan Room
Green Fan Room
7
6
9
1 B
3 B
2 B
9
9
9
21
Compressor Room
Office
#13
11
Wind Room
#12
Rain Room
13
14
9
12
Shop
Area
4 B
5 B
6 B
7 B
8 B
9 B
Office
41
43
15
10
16
17
18
19
Laboratory
42
8
42
6
7
Yellow Fan Room
Orange Fan Room
7
6
Up
20
32
33
31
8
42
Darkroom
Supplies
Storage Room
21
22
Studio
Chilled Water Tank
23
24
25
26
27
28
29
30
21
21
35
36
37
40
Purple Fan Room
Red Fan Rm.
Transformer Vault
7
6
25
34
7
6
38
38
39
39
0 5 10 15 20 25 Feet
0 1 2 3 4 5 6 7 8 Meters
N

Clark greenhouses which were incorporated in the laboratory, a total of 15,000 sq. ft. of floor space was available, and in the finished building this is divided as shown in TABLE 1.

The remaining space of approximately 1400 sq. ft. of floor space is given over to corridors, elevator and stairs.

All 544 ballasts for the fluorescent tubes in the artificial light rooms are installed in the attic, which also houses the ventilators for the light panels.

The space distribution as shown in TABLE 1 was considered best for the specific purposes of the Earhart Plant Research Laboratory. In other laboratories the proportion between space may be different. It may be possible, *e.g.*, to use existing office and laboratory space in nearby buildings, or, on the other hand, a fully self-contained unit should have more laboratory and service space than the Earhart Laboratory has. Yet the 1:1 proportion between growing space and machinery is essential. And the 2:1 ratio between growing space and plant handling area is also rather inflexible when the growing program is intense.

The exact proportions of the individual rooms are largely determined by a number of secondary considerations:

1) In all cases the 8 ft. fluorescent Slimline tube is used as the source of artificial light. In 1948 this was considered the best available artificial light source, and it still is. To make best use of space, the width of the artificial light rooms is slightly over 8 ft., allowing the tubes to cover the whole width of the rooms. If the rooms had been made wider using the same light panel width, the light intensity for the plants at the sides would have dropped off more rapidly; at present the reflection from the white side walls close to the plants causes a fairly even light distribution.

2) In connection with a room width of 8 ft., the wheeled tables or trucks on which the plants are grown had to be either 2.5 ft. or slightly under 2 ft. square. The latter size was preferred because of the greater ease of handling trucks of that size, particularly when moving them through doors. It was decided to make all trucks of uniform size, 20 × 20" in surface (= 51 × 51 cm.). This again determined the other dimensions of the artificial light and dark rooms: they had to be in multiples of 2 ft., and actually are 4 ft., 8 ft., or 12 ft. long.

3) The height of the rooms was determined by three factors: in the first place, to be able to grow as large a selection of plants as possible, the rooms should have the maximal height consistent with proper operation; in the second place, the doors into

---

FIGURE 5 (*opposite*).— Basement floor plan of Earhart Plant Research Laboratory: 1, evaporative condenser; 2, boiler stack; 3, boilers; 4, hot water circulating pumps; 5, waste water sump and pump; 6, air washer spray pump; 7, air washer; 8, work table; 9, air-conditioning unit; 10, charcoal air filter; 11, wind tunnel; 12, deep freeze and compressor; 13, rain room sump and pump; 14, rain room pressure pump; 15, precipitator; 16, main air supply fan; 17, air compressor controllers; 18, air compressors; 19, de-ionizer; 20, kathabar dehumidifier; 21, refrigeration compressors; 22, chilled water sump and pumps; 23, chilled water supply pump; 24, chilled water circulating pump; 25, roof spray pump; 26, autoclave; 27, elevator sump and pump; 28, steam generator; 29, elevator; 30, elevator pump and tank; 31, main power panel; 32, emergency power contractors; 33, 400 cycle generator; 34, roof spray water filter and tank; 35, nutrient solution tank; 36, nutrient pressure pump; 37, nutrient pressure tank; 38, transformer; 39, air duct; 40, sand trap and dilution tank; 41, water heater; 42, sink; 43, screen air filter.

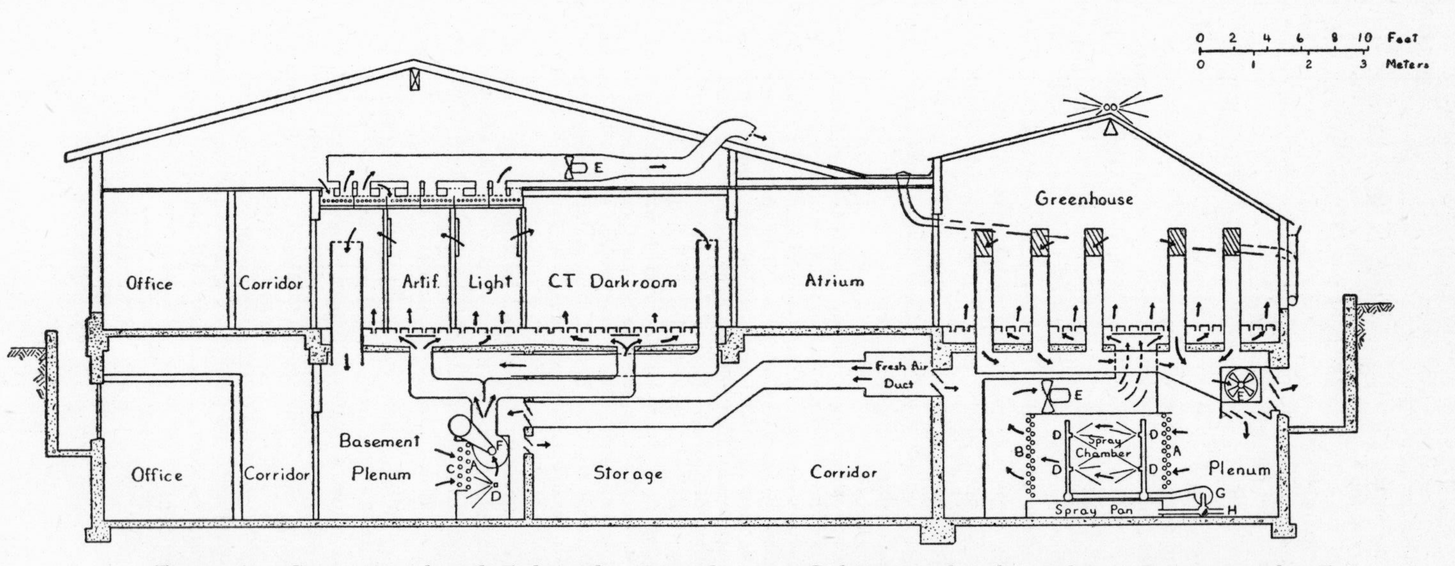

FIGURE 6.— Cross section through Earhart Plant Research Laboratory, showing air circulation (*bold arrows*) through constant temperature room with dark and light sections, and through greenhouse: A, preheating radiator; B, reheating radiator; C, heating and cooling radiators; D, spray nozzles; E, axial flow fan; F, squirrel cage fan; G, air washer spray pump; H, three-way modulating valve for injection of chilled water into airwasher spray.

the greenhouses, being on the low side of the sloping glass roof could not be higher than 7 ft. without raising the height of the side walls of the greenhouses unnecessarily. In the third place, in the artificial light rooms the light panels should be as close to the plants as possible to make full use of the emitted light. To keep the plants within reaching (watering, observation and measuring) distance, the light panels could not be higher than 7 ft. The compromise height was chosen as 7 ft.; the doors of the artificial light rooms are actually only 6 ft. 6 inches, whereas the lower side of the light panels reaches up to 7 ft. (*see* FIGURE 6). The greenhouses vary in height. On the side of the doors they are 9 ft. 6 inches high, rising to 12 ft. in the center, and decreasing to 6 ft. at the other side. This gives sufficient head room to occasionally grow taller plants (when this is done, however, the plants cannot be moved between greenhouses), and it does not create excessive overhead space, the conditioning of which would pose special problems. As water is run over the glass roof to filter out the useless infrared radiation of the sun, the slope of the roof is only 3:12 or 7:12 which allows a thicker water layer on the glass than if a greater slope had been used. Since the side walls of the greenhouses are solid, they had to be kept as low as possible to have the highest possible light intensity inside the greenhouse.

4) In more northern regions, where during the winter the sun does not rise far above the horizon, it may have some advantage to have the sides of the greenhouses constructed of glass (*see* SCHOUTE 1935). At the latitude of Pasadena (34° N.) even in winter the sun comes high enough above the horizon to penetrate the greenhouses in spite of the fact that the sides are solid, and not more than a small percentage of the available light is cut out. Since usually a certain number of shade plants, such as *Cymbidiums* and other orchids, *Saintpaulias,* ferns and mosses are being grown, they can occupy the shady side of the greenhouse, and thus no space is lost. Nearby shrubs, trees and structures do not allow the early and late afternoon sun to reach the Earhart greenhouses anyway, so this fact makes glass side walls useless for increased light supply. Also, as glass side walls would have posed special problems in connection with water cooling, return ducts for the air-conditioning, etc., they were not further considered, and the solid side walls have not seriously interfered with the experiments.

5) The whole operation of the Earhart Laboratory is based on exchange of plants between the various greenhouses, artificial light rooms and darkrooms. Since in most cases this is a daily exchange, twice every day trucks have to be moved back and forth between these rooms. One third to one half of all plants grown are thus moved and this necessitates several basic construction details.

In the first place, the distance between all growing rooms is kept at a minimum (*see* FIGURE 4). This has been accomplished by placing them around a central hall, the Atrium, and only the original Clark greenhouses (Red and Purple*) are outside the perimeter of a 100 × 60 ft. rectangle, which encloses the Orange, Yellow, Green and Blue greenhouses, and nine constant temperature rooms. By keeping the higher temperature rooms close together, and likewise the low temperature rooms, the distance over which the trucks have to be moved can be kept to a minimum. Extremes in temperature change are less frequently required in experiments than exchanges within a narrow temperature range.

A second structural requirement is a large Atrium, necessary to move plants back and forth between conditions. This had to be large enough, so that about 30 per cent of all trucks to be moved could be assembled in it. In the case of the small artificial light rooms, the trucks have to be moved

* For the meaning of these color designations of the greenhouses *see* p. 61.

out of them before new ones can be moved into them. This means a considerable number of trucks have to stand somewhere temporarily before being placed in their final positions.

The third consideration in connection with space allocation is the total area of the growing space. If the different experimental conditions are realized by the moving of plants, then the absolute size which is manageable is limited by the considerable time it takes to move the trucks back and forth. In the Earhart Laboratory the regular daily moving is usually carried out by two gardeners plus one or two persons who have other duties in the laboratory. A normal operating load (*ca.* 250 trucks to be moved each morning and afternoon) takes approximately 30-45 minutes. If the moving time were much longer, the accuracy of control over growing conditions of the plants would be lost. It would be possible to devise methods shortening the time required for moving trucks, but this would have complicated construction details, and would have to be worked out long before the final plans of the building were made (an overhead trolley system is probably best).

As long as sowing, potting and replanting of plants is done on the same floor, the location of those facilities did not necessarily have to be close to the growing space, as all plants are grown on trucks, and thus can easily be moved towards the service areas. The Earhart Laboratory potting area has been projected so that trucks can easily reach the gravel and sand bins from the outside. In this way no secondary moving of material is necessary. Steam sterilization of the sand and gravel is carried out inside the bins, after which they can be opened from the inside, making available sterile growing medium in the same area where the potting is done. Because the potting area is accessible by truck from the outside of the building, the general sterilizers and fumigation tunnel are also located there.

Because so much effort is being spent in the Earhart Plant Research Laboratory to control the aerial environment of the plants, all other conditions have to be controlled to the same extent to make these efforts fully effective. Whenever possible, genetically uniform plant material is used in the experiments, either in the form of vegetatively reproduced clones (potatoes, strawberries, orchids, *Saintpaulias*), or as selected seed. The extent to which the root environment, nutrition and water supply are controlled will be discussed in later chapters. Probably the most important remaining variables in the growing of plants are pests and diseases. Therefore, the laboratory has been designed so as to eliminate infection of plants and prevent introduction of plant pests. In this way, neither damage by parasites nor unknown physiological effects by insecticides or fungicides complicate the results.

Chapter 2

CONSTRUCTION DETAILS OF THE EARHART LABORATORY

After the general principles of construction of the laboratory had been established, the architect, Mr. PALMER SABIN, the mechanical engineer, Mr. ARTHUR J. HESS, and the electrical engineer, Mr. WILLIAM J. KAUPP, started to incorporate the principles into a construction plan. In addition, they had to consider stringent building codes, limitations in available building site and its use, as dictated by the Pasadena City Planning Commission, and the wishes of the neighbors. Building materials and machinery were not obtainable in unlimited amounts in 1946-48, and building costs were rising rapidly, which necessitated many simplifications to make the available money produce as much as possible.

Actually, these three men, with the help of scores of others, have managed to satisfy the donor, the scientist, the administration, the neighbors, the City Planning Commission, the building inspectors, and many other interested parties. They have designed a building, pleasing to the eye (PLATE I), and operating according to the specifications of the scientist. Only a few alterations turned out to be necessary in the subsequent six years of operation; several of these were already anticipated, but in the interests of economy, were left out of the original plans. Yet on the whole, the original construction plan has proved to be entirely satisfactory and no major improvements could be suggested at present. FIGURES 4 and 5 show the floor plans of the basement and ground floor of the Earhart Plant Research Laboratory. A short description of the laboratory was published earlier (WENT 1950).

The design of the greenhouses, artificial light rooms, and other special features will be discussed in detail later, but there are several general construction problems which seem worth mentioning.

General Construction:— The basement of the building is reinforced concrete, and special precautions were taken to make it insect-proof from the beginning. All pipes were installed first and then the concrete poured around them, being particularly careful to vibrate sufficiently to insure the removal of bubbles. These precautions have proved successful as the basement has remained impenetrable to ants, termites, and other insects. It had to be deep enough to provide head room for proper working conditions, and, in addition, space for all air ducts, pipes, and tubes. The electric conduits were all enclosed in the walls and floors. The walls of the nutrient solution tank, the chilled water tank and the gas rooms are of concrete; all other interior walls are lath and plaster.

The above-ground parts of the laboratory are of wooden framework covered with lath and plaster. For insulation, aluminum foil was tacked in the air space between the plaster, and has proved very effective. The lower foot of the first floor walls are all concrete, so that they will not be dented by the trucks when the latter are being moved. All floors are smoothly finished concrete, except in the artificial light rooms and greenhouses, where they are slotted steel. There are no doorsills in any part of the building, so that trucks and wheeled tables can be moved from room to room without difficulty. An elevator allows plants and other materials to be brought back and forth from first floor to basement.

The roof is aluminum sheet over wooden slats (*see* PLATES I and II). During the day, this roof transmits a lot of heat to the attic, where 600 130-watt transformers and ballasts already constitute a heavy heat load. But since the fluorescent tubes in the artificial light rooms operate best at an envelope temperature of 40°-50°, the hot attic air can be put to good use in the light-bank air-conditioning systems, and the high temperature is permissible as long as a large enough volume of air is moved past the tubes. The attic, and also the basement, is supplied with an automatic sprinkling system to reduce the danger of fires spreading.

The windows are never opened, of course, but have fine screens on the inside so that no insects can get in if a pane is accidentally broken. It was also decided that it would not be necessary to have a small gutter around the outside of the building to keep back ants and other crawling insects. But to insure the exclusion of insects from the building, the sills and seams around the outside doors are regularly sprayed with Chlordane or, more recently, with a mixture of equal parts of the Isotox Number 200 and Orthomite 2 (containing aramite).

The offices and downstairs laboratory have a separate air-conditioning system which keeps the temperature at a comfortable level. The entire building is under positive pressure, which is supplied by relief dampers from one of the greenhouses.

This air leaves the building either through the front door, or by way of three vents in the ceiling of the first floor. From there the air is distributed through the attic, and passes either through the lamp-ventilation fans, or through the roof itself, which is not completely airtight. The positive pressure in the building as a whole prevents insects from being sucked in passively. Only a few houseflies have been able to fly against the airstream into the building through the front door.

There are separate exhaust fans in the spray room, the grinding room, and in the vestibule of the gas and radioactivity rooms. The basement doors to the greenhouse air-conditioning units are tightly closed because the basement room acts as a plenum for the greenhouse above.

The walls of the greenhouses and all the rooms provided with artificial light are painted with waterproof aluminum paint to give as much reflection as possible. It is satisfactory as long as the insides of the walls are kept dry. All other walls in the laboratory are painted either light green, light grey, or cream-color, which gives the rooms a cheerful yet sanitary appearance. Only the darkrooms are painted black.

Growing Room Construction:— The original Clark greenhouses, constructed in 1938-39 and described earlier (WENT 1943*a*), have been incorporated in the Earhart Plant Research Laboratory as the Red and Purple greenhouses. Their surface, 15 × 15′, is about half that of any of the four new greenhouses and they are used for the most extreme conditions, which are not in as great a demand. They are lean-to houses, facing South, 6′ high at their lowest point and 10′ at the North wall. The roof rafters are 2″ × 6″ redwood (on edge, with grooves) in which the glass is sealed with putty. Every two years the rafters have to be repainted, and the houses must be reglazed because the putty deteriorates, and the water running over the roof leaks in. This painting and reglazing every two years is a major operation, for the rooms have to be closed off from the rest of the building, and then they must be thoroughly fumigated before plants can be put back in them.

The conditioned air is introduced through a 3 × 4′ opening in the middle of the concrete floor. To distribute this as evenly as possible a diffuser with adjustable slots is placed over it. In spite of our best efforts, however, there are many dead air spots in the corners and over the center table, built above the diffuser, in the two original greenhouses. To help overcome these dead air pockets, an oscillating fan mixes the air at plant level. The air is removed from each greenhouse through an exhaust duct near the highest place in the North wall.

The operating of the Clark greenhouses has been satisfactory for the first ten years, but they have shown where improvements could be made in the construction of the Earhart Plant Research Laboratory. Their main weakness lay in the method of air introduction. Therefore, a large-scale model was built of wood to study the possibility of introducing the air over the whole width of the floor through slots. By experimenting with the width of the slots, and the location and size of the return ducts, it was found that when introduced at a speed of at least 100 m./min. (300 ft./min.) through 9 mm. (⅜″) wide slots, the air would mix almost immediately with the greenhouse air and then would rise evenly through the whole greenhouse without channeling ("drafts"). It would even move upward between plants placed rather close together on tables with perforated tops. When the return ducts were wide enough so that the air resistance in them was less than in the air introduction slots, their location was relatively unimportant, and when placed at plant height (4′-6′) did not interfere with an even air distribution.

In the greenhouses and artificially lighted growing rooms of the Earhart Plant Research Laboratory this method of air distribution through a slotted floor was generally adopted (*see* cross section in FIGURE 6). Each of these greenhouses and rooms has a double floor, the upper one consisting of steel channels spaced ⅜″ apart (*see* PLATES III and XIX), and the lower one,

18″ below, being a solid concrete subfloor. Between these the conditioned air is introduced. In this space between the two floors the kinetic energy of the air stream leaving the air-conditioner has to be transformed into static pressure, which is done by placing bricks upright at different distances from the introduction duct. The subfloor slopes slightly towards the center, where a drain carries off all excess water from watering plants or cleaning. It has been found that no difficulties arise from plugging of the slots between the steel beams with dead plant parts or gravel, and that a 2″ drain in the subfloor duct handles all refuse without difficulty. For proper cleaning of the subfloor the steel beams have to be taken up once every few years.

The steel floor consists of 4″ wide steel channels 1½″ × 4″ × 12′ in length, which are laid over joists 6′ apart. At their ends, ⅜″ spacers are welded, so that over their whole length, the steel beams leave a ⅜″ slot between them. They are fastened to the crossbeams with counter-sunk screws, leaving a smooth surface over which the wheeled tables can move smoothly. The steel beams are galvanized and do not show any signs of rusting after six years. The galvanization was done after the beams were fitted, which posed a special problem in preventing warping. By careful readjustment an acceptably smooth floor has been obtained. In the North and South walls, 6″ × 16″ ducts (*see* PLATE XIX) return the air from each greenhouse to its basement air-conditioning room.

The roof is constructed with aluminum rafters (*see* PLATES II and III) which are laid over a steel ridge pole constructed in such a manner as to intercept the least amount of light. The glass is laid in the aluminum rafters without putty; instead aluminum springs hold the 24″ wide and 6′ long panes tight against their seats. Between the overlapping glass edges Neoprene tubing makes a positive seal. This construction has many advantages: there is practically no leakage between glass and rafters, which is aided by the positive air pressure within the greenhouse. Such leakage is a special problem because of the continuous flow of water over the roof. In the second place, the replacement of broken panes is very simple, and involves only removal of the aluminum spring. The glass panes are double-strength, and after care was taken that expansion and contraction could take place freely, very few panes have been broken during the last three years. During replacement of a broken pane as great a volume of air as possible is blown into the greenhouse, which minimizes the danger of insects entering from the outside. Only at the last moment, when the pane is set, must the fans be turned off. As in the Clark greenhouses, there is no glass in the side walls, which are solid. Along the South wall, two shelves, 12″ wide, are placed 4½′ and 6½′ above the floor. Otherwise, the greenhouses are free of solid benches or other structures, giving greatest flexibility of use of space. Along the walls are outlets for electricity, de-ionized water, nutrient solution, compressed air and other utilities. Overhead electric lights are provided, but are to be used only for finding one's way about at night. More recently, in each greenhouse a set of overhead lights has been installed, which provide additional light during part of the night so that all plants in the greenhouses are subjected to an even 16-hour photoperiod throughout the year. These lamps are two 1000 watt incandescent lamps, with reflectors, producing a 25-75 ft.-c. intensity at plant level. Because the reflectors intercept too much daylight during day, these two lamps are pulled along trolleys against the wall, and only during night are they in position.

The double doors to each greenhouse are aluminum covered wood, and are located in a corner in the East walls. At moving time, both doors are opened to allow free passage of trucks in and out from the Atrium (*see* PLATE IV), a wide corridor leading towards the darkrooms.

The darkrooms and artificial light rooms are constructed in the same manner as the greenhouses (*see* PLATE V). They also have a slotted steel floor and solid side walls with all utilities. The doors are single, and the ceiling is plastered or has glass panels over which the artificial lights are mounted. For structural reasons the return air-conditioning ducts are not located in the walls but are mounted in the rooms themselves which takes away some room space, but does not seriously interfere with the placing of the trucks. It would have been advantageous, however, to locate two ducts per compartment in the side walls with flush-mounted grilles.

Most of these air-conditioned rooms are 8′ wide and 24′ long and are separated into light and dark compartments by light-tight partitions with sliding doors. Thus, no growing space is taken up by swinging doors. Originally, black curtains were used between the compartments, but they did not close tightly, and started to disintegrate after two to three years' use. They were then replaced with plywood partitions and sliding doors, also made of plywood. To prevent warping, the plywood was reinforced with angle-iron. It also was necessary to provide air passages through the partitions, which were made by filling frames of 2″ thickness with black excelsior which allows air, but no light, to pass through (*see* PLATE V). Commercially available darkroom louvres are better. Not only are there partitions between the light and dark sections, but the light-section is again divided into 4 ft. wide sections. This allows plants to receive different photoperiodic treatments without moving them at odd times during evening or night.

The three coldest constant-temperature artificial light rooms are built as a unit which is insulated against the outside with a 6″ layer of cork. Within this unit, the rooms are separated by lath and plaster walls with aluminum insulation. By sloping all electric conduits in the walls towards a drain, one avoids the condensation of water in them, thus no shorts have occurred in the electric wiring.

The rainroom in the basement is constructed like the other artificial light rooms, except it has no basement plenum for the air-conditioning unit. It has, however, a lining of water-proof plaster. This has given a great deal of trouble, and finally a water-proof tar seal was made between the concrete wall and the water-proof surface. The outlets in this room are all water-proof, of the outdoor type. The subfloor drains into a sump from which the rainwater can be recirculated through a pressure pump. A separate sump pump removes the excess water from the system.

The gas rooms are closed off airtight from the rest of the building, and can be reached only through an air-lock consisting of a series of two portals, one with a separate exhaust. Thus, contamination of the air in the rest of the laboratory is reduced to a minimum. Each of these rooms has a built-in air-conditioner, which circulates the air within the room, but does not blow it up through the floor, and has a separate exhaust towards the outside. The rooms can receive either air from the general laboratory supply, which is filtered through another set of carbon filters, or outside air that has not been filtered through charcoal. This allows studies of plants in smog-contaminated air in at least one room of the laboratory.

The air-conditioners for the artificial light rooms on the first floor are located in separate rooms immediately below them in the basement (*see* FIGURE 6). These rooms act as a plenum (space where fresh and return air are mixed and conditioned) and, thus, have approximately the same constant temperature as the room upstairs. The same utilities are present in them and, thus, they can be used in experiments requiring constant temperature.

Air-conditioning:— The range of temperatures for active plant growth is from 0°C to 40°C at its greatest. Actually the most effective range has been found to be from 10° to 26°C; the optimal temperatures for developmental mechanisms of most temperate-zone plants lie within this range. Tropical and alpine plants may grow well over wider limits, but their optima mostly lie between 10° and 26°C also.

After six years of operation, we have set up and stabilized the temperatures in the artificial-light controlled temperature rooms and the greenhouses in a way that seems to accommodate the largest number of plants and experiments. Our constant temperature rooms range from 4° to 30°C; the actual thermostat settings are as follows: 4°, 7°, 10°, 14°, 17°, 17°, 20°, 23°, 26° and 30°C (see FIGURE 4). An increment of 3°C, as we have here between successive rooms, seems small, but in the sensitive range the comparative growth differences are large. Therefore the temperature settings must be accurate, for a variation of plus or minus 1°C causes considerable differences in growth.

The greenhouse temperatures range from 17°-30°C, also in 3° increments. Here the arrangement is a little different from the constant-temperature-artificial-light rooms, because the temperature in each greenhouse is lowered about 6°C each night at 16:00, and kept low until 08:00 the next morning. Previous experiments in the Clark greenhouses showed that having the night temperature lower than the day improved the growth and fruit-set of most plants. If tomato plants were kept, *e.g.*, at 26°C all day and all night, they were spindly and fruit-set was poor. When the night temperature was lowered, fruit-set was much better. Although not all plants depend on night temperature to the extent that tomatoes do, it is true that the adaptation of plants to their surroundings has gone so far as to follow the daily fluctuation in temperature. Therefore, this nightly change in temperature gives better growth, and, as described in the discussion of the laboratory schedule, makes it possible for the plants to receive optimal day and night temperatures in the same greenhouse. Humidity is also a possible factor in plant growth. In the artificial light rooms it is only controlled to the extent that a fine water-spray is turned on when the relative humidity drops below 70 per cent. In the greenhouses humidity is controlled more positively, by adjusting the temperature of the spray-water. Although the units used for temperature control of the greenhouses and the artificial light rooms are somewhat different, they work on more or less the same principle. The temperature is adjusted by hot and chilled water coils through which the air is passed in succession; humidity is adjusted by sprays. Both greenhouses and artificial light rooms receive filtered air from the same intake system, which is described in Chapter 3.

However, because the arrangements in the rooms are slightly different, it might be well to describe the particulars of each separately.

Constant-Temperature, Artificial-Light Rooms:— A schematic cross section of the rooms is given in FIGURE 6. This shows the relative position of the rooms, where plants are grown, and the basement room, where the air-conditioner is situated, and supply ducts that carry conditioned air to the growing room, and the return ducts that bring the air back to the basement, where it is reconditioned. The circulation of air is, then, a closed system, dependent on the one fan in the air-conditioner; the basement room acts as a plenum. Into each basement room there is a duct which comes from the air intake source that supplies the entire building. Fresh air is taken into the rooms from this duct when it is needed. The intake is controlled by dampers which are opened or closed by a pneumatic motor. The controls for this motor are adjusted manually in the control room, so that any desired volume of fresh air can be added to the system. The pressure inside the rooms and basement is positive; this keeps unconditioned air from leaking in from the rest of the building. However, the pressure must be kept at a fairly even level to insure good circulation; therefore, any excess is bled out of the basement room through a set of dampers operated by pressure inside the room.

Now that we have an idea of the movement of the air throughout the constant-temperature-artificial-light room, we can consider how this air is conditioned, and how the temperature and humidity are controlled. The air-conditioning unit in this case is a Drayer Hanson Package Unit. This unit contains two heat-exchange coils, one for hot and one for chilled water. The air is driven through these coils and out by a centrifugal fan which is powered by a ¾ horsepower motor. Between the coils and the fan is the humidifier spray nozzle which is operated with a humidistat. The relative amounts of hot and chilled water in the coils are controlled by a pneumatic thermostat. Both controllers are situated over the air-return duct in the dark section of the room upstairs.

The thermostat operates in the following manner: all the pneumatic controls are run on 15 lbs. pressure. A main line leads from this system to each thermostat. From there the branch lines go to the two valves which regulate the flow of hot and chilled water into the air-conditioner coils. In one end of the thermostat is a small bellows; in the other a hole through which air is bled off. The valve for the chilled water supply is fully open when the pressure in the branch is 13 lbs., and fully closed at 9 lbs. The pressure needed to open and close these valves is regulated by a thermostat; when the air grows warmer, the bellows in the thermostat expands, and shuts off the bleeder-hole. Therefore, pressure will build up in the air line leading to the valves. When it builds up to 13 lbs., the chilled water valve will be wide open and the coils will have the maximal flow of chilled water. As the air in the air-conditioning system becomes cooler, the bellows in the thermostat contracts again, and air in the line is bled off through the bleeder-hole, and the air pressure in the valves drops. When it reaches 9 lbs., both chilled and hot-water valves are closed; the air in the rooms is now adjusted to the desired temperature. When it begins to get too cool, more air is bled off through the hole in the thermostat, and the pressure near the valves falls below 7 lbs., at which time the hot-water valve begins to open. If the pressure drops as low as 3 lbs., the hot-water valve is wide open, which gives maximum flow. As these are modulating controls (meaning that the valves can be maintained at any degree of opening), the amount of hot or chilled water supply is adjusted to the demand for heating or cooling. In construction and operation great care should be taken to adjust the flow of chilled and hot water through the valves to the rate of response of the thermostat; if the flow is too slow, temperature adjustments are slow; if the flow is too fast, so-called "hunting" occurs where the temperature overshoots the limits of the thermostat. These modulating controls, when properly adjusted, are able to keep the temperature constant within a fraction of a degree over long periods of time, because they adjust the amount of heating or cooling to the actual demand. The older type of thermostat which either is "off" or "on," operates not with a modulated flow of heat or cold, but supplies the full amount of heating as long as the thermostat is below the set temperature, and then suddenly cuts off the heat completely when the set temperature is reached.

The humidity in these rooms is adjusted by forcing tap water and compressed air (4 atm.) through an atomizing nozzle. The water and air flow is controlled by two solenoid valves which are opened and closed by a pressure switch which is operated by a hair-type humidistat. A rise in humidity gives a rise in air pressure which closes the solenoid valves. When the humidity drops, the pressure is reduced and the solenoid valve opens. The humidistats are set so that the relative humidity in the rooms will not drop under 70 per cent. This applies only to temperatures between 14° and 26°C. In the colder rooms (4°-10°C) the relative humidity goes up as high as 95 per cent. These facilities allow us to *increase* the humidity, but not to lower it. The air in the rain, wind, and special gas rooms is conditioned in the same way as it is in the 14°-26°C rooms. In the three cold rooms (4°, 7°, 10°C) the chilled water is not cold enough to do the required amount of cooling, so the coils in the air-conditioners are filled directly with refrigerant, and are of the so-called direct-expansion type. The refrigerant is re-compressed by a 7½ h.p. compressor; the condensing of the refrigerant was formerly accomplished by the roof-spray water (*see* Roof Spray section), but it was found that there was insufficient water to supply cooling for both the 60 and 7½ h.p. compressors. Now a separate evaporative condenser services the 7½ h.p. compressor.

The flow of refrigerant in the coils is regulated by solenoid valves, which are in turn controlled by the pneumatic thermostats in the rooms upstairs. A pneumatic-electric relay opens or closes the valves. This system is non-modulating, and the valves are either completely open, or completely closed. Therefore, the temperature control is not quite as close as in those rooms which have modulating valves. The variation is about plus or minus 1.0°C (*see* FIGURE 16).

In the 4°C room, the temperature of the refrigerant in the coils must be below freezing in order to cool the air to the 4°C mark. Because of the high humidity in the room, the coils ice up rather quickly, preventing further air flow through them. Therefore, it was necessary to install spray headers, operated by a solenoid valve connected to a time clock on the control panel, in front of the coils. The time clock is set to give a 10-minute spray of tap water on the coils at 08:00 and 16:00, which is sufficient to melt the ice formed in the intervening period. These two periods coincide with moving time, when the temperatures in the cold rooms are fluctuating anyway, so no additional rise in temperature is incurred.

Greenhouses:— The air-conditioners for the greenhouses have to handle large quantities of air and, consequently, they are much larger than those for the artificially lighted rooms. Because under appropriate conditions they have to cool the entering air by evaporation of water, they differ considerably from the unit air-conditioners just described (*see* FIGURE 6). They consist of a spray chamber with a face area of 50″ × 54″ and 84″ long in which a coarse water spray is produced by nozzles fed by a circulating pump of 2 h.p. All air has to pass through this spray chamber, and there becomes saturated at the temperature of the spray water. By regulating the temperature of the spray water, the wet-bulb temperature of the air leaving the spray chamber can be controlled. Cooling is regulated by a 3-way valve, which normally returns the water from the spray pan to the circulating pump, but upon opening mixes more or less chilled water with the spray-pan water. The opening is controlled by a modulating air motor, operated by a thermostat in the spray-pan water. When the thermostat calls for heating, the 3-way valve closes off the chilled water, and another modulating motor opens the hot water valve in a radiator placed in the air stream entering the spray chamber.

To bring the air to the proper dry-bulb temperature, which is required in the greenhouse, it passes through a re-heat coil in which the flow of hot water is regulated by a modulating valve which responds to a thermostat set in the greenhouse, in the return air duct. During the day, a considerable amount of required heat is derived from radiation. The driving force for the air is supplied by an axial flow (or blade-type) fan of 5 h.p., which forces the conditioned air into the double floor under the greenhouse. In the return air duct another 2 h.p. axial flow fan pulls the air out of the greenhouse, and delivers it into a space which has two sets of dampers which are inter-connected and are operated by an air motor. One set of dampers opens to the outside for air exhaust and the other opens into the air-conditioning equipment room which acts as a plenum. Into this same plenum the fresh air-supply duct opens. Another control motor interconnected with the exhaust damper motor controls any amount of fresh air taken in. The regulation of these dampers is critical for the proper operation of the greenhouses. The pressure in the space connected with the outside dampers has at all times to be positive, otherwise unfiltered outside air is drawn into the greenhouses. This is accomplished by having the air-supply dampers always sufficiently open to offset the suction in the basement plenum room caused by the greenhouse supply fan (E in FIGURE 6). As long as the greenhouse exhaust fan (E) is in operation, it produces a positive pressure in the plenum.

In the operation of these greenhouses the following points are of importance. Since the optimum growing conditions require a different day and night temperature, there are two thermostats in the spray pans and two in the return air duct. During day one set of thermostats is connected with the valve motors, and during night time the other pair, set for different temperatures, is in control. A 3-way valve switches over the thermostats for day to those for the night operation (*see* PLATE VI). This switching can be done either manually, or by a time clock, or by a light master control. The latter is a double thermostat of which one bulb is blackened and the other shielded from radiation. The temperature difference between the thermostats is a function of the total radiation. It is possible to set the double thermostat at any temperature differential which corresponds to any amount of radiation. Below this critical radiation, the greenhouse is operated by the night thermostat, and above it, the day thermostat regulates. Most of the operation is regulated by a time clock which shifts at 08:00 from night to day thermostat and at 16:00 from day to night. Since at these times plants are being moved from one greenhouse to the other, the temperature change for the plants being moved coincides with the temperature change in the air around the plants left in the greenhouse.

Since the relative humidity is not of paramount importance in the growth of plants, it is not kept constant from day to night, as this would involve a much greater operating expense. During day, when the air is heated 4 to 5 degrees by radiation, it is impossible to keep humidities higher than 70 per cent, because the radiation raises the dry-bulb temperature of the air without raising its wet-bulb temperature. During night, when no radiation enters the greenhouse, very high humidities can be maintained. This is very economical to do, because then little re-heating of the air leaving the spray chamber is necessary.

To decide whether the air should be largely re-circulated or removed, both the greenhouse temperature and the humidity of the outside air has to be considered. At any time during day with a high degree of radiation, the air leaving the air-conditioner for the greenhouse must be at least 5° cooler than the thermostatically set temperature. When this temperature lies above the wet-bulb temperature of the outside air, cooling by refrigeration is necessary. The higher this temperature differential is, the more refrigeration is needed. As soon as the amount of heat picked up inside the greenhouse is less than the amount of refrigeration required for cooling the outside air in the spray chamber, then the greenhouse air should be re-circulated for most economical operation. At lower outside temperatures, complete renewal of the greenhouse air without re-circulation is most economical, until much pre-heat has to be applied. Then more and more re-circulation should occur with only so much make-up fresh air that no refrigerative cooling is necessary.

At night, air can be re-circulated under all conditions; since so little heat has to be removed and at that time, it is largely a matter of supplying heat.

In one room (number 9 in FIGURE 4) the humidity of the air can be regulated accurately with a Kathabar air-conditioner. This is located in the basement (20 in FIGURE 5) and the air of room 9 can be circulated through it. This air is passed through a spray chamber, where its vapor pressure comes in equilibrium with that of droplets of concentrated lithium chloride. By regulating the temperature of the air and the lithium chloride, any relative humidity of the air can be produced and maintained. At 26°C the relative humidity can be reduced to 17%, which corresponds to extreme desert conditions (at higher temperatures, lower relative humidities can be produced; if the temperature were raised to 40° without changing the vapor content, the relative humidity would be 8%).

Refrigeration:— All greenhouses and artificially lighted rooms, which are kept above 10°C, are cooled with chilled water which is kept at about 5°C by a 60 h.p. compressor (21 in FIGURE 5). This compressor operates with freon. The refrigerant goes through expansion coils which are divided over four big chillers. A 5 h.p. pump circulates water through these chillers. The chilled water is kept in an 18,000 gallon tank which forms at the same time a storage of cold water which is available for the hours when the refrigeration load is greatest and also in case of power failure. After expansion, the refrigerant is returned to the compressor and is liquefied again in a condenser through which the roof spray water passes.

A pressure switch in the refrigerant line starts or stops the big compressor and maintains an even water temperature which ranges from 4°-6°C. A thermostat in the chilled water tank is set at 3°C to cut off the main compressor to prevent icing of the chillers in case the pressure switch fails to work. The compressors themselves have all the regular safety and control devices customary in these systems.

Although a leakage of freon has occurred several times, no definite damage to the plants in the laboratory could be attributed to it. It, therefore, seems that freon is a safe refrigerant that can be used in greenhouses. Only on the warmest days is the capacity of this refrigeration system insufficient; on such days, however, shutting off the chilled water from one or two greenhouses and using only evaporative cooling, the temperatures in the rest of the building can be maintained.

The chilled water is circulated throughout the building and provides a very effective method of cooling greenhouses and artificially lighted rooms. Only the rooms kept at 10°C or below require a different type of cooling. The air-conditioners for the latter have direct expansion coils operated by a solenoid valve. For economy, the three coldest rooms are serviced by a single 7½ h.p. compressor, which poses difficult problems in balancing the refrigeration. Another 5 h.p. compressor cools through direct expansion the Purple greenhouse, of which the air-conditioning system is not connected with the chilled water system. The walk-in refrigerator has a separate 2 h.p. compressor.

Heating:— All heating in the laboratory is performed by warm water, which is circulated continuously through the supply-and-return pipes. The water is heated in a double gas-fired boiler (3 in FIGURE 5), which is located in the extreme Northwest corner of the building in a special boiler room. Access to this room is only through the outside, so that no exhaust gases can enter the building. The exhaust gases escape through a stack, which reaches above the roof level. The prevailing wind, which is either Northeast during night, or Southwest during day, carries this exhaust away from the building. The two boilers operate independently; under normal conditions, only one is in operation, and is controlled by a thermostat in the side where the water leaves the boiler. When, on cold days, the one boiler is insufficient, the temperature of the water will drop below the cut-in point of the second thermostat. At this point, the thermostat of the second boiler is activated which then turns it on. The gas flames are operated in the regular manner with all necessary safety devices. An alarm system indicates when the temperature of the hot water supply has dropped below 70°C, or when the circulating pumps have stopped.

A small separate boiler (28 in FIGURE 5), also gas fired, produces low pressure steam, which is used for the autoclaves or for steam sterilization of sand and gravel in the storage bins.

All other heating in the laboratory is electrical, so as not to produce fumes from incomplete gas combustion which might damage plants; where open flames are needed, such as in sterile culture work, an alcohol burner is used.

Roof Spray:— A continuous film of water is maintained over the glass roof. The primary purpose of this water is to remove the long wave lengths from the entering radiation. Calculations show that about 20 per cent of all radiation is removed in this way, since the wave lengths above 12000 Å are absorbed by water, even in very thin films. These wave lengths do not affect plant growth other than by supplying heat. The roof spray water is at the same time used in the condenser of the 60 h.p. compressor, which obviates the necessity of building a big cooling tower. As a third function, this water diffuses the sunlight in the greenhouses so that the rafters do not throw sharp shadows. In the fourth place, this water washes dust, leaves, and other extraneous matter from the glass surface. And finally, it evens the temperature of the glass, whereas during the summer strong evaporative cooling keeps the temperature of the spray water below the air temperature, in winter this water may be above the air temperature because it carries the heat from the refrigeration condenser. This reduces condensation against the glass inside the houses.

At first considerable difficulty was encountered in making the roof sprays efficient as a cooling tower. Not until conical sprays were installed throwing most of the water upwards before it falls on the roof, was sufficient cooling obtained (*see* PLATE II). The water, when only rippling over the glass roof, does not have sufficient surface to act as a cooling tower. In addition, some extra conical sprays are pointing upwards to increase the water surface in contact with the outside air.

The greatest difficulty in connection with roof spray water is to keep algae from growing in it. Originally, periodic injection of bromine proved an effective method of algae control, and only because of repeated mechanical difficulties with the injector was this method abandoned. It was found that if water saturated with bromine was injected for one hour into the roof spray water this was sufficient to kill all algae; however, the injection had to occur very early in the morning so as not to cause an excessive evaporation of bromine before it had run down the roof. For several years, the bromine injector was disconnected and the algae were controlled by adding 3 lbs. of Santobrite once every week to the 1000 gallons of roof spray water. Now, with an improved injection system, bromine is again used, at a higher rate, for half an hour once every 4 days.

With continuous evaporation of the spray water, a very high salt concentration would be reached, if it were not for continuous slow bleeding off. The water bled off and the proportion evaporated is made up with ordinary tap water. To prevent excessive scale deposition on the glass, the make-up water passes through a Micromet apparatus which supplies sodium hexameta-phosphate which keeps calcium and iron in solution and prevents corrosion.

Although the algicides are very toxic to all plants, no difficulties have been encountered in the greenhouses from dripping roof spray water. The aluminum roof construction closes very tightly and, also, the positive pressure in the greenhouses helps prevent the roof spray water from entering.

Light:— Artificial light sources have in the past been developed along two lines: an increase in light intensity per source and a decrease in surface intensity coupled with an increase in surface. From candle to oil burner or gas jet there was not much improvement, until surfaces were made to emit radiation with the heat of the flame. Thus, the incandescent gas burner appeared which was the first artificial light source of sufficient intensity to attempt to grow plants with. Very soon afterwards the electric arc appeared, and for more than half a century this has been used successfully in the growing of plants. The most experience with carbon arcs in plant growing has been gained by PARKER and BORTHWICK (1949) who use specially prepared carbons to obtain proper spectral composition of the light produced; yet, they obtain somewhat better growth by adding light from incandescent electric lamps to the carbon arc light. The main advantage of the carbon arc is its very high luminosity, which can be raised to almost any desired level. Disadvantages are: (*1*) discontinuous operation, due to the need of periodic renewal of the carbons, (2) fluctuating intensity, due to a continuous shift in the crater location in the carbon, (3) production of undesirable gases, which have to be removed (ozone, oxides of nitrogen), (*4*) point source of light, with concomitant rapid change in intensity upon change in distance from light, and (5) high proportion of ultraviolet light. By filling the core of the carbons with different materials, one can vary the spectral distribution of the emitted light.

The incandescent electric lamps proved to be very useful as light sources for the growing of plants. The Nernst Lamp, in which a porcelain resistor is made to emit an intense white light, was used in some cases, but technical difficulties prevented it from becoming a useful light source. With the production of filaments of higher and higher melting point, the metal filament incandescent lamp became a better light source, until some 30 years ago it had replaced almost all other artificial light sources for the growing of plants. The main advantages are: (*1*) cheap elements and low installation costs, (2) ease of renewal of burned-out elements, (3) steady light intensity, (*4*) good growth of plants in its light, (5) safety of operation, and (6) flexibility of operation. But among the disadvantages of the incandescent electric lamp have to be counted: (*1*) its low efficiency in transforming electrical into light energy, (2) the inflexibility of its spectral emission, (3) the high proportion of heat radiation requiring special heat filters when used for growing plants, and (*4*) the low proportion of shorter wave radiation in the visible spectrum.

The incandescent lamp is still essentially a point source of radiation, like the carbon arc, but its cheapness and convenience in installation make it possible to install such large numbers, that essentially a continuous light source is available. The amount of heat which has to be removed is so large that the only practical arrangement is to have a sheet of running water between the incandescent lamps and the plants. In some installations (VAN DER VEEN 1950) the temperature control is achieved by the rate of flow of the cooling water between lamps and plants.

The advent of the gas discharge lamps, such as neon, helium, sodium vapor and mercury vapor lamps has completely changed the growing of plants in artificial light. Although at first the spectral distribution of these different sources was not proper for plant growth, fluorescent coatings can produce any spectral range in the visible region. Before the fluorescent lamps were available, fairly successful attempts were made in using neon and mercury vapor lamps (for instance, Cooper-Hewitt lamps in the Clark greenhouses of Caltech).

From a human comfort standpoint, the fluorescent electric lamps are almost ideal in that they have a relatively low surface brightness which prevents blinding; besides, they emit approximately five times as much visible radiation per unit electricity as incandescent lights. Against these

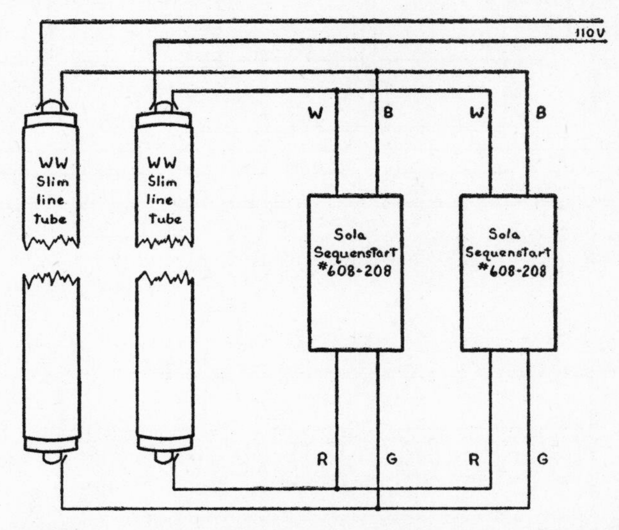

FIGURE 7.— Wiring diagram for installation of 8′ Slimline fluorescent tubes, when two are connected with two 2-lamp transformers to run on 400-500 m.a.

advantages we have to weigh the following disadvantages of fluorescent lights for the growing of plants: (*1*) low surface intensity at the plant level, (2) their installation costs are high due to their high starting voltage and the necessity of ballasts to counteract their negative voltage-amperage characteristics, (3) the high cost per individual lamp, (4) the extra safety precautions needed on account of their high starting and operating voltage, and (5) toxicity of some phosphors. The toxic beryllium phosphors are not being used any more in the new fluorescent tubes. Taking all advantages and disadvantages into consideration, fluorescent lamps today are the most practical source of light for the growing of plants.

As light source in the artificial light rooms of the Earhart Plant Research Laboratory, the eight-foot Slimline fluorescent tube was selected as the most economical, giving the highest light intensity. They are arranged in panels of ten tubes each, separated from the growing room by glass panes set in an aluminum window frame of two by eight feet (*see* PLATE V). This window serves several purposes: (*1*) it separates the plants from the high voltage of the tubes, and (2) it allows separate ventilation of the lights. This is very important, because the fluorescent lamps operate at their highest efficiency at an envelope temperature of about 50°C. Near freezing, the lamps may not start at all and their light emission is very low. Therefore, to get uniform light intensities in rooms of different temperature, it was necessary to ventilate the fluorescent lamps separately so as to keep their surface temperature between 40° and 50°C. This is accom-

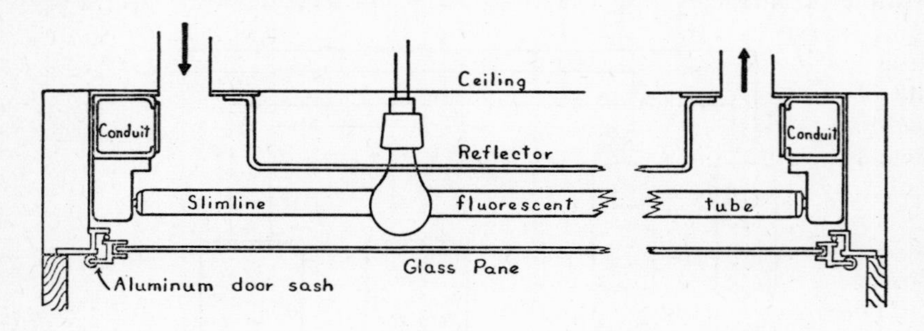

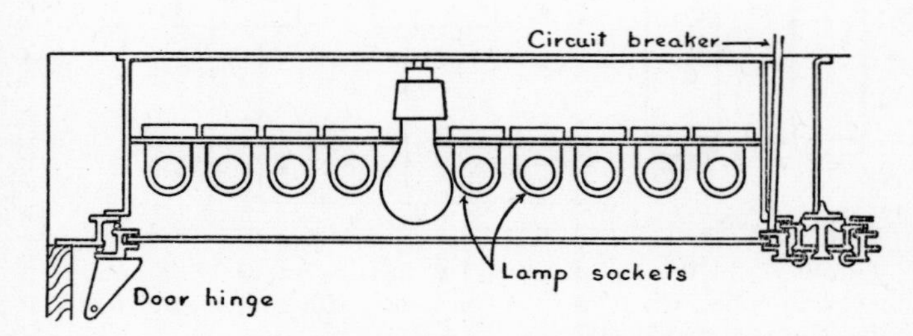

FIGURE 8.— Cross sections through artificial light panels. Air is circulated (*bold arrows*) past lamps between reflector and glass panes. The conduits carry the wires from the lamps to the transformers in the attic.

plished by thermostats in the ventilating system of the lamps. As soon as the air temperature around the lamps becomes too high, fans start to operate to remove this hot air and replace it with attic air, which is warm at all times.

To obtain a higher surface intensity of the lamps, they are operated at a higher amperage than ordinarily recommended. Instead of using 100 milliamps, the tubes are operated at 290 milliamps each by paralelling two 200 m.a. ballasts (*see* FIGURE 7). In addition to the fluorescent lamps a certain number of incandescent lamps are used at the rate of four 60-watt incandescents to every eight or nine Slimline fluorescents. FIGURE 8 shows cross sections through a two-by-eight foot light panel which is arranged in groups of two per light compartment; both are usually operated simultaneously. Between each group of two panels, sliding doors can be closed to obtain different photoperiodic treatments. The light intensity varies according to the distance from the light panel. Because the walls are highly reflective, being coated with aluminum paint, the intensity drops only slightly towards the edge of the light compartments. At a distance of 10 cm. from the glass panel, the average intensity is 1300 ft.-c., at 20 cm. it is 1150 ft.-c., at 50 cm. it drops to 1000 ft.-c., at 100 cm. distance it is 700 ft.-c., and at floor level 300 ft.-c. These figures refer to intensities without shading. By placing the plants on trucks which are adjustable in height, it is possible to subject plants to any desired light intensity below 1300 ft.-c., and to maintain such light intensity by gradually lowering trucks as the plants grow up. The lamps are separated from the room by a glass partition (*see* PLATE V and FIGURE 8) so that the room air does not get in contact with the lamps. At air temperatures below 10°C fluorescent lamps emit only a small fraction of their potential light output. In the 26°, 23°, 17° and 10°C rooms, the average light intensity at 60 cm. below the light panels is 980, 970, 920 and 930 ft.-c., since the lamps all operated at approximately the same envelope temperature.

The ballasts for the fluorescent lamps are all mounted outside the light panels themselves, so that their heat does not have to be removed by the lamp ventilating system. In all cases, even for the lights in the basement growing rooms, the ballasts are installed in the attic. This attic is thus heated, and this warm air is then used to ventilate the lamps. A thermostat in the exhaust duct of the lamp ventilators operates an exhaust fan. Since a number of panels are ventilated by the same exhaust fan, and these panels are operating on very different schedules, this arrangement is not very satisfactory. A much better arrangement involves continuous operation of the exhaust fans, whereas the air flow through each panel is regulated by a separate thermostatically controlled damper. The thermostat should be installed on the exhaust side of the panel fairly close to the lamps.

More recently a new method of operation of the fluorescent tubes has been described. The eight foot fluorescent Slimline tubes are operated on 360-cycle current. This makes it possible to omit the ballasts, provided a proper condenser is put in the light circuit. The available frequency converter will operate 50 tubes at a time at a much higher light intensity than is possible on available ballasts, and in this way plants can be grown in over 2000 ft.-c. intensity. This high frequency practically eliminates the flickering of the fluorescent tubes. There are two drawbacks to the use of the frequency converter. One is the high price, the other is the inability to operate only a fraction of the 50 tubes: they have to operate all at the same time.

In designing artificially lighted plant-growth chambers, not only the light source has to be considered. If possible, the lamps should cover the whole surface of the ceiling, being immediately bordered by highly reflecting walls. This prevents the rapid dropping off of the light intensity near the perifery of the light panels. By installing lights along the sides of the chamber, the light intensity at a certain level of height is not constant and drops from the sides towards the center. This makes it very difficult to subject a whole group of plants to the same light intensity. When all lights are installed in the ceiling, and when the walls are adjacent to the lamps, the light intensity at any given distance from the lights is fairly even and can be adjusted by raising or lowering the plants under the lights.

Another recent improvement is to replace in each light panel the ordinary incandescent light bulbs with incandescent strip lamps (lumiline). This evens the light intensity even more.

Electrical Power Supply:— In the Earhart Laboratory all motors have a combined capacity of 180 h.p. Near each motor there is a power cut-off and in the basement there is a general switchboard panel with automatic contacters and manual switches for all motors and lights. The contacters of the major motors each have a microswitch attached which operates an indicator light on the indicator panel in the control room (*see* PLATE VI). In this way, it is possible to see at once which motors are running and which are not. Each motor which is running shows this with a white indicator light. Motors which have to operate continuously show a red light when they are off; intermittently running motors (such as nutrient solution pump, air compressors, etc.), show an orange light when not in operation. Thus, the appearance of a red light indicates the necessity for immediate attention.

The electricity is received in the transformer vault at 2300 volt. Two transformers step this voltage down to 220 V. 3-phase, or 110 V. single phase. Only the 60 h.p. main compressor motor runs on 2300 V. and has its cut-off and fuses in the transformer vault. All motors of 1 h.p. or more are 3-phase motors.

Since there are no ventilators in the greenhouses, a power failure during daytime would be disastrous for the plants. For this reason, an emergency power supply is available in the form of a 30 KW gasoline-powered motor generator (29 in FIGURE 4). When for some reason the power supply in the laboratory fails, the generator starts automatically and furnishes 220 V. 3-phase current to the most essential functions (circulating fans and spray pumps in the air-conditioners of the greenhouses, air compressor, sump pumps, heating controls, alarms, chilled water supply pump, emergency lighting). These are all located on a special panel which can be energized either by the regular current or the motor generator.

In order not to overload the generator, the motors are started at intervals of 5 seconds through a multiple switch, operated by a camshaft which is run by a 5-minute time clock. This in turn shunts the starter switches for the various motors. A similar arrangement starts all other motors, too, after the regular electric power supply has been re-established. To indicate when and how long there has been a power failure, two electric clocks are mounted on the indicator panel. Both of them operate on the regular power supply. One of these is self-starting, the other is not. The latter will indicate at what hour the power supply was cut off, the former shows the length of time the power was interrupted. A counter on the motor generator indicator indicates how many hours it has run.

The voltage fluctuations in the power supply are not very large, and motors and lights perform very evenly without a need for voltage regulation.

In every room and greenhouse are outlets for 110 V. a.c., and in addition there are binding posts in all greenhouses and growing rooms, which are connected with a set of terminals in the control room. This makes possible the sending of electric signals or other types of current to the greenhouses or the recording of electric impulses from the greenhouses in the control room. A small motor generator can furnish 10-16 V. d.c., or 100-150 V. d.c. current.

All wires for electric power supply and lighting are TW (plastic insulated). Since all conduits are drained, no water collects in them, and not a single short has developed in any of the conduits in spite of the fact that very high humidities and strong temperature differentials exist throughout the building, and that 13 miles of wire are installed.

All outlets in the laboratories and greenhouses are three-pronged with one of the prongs grounded. In other places, where moisture is not a menace, two-pronged outlets are provided.

Utilities:— In every greenhouse, artificial light room, dark room and basement plenum room there are outlets for ordinary tap water, for deionized water, for nutrient solution, for compressed air (4 atm.), for chilled water and for warm water. The latter outlets are simply connected with the chilled and warm water supply and return pipes which carry the cooling and heating load of the building. The temperature of the water fluctuates considerably, but it can be used for general heating or cooling purposes, and when passed through an automatic "Powers" thermostatically controlled mixing valve, together with tap water, it can be used to obtain constant temperature for small apparatus within each room.

Because the combustion products of gas can be very toxic to plants, no gas outlets are in the laboratory.

Compressed air is generated by two 5 h.p. compressors which work alternately. This prevents overloading. Before entering the pipe-line system throughout the building, the air is passed from the storage tanks through a reduction valve and porous stone filter which removes the oil from the air. In this way, no damage is done to plants by the compressed air. The large capacity of the air compressors is required for the large volumes of air which are needed in the aeration of nutrient cultures and for the humidifier nozzles in the air-conditioning units. Finally, it is used for the regulating valve control of the air-conditioners. To this end, the air is passed into a small after-cooler to remove moisture and oil, then through a 15 lb. regulating valve which keeps the pressure for the control system even at all times.

The compressed air supply in the whole building simplifies experiments on photosynthesis. In this way, only one single source of control air need be analyzed in conjunction with the air passed through individual assimilation chambers.

Control Room:— This centrally located room holds all recorders, indicating panels and time-clocks (*see* PLATE VI). The temperature recorder is connected with thermocouples in each of the growing rooms and greenhouses. In this way, it is possible to see at a glance whether all air-conditioners are functioning properly and a record is obtained by which the performance of each room at each time can be checked. On an indicator panel, the operation of each of the major motors is indicated. Running time meters on this panel count the number of hours that the 60 h.p. compressor and other motors were in operation.

Since all air-conditioner controls are operated by a compressed air system, it was easy to bring branch-lines off the individual control circuits for each air-conditioner up to the control room. There the branch lines are connected with pressure gauges which indicate the operation of the several valves. In addition, each branch line ends in a petcock which makes it possible to control the opening and closing of each valve from the control panel. When the temperature recorder shows aberrations in the set temperatures, the indicator panels will immediately show whether these aberrations are due to improper operation of valves or motors.

Half of one wall of the control room is taken up by the time-clock panel. A total of eleven time-clocks, with cycles ranging from 4 days to one minute and comprising a total of 60 individual contacts with 120 control positions, makes it possible to obtain any desired cycle. Instead of the regular cams supplied with the time-clocks, special cams are made which allow multiple and irregular on-and-off periods throughout one cycle of each time-clock. At the base of this panel, binding posts are connected with the contactors for each of the 62 artificial light panels in the building. By connecting these binding posts with the proper time-clocks, any light-and-dark cycle can be obtained for any of the light panels.

A total of 16 elapsed time counters are mounted on this panel. The current from any of the time circuits can be passed through these counters, and thus the operation of any time-clock-controlled process can be checked.

Another panel carries the terminals for the binding posts in the artificial light rooms and greenhouses. Through this panel, rooms can be interconnected electrically, or nine different signals from the time-clock panel can be transmitted to each of these rooms. It is also possible to record electrical impulses produced in the growing rooms on electric recorders in the control room.

In addition to all these recording and indicating instruments, there is a

Thomas CO_2-analyzer in the control room. From each of the greenhouses and artificial light rooms, two Saran tubes with a diameter of 8 mm. run to the control room, and thus air samples can be removed from any of the rooms to be analyzed centrally.

The superintendent and assistant superintendent have their desks in the control room.

The indicator lights and other electrical equipment generate so much heat in the control room that a separate exhaust fan is necessary to remove this heat.

The Automatic CO_2-Analyzer:— One of the most valuable research instruments in the Earhart Laboratory is the CO_2-analyzer, modified and improved by Dr. M. D. THOMAS after the original description of his CO_2-autometer (THOMAS 1933). To paraphrase Dr. THOMAS's own words (1933): "In view of the important role of atmospheric carbon dioxide in many phases of biology, such as animal and plant respiration, photosynthesis, and air pollution, it is surprising that" . . . the automatic CO_2-analyzer of THOMAS is not more generally used. In the work of THOMAS and collaborators (1937, 1943) it was clearly shown how well adapted this instrument is to the study of photosynthesis and plant respiration. Since 1933 other CO_2-analyzers have been described, using the absorption of infrared light by CO_2 as a quantitative measure of its concentration. Several adaptations of this principle are now available as automatic CO_2-analyzers, which are in use by many botanists. It was decided, however, to use the Thomas method in the Earhart Laboratory, and in 1950 we received from Dr. THOMAS a greatly improved CO_2-autometer. This has been installed and is being described in its present form.

The principle of this apparatus is the measurement of the decrease in conductivity of a weak NaOH solution after CO_2 absorption. To make the determination continuous, a constant stream of air is mixed with a constant flow of NaOH, and the conductivity of the effluent NaOH can then be expressed in parts per million of CO_2 in the entering air.

The analyzer consists of the following parts (*see* FIGURE 9):

1) Distributing valve (O). This valve has 12 inlet ports which discharge in rotation through a common outlet to the Zenith metering pump (P). By means of this valve a different source of air for analysis is selected every 4 minutes.

2) The NaOH reservoir consists of two 100 liter drums, one mounted above the other. The lower one serves as storage reservoir, and new solution is made in the upper one. The make-up water (deionized) is passed through a cartridge in which the calculated amount of NaOH pellets (13.9 gr. per 100 liter) is placed. After thorough mixing inside the upper reservoir by means of a stirrer, the solution can be drained into the lower reservoir. The air thereby displaced from the lower is returned to the upper reservoir. All fresh air displacing the NaOH solution passes through a CO_2 absorbent before entering the tanks. Thus, the concentration of the NaOH remains unchanged for long storage periods. The analyzer uses approximately 10 l. of NaOH per day, so that once every three weeks, two new batches of NaOH have to be made. The NaOH is pumped by a diaphragm pump (E) into the absorption tube. A small geared-down motor moves the diaphragm at a rate of once every 2

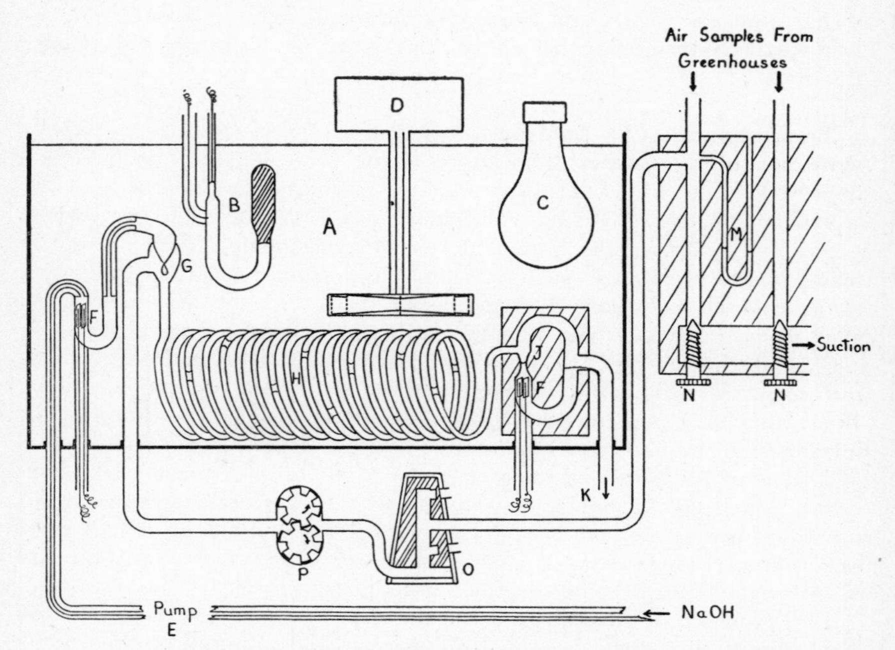

FIGURE 9.— Diagram of the Thomas CO_2-Analyzer. All absorption and measurements of conductivity are carried out in a water bath (A) which is maintained at constant temperature with a thermostat (B) and heating element (light bulb: C). Water is continuously stirred with a centrifugal pump (D). Dilute NaOH comes from 100 l. storage tank and with a pump (E) is introduced past the conductivity cell (F) into the absorber (H) at G, together with the air to be analyzed. At J, air and NaOH solution are again separated, with the latter passing through the conductivity cell (F). At K, the spent NaOH is discarded. The air is pulled from the greenhouses with slight suction. The rate can be adjusted with screws (N), and the actual suction in the line is read with a manometer (M). Samples of this air then pass through the 12-port valve (O), which connects in succession each one of the 12 air sources to the Zenith metering pump (P) by which the air is introduced at G into the absorber (H).

seconds, which results in 0.2 cc. displacement per stroke, or about 6 cc. per minute. The amount of solution can be measured with an electric counter which counts the number of drops entering the absorption tube. This number should be constant per unit time and an occasional check of the counter tells whether the pump is performing properly. Most trouble was encountered in leaking valves of the diaphragm pump, caused by dirt in the NaOH supply line. As a check, the NaOH as it leaves the analyzer (at K) can be titrated, too. The use of rubber in the connections through which NaOH passes is avoided as much as possible because of the solubility of CO_2 in rubber. Glass and tygon tubing is used throughout.

3) The same motor which operates the NaOH pump (E) also drives the Zenith gear pump (P), which delivers an accurately measured amount of air, 300 cc. per minute, to the absorption tube. The Zenith gear pump is designed for liquids which lubricate the gears. When used for pumping air, a small oil container supplies about 0.1 cc. of lubricant per day which is collected at the exhaust side of the pump, from where it can be returned to the oil supply container by a connecting tube. This pump has been completely trouble-free. It has to develop a fairly high pressure, about 1/4 atm., to move the drops of NaOH through the absorption tube.

4) The absorption tube (H) is a particularly neat development of Dr. THOMAS. It is 9 m. long with an i.d. of 4 mm. and is coiled. The air pushes the drops of NaOH through the tube. They are, thus, wiped off along the length of the tube, which brings the air for about 20 seconds in intimate contact with the NaOH which covers about 1000 $cm.^2$ of tube surface. The excess NaOH is pushed out of the end of the tube and by that time has absorbed over 99 per cent of the CO_2 in the air. Since the supply of air and NaOH are both constant, the NaOH leaves the tube also at a constant rate. It is then separated from the air (at J), and flows through a conductivity cell (F) in which two platinum electrodes are separated by the solution of which the conductivity is to be measured. Air bubbles between the electrodes can immediately be recognized by very irregular resistance readings, which vary periodically with the pulses of NaOH passing through the absorption tube.

5) The absorption tube and conductivity cells are immersed in a constant temperature water bath (A), of which the temperature should not vary more than 0.01°C. Irregularities in the temperature of the bath are detected in irregular readings of the zero cell (F) in the supply line of the NaOH. To get best CO_2 absorption the bath temperature should be kept at 40°C., and it should always be above the maximum room temperature. The thermoregulator (B) is sensitive, and the heater element (C) has only slightly more capacity than needed to keep the bath at the required temperature at the lowest room temperature. To get a heater with a very small heat capacity, incandescent lamps with the bulbs immersed in the water are found most convenient, and it is very easy to select one of the proper wattage.

6) The recording is done by a Brown Electronik Recorder, with the interrupter removed, so that the conductivity of the NaOH can be measured with the regular 60-cycle a.c. current, transformed down to about 1 volt. The range of the recorder is from 250-500 ohm. The conductivity cells have about 260 ohm resistance with the 0.003 N. NaOH solution. Their resistance is accurately matched with a variable resistor. At 2000 p.p.m. CO_2 the resistance of the NaOH after absorption is almost a linear function of the CO_2 concentration. At a constant flow rate of air and 0.003 N. NaOH the recorder can be calibrated to read 5 p.p.m. CO_2. To permit reading of the continuous line drawn by the pen of the recorder, and recognition of the records of the different air samples, the resistance cell is momentarily disconnected at each change of air sample, which causes the pen to write a short horizontal line. Since it takes the new air sample 30 seconds to reach the recording resistance cell, the record during the 30 seconds following the change of air sample, gives the true CO_2 value for the air sample which passed through the absorber in the previous period.

7) Once in every revolution of the selector or Blackman valve, the recorder is connected with the resistance cell in the supply line of NaOH during the last minute

of the last sample's record. This gives the zero reading of the recorder, checks the NaOH, and conveniently visually separates the series of samples.

8) For calibration of the CO_2 recorder a number of compressed oxygen tanks are evacuated. An accurately measured amount of CO_2 is injected into them, and then they are filled up with CO_2-free N gas to the pressure calculated to give the desired CO_2 concentration: 200, 350 and 500 p.p.m. for instance.

With the CO_2 recorder it was found that the air turnover in all greenhouses and artificial light rooms of the Earhart Laboratory is always fast enough so that no appreciable difference in the CO_2 content occurs, when compared with the outside air. The presence of persons in any of the air-conditioned rooms is not reflected in increased CO_2 content of the air, nor is a decrease found as a result of photosynthesis. However, the presence of one or more persons in a non-air-conditioned room, like the control room, shows up within a few minutes in an increased CO_2 content of the air.

When dry ice was stored in an insulated container in one of the artificial light rooms, a constant increase in CO_2 content was obtained. This is actually the easiest method of increasing the CO_2 content of the air in these rooms; the degree of insulation of the dry ice container controls the release of CO_2, and the constant amount of make-up air keeps the concentration in the air constant.

Chapter 3

MAINTENANCE OF RELATIVE STERILITY

The Earhart Plant Research Laboratory consists basically of a number of greenhouses, artificially lighted and dark rooms and, in addition, all the necessary machinery to make them function. Investigators are only concerned with research problems; the technical staff, headed by the superintendent, takes care of watering, moving trucks, keeping the machinery working, etc. In the following chapters a number of these technical matters will be discussed, because so many of them are of more general interest. It is, *e.g.*, possible to get an impression of how much work is involved in keeping greenhouses insect- and disease-free, what difficulties are encountered with air-filters, how we have solved problems of growing, watering and staking of plants, etc.

Since so many precautions are taken to control the environment of the plant as far as light, temperature, humidity, soil, nutrition, etc. are concerned, every effort is made to keep other disturbing influences such as pests and diseases out of the laboratory. To this end, all persons, materials and air entering the Earhart Plant Research Laboratory have to be decontaminated, sterilized or filtered. To get an idea of the magnitude of this activity it can be stated that, per year, about 100 tons of gravel, materials and supplies have to pass through the sterilization procedures. On an average of about 50 times per day persons enter the building which amounts to 18,000 entries per year. Each day about 1,000 tons of fresh air are filtered and decontaminated. A number of procedures have been adopted more or less arbitrarily to achieve this sterilization and decontamination and the results have borne out the effectiveness of these measures, since for a period of one and one-half years actually no insect infestations have occurred at all and no serious parasitic diseases have been observed.

Decontamination of Personnel:— Persons entering the building could bring in either insects or plant diseases. To minimize this possibility everyone entering the building has to change clothes. Once a person becomes aware of the fact that he may be a vector of insect-spreading, it is amazing to observe how many aphids or other plant pests are carried on one's clothing. All outer garments, which were in contact with the outside and on which aphids and other insects or spores of diseases might be carried, are removed in the dressing room. This outer clothing is then placed in cupboards designated for street clothes. The regular workers keep a set of laboratory clothes in the dressing room, which they put on instead of their street clothes. These laboratory clothes are left hanging in a separate cupboard in the dressing room. When these clothes are freshly washed and ironed, they are insect- and disease-free, and can be brought into the building without further sterilization, provided they were kept in a tightly closed bag immediately after ironing, and the bag removed only after entry into the building. The following routine for changing clothes has been adopted: first the person removes all his outer clothing, then he combs his hair and washes his hands. It is then fairly certain that he has removed all insects and readily detachable disease spores from himself. He then puts on laboratory clothes. Shoes are also changed, since it became evident that our original procedure of spraying them with D.D.T. was probably not sufficient to eliminate all chance of contamination. Now, every person has a pair of laboratory shoes which are sterilized before they are taken into the building and then are left there on special shelves. This procedure would still leave the possibility that insects could be tracked into the dressing room and then could be transferred to the laboratory shoes by way of the dressing room floor. To prevent this, the floor is regularly washed with chlordane or lindane which leaves a residue which is effective for several weeks. There is now no indication that any insects or diseases are brought in by way of shoes. Unless the washing of hands is strictly adhered to, viruses like tobacco mosaic are transmitted.

The number of visitors is kept to a minimum to prevent the possibility of their being vectors for pests or diseases and, also, because they pose a special problem as far as laboratory clothes are concerned. After removing their outer clothes the same way that the regular laboratory workers do, they are supplied with freshly laundered hospital gowns and caps or the regular doctor's uniforms used in operating rooms. The shoe problem is solved by supplying rubber galoshes, which can be put over the outside shoes, and which are kept in containers with ethylene dibromide, providing continued sterilization of the galoshes while they are not being worn. Workmen and maintenance men who come in only occasionally are supplied with overalls and rubber galoshes.

Since most workers eat lunch in the laboratory in a special place away from the growing plants, these lunches can be brought in without special sterilization. The container in which the lunch is carried has to be further enclosed in a paper bag which is removed upon entering the building. All fruits and fresh vegetables which can carry aphids are banned, but easily washed vegetables and fruits are allowed to be brought in provided they are thoroughly scrubbed before entering the building. All other materials, such as notebooks, which have to be taken into the building, are fumigated the same way as other materials.

The few times that insect pests entered the building, the whole laboratory had to be gassed, which caused damage to plants or ruined experiments. It is clear that the 10 to 15 minutes per day it takes to change clothes is an insignificant amount of time when weighed against the advantages of working under insect- and disease-free conditions. The essentiality of any of our precautions is not known, but, because of the success achieved so far, no further experimentation is carried out. The system depends, of course, on the complete coöperation of all workers in the laboratory, and this coöperation in adhering to all laboratory rules has been excellent.

Sterilization of Material:— Fortunately, absolute sterility such as in the laboratory of Professor REYNIERS at Notre Dame is not necessary, provided all organisms causing injury or diseases to plants are kept out. To this end, fumigation or washing with soap and water has proven to be sufficient. The greatest difficulty lies in sterilization of the root medium of plants, and this is largely solved by using only gravel and vermiculite as the root medium.

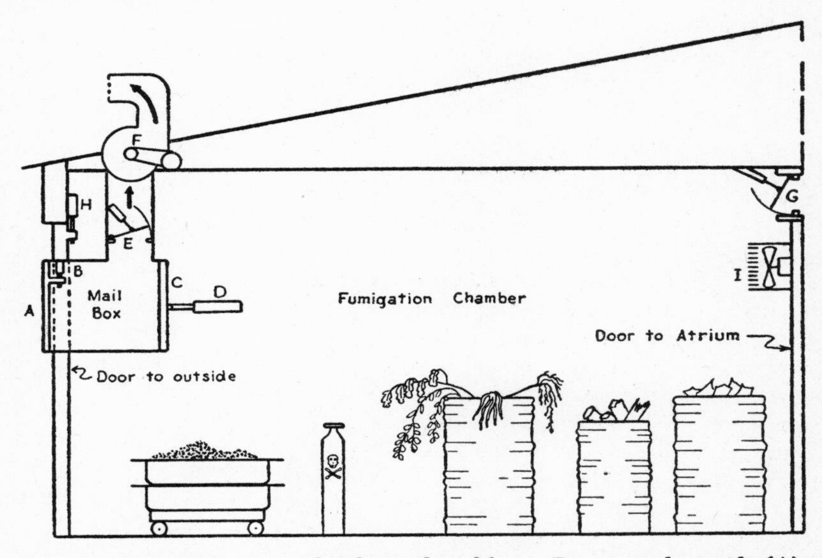

FIGURE 10.— Fumigation chamber and mail box. Door towards outside (A) and inside (C) of mail box. Outside door is locked with electrically controlled bolt (B), inside door is opened with pneumatic lever (D). Pneumatically operated damper (E) opens mail box towards exhaust fan (F). To aerate mail box after fumigation, (C) and (E) are opened with fan (F) operating; to aerate the fumigation chamber itself, damper (G) is also opened towards the atrium.

Most of the plant material enters in the form of seeds which makes disinfection simple and keeps out most viruses. In the few plants where the seed coats seem to carry viruses, such as in beans, these seed coats are removed as far as possible before planting. When mature plants have to be brought in, every precaution is taken to assure freedom of diseases before they are brought into the building. Our potatoes had been tested against virus diseases, strawberries were from certified disease-free material obtained from reliable growers; the same thing was done with carnations, roses and other plants. Fortunately most of the systemic diseases, which are brought in on living plant material, are specific to those plants.

Fumigation of materials with methyl bromide has proven to be entirely effective. To this end, there are three spaces of different sizes to fumigate both large and small amounts of material. For the first two and one-half years, everything was brought in through a large mattress-sterilizer (steam-autoclave) measuring 4 × 4 × 8′, and opening both inside and outside the building. Objects to be fumigated were put in through the outside door, while the inside one was sealed. The gas was then turned on and circulated inside the autoclave by a fan. When the fumigation period was over, the autoclave had to be aired by opening both doors a crack simultaneously and letting the air from the building (which is under pressure at all times) blow the gas out. After a few minutes of airing the outside door was shut and the fumigated material brought inside. Since the addition of the new fumigation chamber and the mailbox (FIGURE 10), the autoclave is used much less. The chamber is 15 × 7 × 8′, and opens both outside and inside to the Atrium. A mailbox (20 × 20 × 24″) is built into the wall next to the outside door, and has separate inside and outside latches of its own. There is an air duct to remove the gas and dampers (G) will admit air from the Atrium to replace the exhausted gas. It has an electric fan (F) and a pneumatically controlled damper (E) which is closed when fumigation is in progress. The air duct is situated over the mailbox so that the mailbox can be used separately from the tunnel when only small amounts of material are being brought in. Both sets of doors have automatic locks (B and H) and signal lights to prevent accidents. The fan, damper, and inside door of the mailbox (C and D) are all remotely controlled from a special panel inside the building. The fumigation chamber also serves to remove spent vermiculite, plant material, paper and trash from the building.

The dosage of methyl bromide we use is 2 lbs./1000 cu. ft./2 hours at 21°C. Both the autoclave and the fumigation chamber have thermostatically controlled heating elements to keep them at proper temperature and fans to circulate the gas; the mailbox has no heating element, so the amount of methyl bromide is varied according to the temperature of the air inside the mailbox at the time of fumigation.

Methyl bromide is injected from a 10 lb. cylinder, which is equipped with a measuring gauge. The mailbox, which takes only from 3 to 5 cc., has a gauge glass of its own, which can be filled with the proper amount from the cylinder.

All our precautions with plant material would be in vain, if the growing medium were not sterile also. Therefore, ordinary soil is banned from the laboratory, and vermiculite (heat-expanded mica), sand or gravel is used instead. Vermiculite needs no sterilization, for it is baked at a high temperature during its manufacture, and sealed in heavy paper bags, which need only to be passed through the fumigation chamber, like any other solid object. Sand and gravel are kept in 5-ton, rubber sealed bins which open inside and outside the building. When a new load is put in, the inside lids are shut while the outside ones are open. After the load has been dumped from the truck, which can drive right up against the bin, the outside lids are sealed and locked, too, and the sand or gravel is steamed for 24 hours. Only after this is the inside lid opened; the material can then be used without further transfers. Steam-treating the sand has prevented "damping off" in cuttings and seedlings as caused by *Phycomycetes* or other fungi. There has only been one case of "damping off" (on a *Begonia*) since the laboratory was opened.

Occasionally, soil samples or peat moss must be brought in for special projects. After spreading them in layers of not more than 3 cm. thickness, they are fumigated with the regular dose of methyl bromide, but for four hours instead of two. The longer exposure allows the gas to penetrate all through the material, which it must do in order to be effective. Yet, in spite of these precautions, saprophytic nematodes and gnats have come into the laboratory with leaf mold so that at present, only peat moss is allowed inside, if an organic root medium is required (as *e.g.* in *Cypripedium*).

Filtration of Air:— Considering that the greenhouse air is cooled mainly by evaporation, and that there is an air-change every ½ minute, it is obvious that much air is taken into the building each day. The maximum rate of intake under the heaviest cooling load is 30,000 c.f.m. (or 1 ton per minute), but the average is 1000 tons per day. This large volume of air presents another cleaning problem, for the outside air in any metropolitan area does not only contain insects, but also is full of gaseous impurities which are more or less detrimental to plants.

When the laboratory was opened, the air intake was equipped with a Farr (mechanical) filter and an electrostatic precipitator (13,000 V. on the external grids, 6,500 V. on the plates) to keep out solid particles and insects. However, these filters did nothing to remove the "smog," which severely damages thin-leaved plants, such as tobacco, beets, *Hyoscyamus* and inhibits the growth of other plants such as the tomato (KORITZ and WENT 1952, HULL and WENT 1954). This smog damage was found to be due to peroxides and ozonides of hydrocarbons (HAAGEN-SMIT *et al.* 1951), which are formed in Los Angeles area air from gasoline vapors under the influence of sunlight. Experiments showed that activated carbon would remove these compounds, and in 1951, carbon filters were installed in the air intake of the laboratory. Since that time, there has been no further damage to even the most sensitive plants, and the differences between plants grown inside and outside the laboratory are quite spectacular. Only on days with exceptionally heavy smog, on the average once a year, this degree of filtering is insufficient and plant damage occurs. On such days, it is possible to prevent smog damage by recirculating all air in the greenhouses. Under those conditions, not enough refrigeration is available to keep the greenhouses at the desired temperatures so that freedom from smog has to be paid for by inconstancy of the temperature.

The size of a smog filter depends on the load of air to be cleaned, the concentration of the pollutants and the degree of purification desired. The first fact especially must be taken into consideration, for the air must be in contact with the carbon for a certain length of time to be completely purified. This time under our conditions is approximately 1/10 of a second and this removes 95-98 per cent of the smog as expressed in oxidant-level. This is sufficient except under the heaviest smog conditions; therefore, it is advisable on days with heavy smog to reduce the amount of air to be taken in.

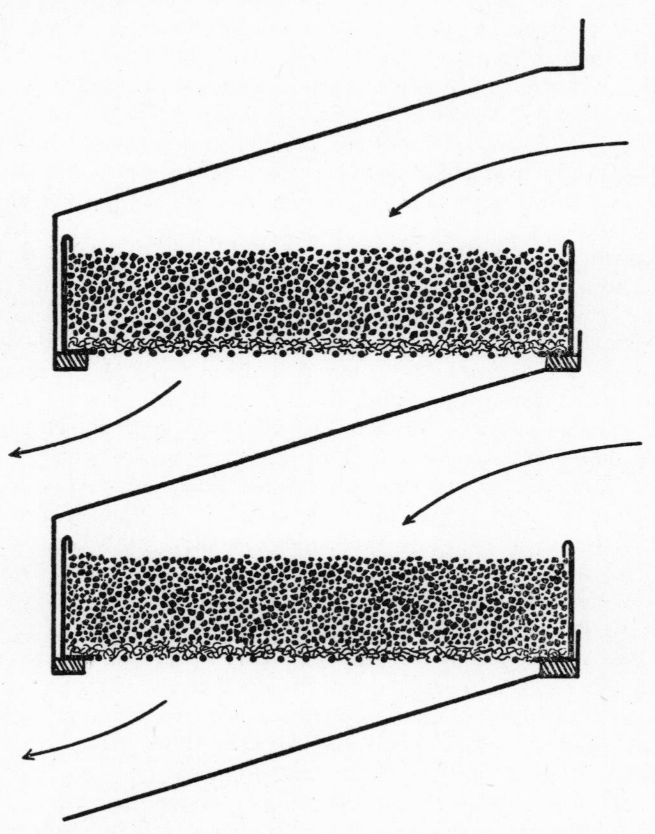

FIGURE 11.— Cross section through part of the charcoal absorber, with 2 trays. These are fitted with a sponge rubber gasket into the metal framework, which causes the air (*arrows*) to pass through the charcoal in the trays.

The filter in our laboratory (FIGURE 11) consists of 125 20 × 20 × 2.5-inch trays filled with 6-12 mesh-size carbon particles (Norit C). These carbon filter trays are arranged in tiers in the chamber where the mechanical filter, precipitator and 10 h.p. main air-intake fan are located. The outside air is drawn downwards through the trays by the fan which then distributes the clean air to the greenhouse air-conditioning systems.

Under Pasadena conditions the carbon in the trays has to be changed once a year after about 300,000 tons of air have passed through the 200 Kg. activated carbon in the trays, removing an estimated 30 Kg. of oxidized hydrocarbons. The carbon gradually compacts and becomes clogged with dust. This increases its air resistance; when it has reached a resistance of 5 cm. water pressure, the carbon has to be replaced.

More recently, we have reduced the thickness of carbon in the smog filter trays. This reduces the pressure-drop in them, and since such a high percentage of the oxidants is removed, a 90 per cent efficiency is still sufficient for our purpose, and it greatly increases the total air supply to the whole building.

Freedom from Pests and Diseases:— It may be of some interest to analyze each of the pest and disease infestations which have occurred in the Earhart Laboratory since its opening.

Virus diseases.— When living plants rather than seeds had to be introduced into the greenhouses, the chance of bringing in virus with them was rather great. Actually, our *Cymbidiums* all have the black spot virus, which has not spread to other plants. Once a serious virus infection occurred on *Hyoscyamus,* which was completely suppressed by removing all plants which had been in contact with infected material, and by not touching any infected or suspected plants. Several times a few tomato plants showed the first symptoms of tobacco mosaic. Removal of the infected plants was sufficient to prevent further spreading. In the latter case, the virus was probably introduced by insufficient washing of hands before entering the laboratory, for it only occurred when a smoker was handling the plants.

In previous work in the Clark greenhouses, when no complete quarantine was possible, it had been found that invariably tomatoes became infected with tobacco mosaic in 3-6 months, especially when students had been working with the plants. It was then found that at high nyctotemperatures (26°-30°C) the mosaic symptoms on the tomato plants were very severe, and that they decreased in severity with decreasing nyctotemperature until at 8°C the plants were outwardly completely healthy.

Twice, groups of *Melilotus* plants, infected with the wound tumor virus, were deliberately introduced into the laboratory. Since the insect vector for this virus was rigorously excluded, the virus has not spread and only the previously infected plants came down with the disease, whereas none of the control plants developed root or stem tubers.

Therefore, by excluding the vectors for virus infections, by properly washing hands before entering the building, and by introducing only seeds or virus-free plants, a completely virus-free condition can be maintained almost indefinitely in greenhouses and, thus, *e.g.*, problems of degeneration of vegetatively propagated plants can be studied without interfering viruses.

Bacterial and fungus diseases.— *Botrytis* rot affected strawberry plants under low light intensity and in excessively high humidity, but since *Bo-*

trytis is a facultative parasite proper cultural conditions keep this fungus in check.

One of the clones of *Poa,* which Dr. HIESEY used, was infected with mildew and fumigation with CH_3Br did not eliminate it. Due to the great specificity of mildews, it did not spread to other grasses or plants.

After an initial mildew-free period of several months, *Cucurbita* plants became infected with mildew, and soon each *Cucurbita* grown in the Earhart Laboratory developed mildew to such an extent that it had to be discontinued as an experimental plant.

This mildew infection was probably due to air-borne spores, for during the first year the electrostatic precipitator was frequently out of commission. Since the mechanical and the smog filters have been installed, a new attempt to grow *Cucurbita* in the Earhart Laboratory has been made, and for at least eight months the plants have been mildew-free.

Dr. ELLIS DARLEY investigated the number of bacterial and fungal spores present in different locations in the Earhart Plant Research Laboratory. On January 13, 1950, 70 petri dishes of 10 cm. diameter with nutrient agar were exposed for 30 minutes each in 14 different places; the following data are averages of 5 individual agar plates exposed at 08:00, 10:00, 12:00, 14:00 and 16:00:

Red Greenhouse: 4 yeasts, 1 fungus
Yellow Greenhouse: 13 bacteria, 2 *Penicillium,* 1 *Hormodendrum*
Blue Greenhouse: 15 bacteria, 1 yeast, 3 *Penicillium,* 1 other fungus
Darkroom Number 8: 2 bacteria, 1 yeast, 2 fungi
Darkroom Number 5: 5 *Penicillium,* 1 fungus
Darkroom Number 2: 2 yeasts, 2 *Penicillium*
Atrium: 1 bacterium, 3 yeasts, 2 *Penicillium,* 1 *Hormodendrum*
Potting Area: 5 yeasts, 4 *Penicillium,* 1 fungus
Laboratory in basement: 4 bacteria, 4 yeasts, 10 *Penicillium,* 2 fungi

Considering the very large amount of air which passes through the greenhouses with attending turbulence, the air can be considered very clean for a greenhouse or growing room; probably most of the spores present were produced by fungi already inside the building. With improved operation of the electrostatic precipitator which often fails, it is possible to maintain complete freedom of disease inside greenhouses.

Insect pests.— Concerning insect infestations, the following can be said. In March 1950, aphids were discovered on *Potentilla* plants. They occurred all on the same clone of *Potentilla,* growing in different greenhouses, and they had not spread to neighboring plants on the same truck. Therefore, it is fairly certain that resting stages of the aphids had survived CH_3Br fumigation in December 1949, when the *Potentilla* rhizomes were brought into the laboratory. This fumigation had deliberately been light to spare the plants, which indicates that the recommended fumigation should be rigidly adhered to. Twice repeated parathion fumigation of the affected trucks eradicated these aphids.

In March 1955 another aphid infection was noted, when one truck with barley plants was badly infected. This infection was probably due to carelessness of a person entering the greenhouses; two Isotox fumigations of the whole building removed every trace of these aphids.

For about two years a periodically recurring infestation of root aphids has plagued us. Series of three parathion fumigations at weekly intervals temporarily checked the insects, but after about six months they reappeared. Finally, a drastic Isotox watering of every plant container has killed them, but this treatment did much harm to a number of plants, especially tomatoes. Systox spraying was ineffective. It is likely that these aphids entered with leafmold or potted plants; now, all plants introduced into the greenhouses are bare-rooted and leafmold is not permitted in the Earhart Laboratory any more.

The *Cymbidium* plants periodically become infested with scales, which have resisted Systox, Isotox, Parathion and methyl bromide treatments. Fumigations always temporarily checked the infestation, but apparently did not kill the insects located in the overlapping bases of the leaves. The very limited mobility of these scales made it possible to restrict them to relatively few *Cymbidium* plants.

There have been three independent red spider infestations. The first one, in the spring of 1950, was not discovered until it had spread through most of the building. Therefore, it is impossible to trace its source. Most affected were *Xanthium* and *Fragaria,* and particularly in the warmer greenhouses. But most other plants remained completely (tomato) or almost completely (tobacco) free from red spiders.

A standard Parathion fumigation killed all hatched red spiders, but within a few days living young red spiders, hatched from eggs, were found again. A second fumigation a week after the first killed also these. But a few weeks later red spiders reappeared. A series of 3 Parathion fumigations, spaced 6 days apart, brought the red spiders under complete control and they did not reappear for another half year.

Then another red spider infection was found in the warmest greenhouse, on corn and *Xanthium,* but was again controlled with thrice repeated Parathion fumigation of the warm greenhouse, and twice repeated for the whole building.

In May 1951 again red spiders appeared in the warm greenhouses, on corn and *Amaranthus fimbriatus,* in the same corner as before, but again the infection was controlled with 3 Parathion fumigations.

It is certain that these three red spider infestations were due to three separate infections. Since the last two appeared in the same corner of the same greenhouse (Red), and since this house is not specifically insect-proofed, it seems reasonable to assume that through cracks or other openings red spiders entered from the nearby Dolk greenhouse, which is a more or less continuous source of red spiders. It seems unlikely that they were brought in by people, because of the same location where the infestation started at least the last two times. Other insect pests, such as white flies, thrips, leaf hoppers or caterpillars, common in ordinary greenhouses, have never been observed in the Earhart Laboratory.

Other non-parasitic insects were occasionally observed inside the building:

1) A few times during the first months ants were found in one or another part of the laboratory. Since the outside of the building, especially around doors, has been regularly sprayed with chlordane no more ants have been observed.

2) For the first three years termites entered the old part of the greenhouse about once yearly. They seem to come from an area filled with soil from which wood waste was not sufficiently removed. All wood was removed from the soil around the new building and no termites have appeared there. Besides, special care was taken to make the concrete perfect and properly seal all pipe and conduit openings.

3) Flies and other fast-flying insects occasionally enter through the doors of vestibule and washrooms in spite of the positive pressure which causes air to rush out when doors are opened. With the aid of small DDT aerosol bombs such insects are killed as soon as observed (not more than 4 times per year).

4) Before mechanical filters were installed, insects, especially large ones, entered through the air-intake for the building when they passed the electric precipitator. Apparently they were able to crawl along the charged plates without being electrocuted and were not held by the oil layer on the plates. The mechanical filters and the smog filters have removed this pathway of insect infestation.

5) A few spiders have been found, which apparently had crawled through unsuspected openings.

6) Saprophytic nematodes have developed in leaf mold which was properly fumigated with CH_3Br before entering the building. This may have been due to improper penetration of the fumigant, or to ineffectiveness on resting stages such as eggs. In general, soil should be fumigated for much longer periods than living plant material.

In spite of the occasional infestations of pests and diseases, which have been analyzed in the previous paragraphs as to their source and method of prevention, it can be stated that freedom from pests and diseases in the growing of plants is not only desirable, but is attainable, if the proper safety devices are installed and maintained, and if unrelenting care is exerted by all persons entering the quarantined building. Whereas in the first years of operation about twice per year plant pest infestations occurred in the Earhart Laboratory, recently, the insect-free period has been increased to one and one-half years, and with our present experience this period could be longer yet.

Chapter 4

HANDLING OF PLANTS

Plant Moving:— As has been mentioned before, all plants are placed on wheeled trucks so that they can be moved around freely (*see* PLATE IV). This has a number of advantages:

1) The plants can be subjected to a much larger number of conditions than are maintained in the laboratory at any one time. The change can consist of either daily shifts or other than daily periods (for instance, a rain or a wind treatment at a particular stage of development of the plant).

2) Better utilization of space is possible. No corridors have to be left in the artificial light rooms; rather, these can be filled completely with trucks. If it is necessary to reach plants in the completely filled compartments, this can be achieved by temporarily moving trucks out of the way.

3) In the greenhouses, only a few narrow walks need to be left between the plants (*see* PLATE III). Again, by moving obstructing trucks out of the way each plant can easily be reached.

4) It simplifies sowing, measuring and harvesting, by making the plants more accessible and moving them wherever it is most convenient to work on them.

5) It simplifies periodic photographing (with the Photorecord camera).

In the Clark greenhouses three types of trucks were used. Two had table space of 20 × 20 inch, and the third a surface of 30 × 30 inch. It turned out that the latter size was too large because the trucks became too heavy to move when fully loaded with plants and were hard to move through regular size doors. Therefore, in the Earhart Plant Research Laboratory all the trucks were made with a standard area of 20 × 20 inch. If occasionally larger surfaces are needed, two or more trucks are wired together. Whereas the original trucks were made of wood, the new ones are made of galvanized steel. There are two types of trucks used in Earhart (*see* PLATE VII). One is made with a fixed table height of 24 inches, which is used in all experiments not requiring artificial light and the other has an adjustable table which can vary from 6 inches to 71 inches from the floor. PLATE VII shows one of these trucks. It is made of angle-iron with a square frame and base in which the four casters are offset slightly from the corners. These casters have three-inch wheels, and have a ball-bearing swivel with double ball race. To keep them in good condition the casters have to be serviced once or twice a year, at which time the shafts are cleaned and oiled and the ball bearing greased. Only the more expensive, fully galvanized casters stand up under the permanent moisture in the greenhouses. The table tops on the adjustable trucks are held in place by two metal rods which are passed through periodic holes in the upright frames. These holes are at 2-inch intervals, and thus allow a whole range of different heights. More recently a new type of adjustable truck has been devised with detachable upright frame of galvanized steel tubing. The upright tubes fit tightly over 8″ long rods welded onto the base frame, and are fixed at the top by a square frame of 1″ wide band-iron. Similar square band-iron frames can also be attached to the single upright tube on the fixed table trucks, to contain branches and foliage of larger plants within the outlines of the truck.

The table tops are made of a frame of angle-iron onto which is welded an expanded metal top which allows free air passage and yet is sturdy enough to hold 70 Kg. of plants.

A special system of identification of the trucks was necessary, by which it would be possible to see at a glance where each truck belongs at any time of the day, and to where it must be moved. To this end, a ring post is attached to one corner of each truck, and extends to a height of 2 m. The ringpost consists of galvanized pipe, from which a wooden dowel extends 12 cm. Over it 1″ high colored rings are slipped (*see* FIGURE 12 and PLATE VII), and secured by a cotter pin through the dowel. Each ring corresponds to one of four time periods during the day (from top to bottom: 08:00-12:00, 12:00-16:00, 16:00-24:00, 24:00-08:00). The color or number on the ring indicates where each truck belongs at each of the four periods. The greenhouses are indicated with a color code (*see* next section). The dark rooms are indicated by black rings, carrying the number of the room in white on three places around the ring, so that it can be read from every side. The artificial light compartments are indicated by white rings with black numbers. Around the bottom of each of these rings is a narrow colored strip which indicates the particular compartment. Thus, all trucks which have to be in Orange greenhouse in the morning have a top ring of orange color; when the next ring is of a different color, it means that the truck will be shifted at 12:00 to the condition corresponding to the number or color of the second ring from the top. This identification by rings has worked out very well. It is easy for the gardeners to tell when and whereto each truck is to be moved; it also makes checking simple, and minimizes mistakes. Once an investigator has installed a particular set of rings on a truck, he is assured that the plants on this truck will receive the desired treatment for as long as the truck remains marked.

The rings are cut from colored plastic tubing or are sections of painted tubing of a uniform diameter. The numbers are secured on them with Scotch tape. Each ring is 2.5 cm. high, which means that from 08:00 to 16:00, 6 mm. of ring corresponds to 1 hour occupancy. If occasionally plants have to be moved at times other than 08:00, 12:00, 16:00 or 24:00, the size of the ring can be cut down accordingly.

The majority of the trucks are moved at 08:00 and 16:00. The period inbetween coincides with full daylight in the greenhouse. By choosing these two times, one may schedule all moving within the eight-hour work period of the gardeners, lengthened by the 1-hour lunch period. As soon as the men arrive in the morning at 08:00, moving of the trucks starts and is usually completed by 08:30. Similarly in the afternoon, moving starts at 16:00 and is completed by 16:30. These particular moving times have another advantage. In those artificial light compartments which are lighted 24 hours a day, the same space can be occupied during day by a truck that is to receive 8 hours of light, and during night by another truck that is to receive 16 hours of light. These rooms, therefore, may do double-duty for both long- and short-day treatments.

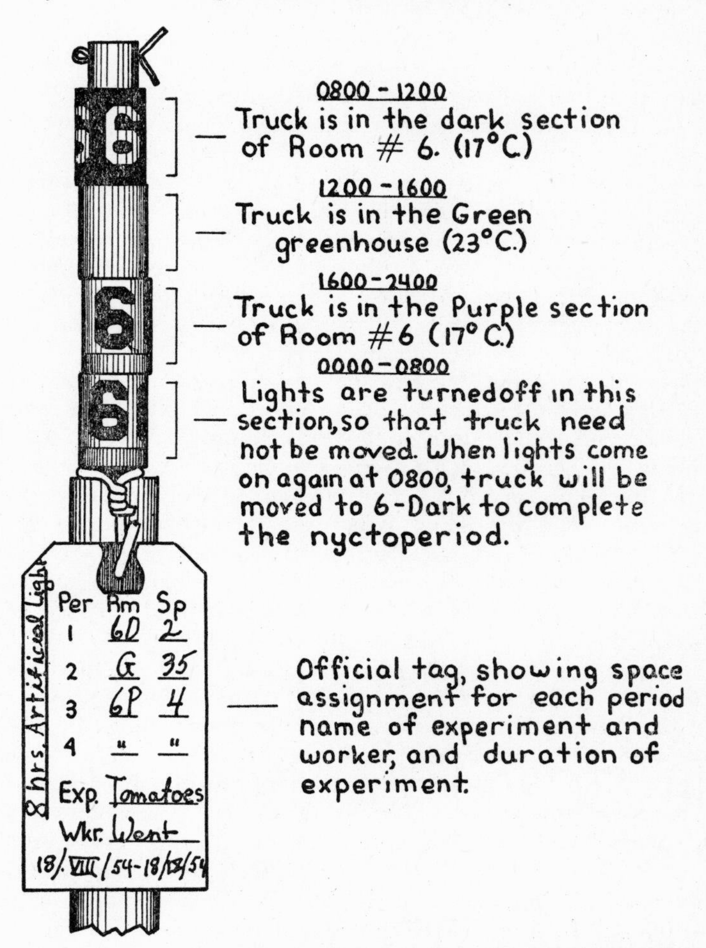

0800 - 1200
Truck is in the dark section of Room # 6. (17°C)
1200 - 1600
Truck is in the Green greenhouse (23°C.)
1600 - 2400
Truck is in the Purple section of Room #6 (17° C.)
0000 - 0800
Lights are turnedoff in this section, so that truck need not be moved. When lights come on again at 0800, truck will be moved to 6-Dark to complete the nyctoperiod.
Per Rm Sp
1 6D 2
2 G 35
3 6P 4
4 " "
Exp. Tomatoes
Wkr. Went
18/VIII/54-18/XII/54
8 hrs. Artificial Light
Official tag, showing space assignment for each period name of experiment and worker, and duration of experiment.

FIGURE 12.— Ring post, attached to one corner of each truck, showing the colored rings in position, together with the truck tag. Upper ring is black with white numbers 6, next ring is green, lowest two rings are white with purple band and black numbers 6.

Moving outside the working hours of the gardeners has to be done by the investigators themselves. It is remarkable how many experiments can be carried out without resorting to night moving. It is likely that the above-mentioned rule is partially responsible.

During the two main moving times, the *modus operandi* is as follows: First, all trucks which have to be shifted are taken from the artificial light rooms and moved into the Atrium (*see* PLATE IV). The order is from the coldest to the warmest rooms. Then as many trucks are put in their new positions in the rooms as is possible without blocking the passageways in the rooms. When this is done, the greenhouses are opened up, and the trucks are moved from there into the rooms or other greenhouses. Finally, each room and greenhouse is checked to see that all trucks are in the correct place, the sliding panels between the light compartments in the rooms are closed, and the doors to the rooms and greenhouses are shut. By always following the same method, the average time that each plant occupies its specific location comes close to 8 or to 16 hours, for the plants moved out first in the morning are also moved first in the afternoon.

It is easy to move two trucks in tandem. When not too many corners have to be negotiated, 3 or 4 trucks can be moved simultaneously. A spirit of competition has developed between the gardeners to see who can turn the sharpest corners with the most trucks. This only works properly when the casters are well oiled and free-moving.

Whereas the moving increases the versatility of the laboratory, it has also its drawbacks. In the first place, leaves and other plant parts which protrude beyond the confines of the truck frequently get injured in moving. This can be prevented to some extent by tying the plants up properly. In the second place, a certain amount of root damage occurs as the trucks bounce over the floors, which are somewhat uneven due to the slots. The degree of damage is unknown, but can be reduced by staking the plants properly and by the use of vermiculite as root medium. A third drawback is that the dark rooms have to be opened for moving, and receive a considerable amount of light during the moving period. Experiments in which absolute darkness is required during the moving times can be accommodated either by using the basement air-conditioned rooms, or by special black covers for the trucks to be protected. Since in most photoperiodic work, the uninterrupted dark period does not need to be more than 16 hours, the moving schedules do not interfere with this requirement.

To reduce the exposure to light as much as possible for those plants which should remain in darkness during moving time, the ceiling lights in the dark rooms are green, which color is least effective in photosynthesis and photoperiodic induction, yet the human eye has its highest sensitivity in that range of wave length. Besides, the walls of the darkrooms are painted black.

The plants growing in the greenhouses are exposed to natural daylight, which in Pasadena ranges in duration from 9½ to 15 hours. To make photoperiodic exposure uniform throughout the year in each greenhouse, two 1000 watt incandescent lamps are installed in them, reflectors insuring a light intensity ranging from 25-100 ft.-c. at plant level throughout the greenhouse. During day the lamps can be slid towards the side of the greenhouses so that the large reflectors intercept as little daylight as possible. They are lighted from 16:00-20:00 and from 04:00-08:00, leaving an 8-hour nyctoperiod throughout the year.

Coding of Growing Rooms:— A simple method was necessary to designate the 54 different rooms and compartments so as to make moving of trucks easy, simplify discussions and at the same time be usable in the bookkeeping. To this end, the greenhouses were color-coded.* The warmest greenhouse (30°C day, 23°C night temperature) was named Red, and on the door, a red band is painted. Trucks which have to stay in the Red room have red rings on the ring posts. The next cooler greenhouse

TABLE 2: *Temperatures (in centigrade) and number of available truck spaces in constant temperature rooms:—*

ROOM NUMBER	TEMPERATURE	DARK SECTION	*Artificially lighted sections* RED	GREEN	PURPLE
1	4°	16	0	8	0
2	7°	16	0	8	8
3	10°	16	8	8	8
4	14°	24	8	8	8
5	17°	24	8	8	8
6	17°	24	8	8	8
7	20°	24	8	8	8
8	23°	24	8	8	8
9	26°	24	8	8	8
10	−10° to 0°	8	0	0	0
11	30°	0	0	16	0
12	14° to 30° (rain)	0	0	16	0
13	14° to 30° (wind)	0	0	8	0
14	14° to 30° (gas)	0	0	16	0
15	14° to 30° (radioact.)	0	0	16	0

is Orange (26°C day, 20°C night temperature), the following two are kept at the same temperature (23°C day, 17°C night) and are coded Yellow and Green; still cooler is the Blue greenhouse (20°C day, 14°C night), and coolest is the Purple greenhouse (17°C day, 12°C night). These colors are suggestive of the actual temperature conditions and make it simple to remember them.

The artificial light and dark rooms are numbered 1 through 15, each number indicating another set of compartments kept at the same temperature. TABLE 2 shows the temperatures at which the different rooms are kept and the number of artificial light sections.

Whereas in principle the Green section of the artificial light rooms gets continuous light, if there are no plants to occupy them during daytime the lights are turned on from 16:00 to 08:00. In the Purple sections the

* All greenhouses have the regular white glass, and the color-code does *not* refer to the color of the light.

lights stay on only until midnight and depending on whether plants stay in the Purple section during day the lights are turned on at 08:00 or at 16:00. The Red sections are generally kept for special experiments or to supplement the Purple or Green sections when they are completely filled up.

Room Number 10 is a walk-in cold box in which temperatures anywhere from freezing to −10°C can be maintained. In Room Number 11, the temperature control is much less precise since it is carried out with on-off thermostats which operate fans to blow in cool or warm air as needed. Rooms 12, 13, 14 and 15 are set at whatever temperature is necessary for a particular investigation, and when not in use for their specific purpose are used as overflow space from the other artificial light rooms.

Bookkeeping Methods:— To make most effective use of the air-conditioned greenhouse space, it must be possible at all times to ascertain how much of the existing growing space is in use and for how long, and how much is available. This is necessary to know in the planning of new experiments and for the continuation of running experiments.

To this end, a card file is kept of all growing space. Every truck space (squares in Figure 4) in each greenhouse, dark- and light-room is represented by a card in this file (*see* Figure 13). And on this card is written for which experiment that space is in use. If not in use, a small colored rider is attached to the upper edge of the card. By looking at these riders, it is possible to see at a glance how much space is available in any greenhouse.

Each card is divided into 4 sections corresponding with the 4 major time periods of the day, as they are represented by the 4 colored rings on the trucks (08:00-12:00, 12:00-16:00, 16:00-24:00, 24:00-08:00). On this card is marked the name of the worker who requests the space, the experimental plant, the date of beginning of the experiment, and its presumable termination. When a truck occupies space in different greenhouses at different times of the day, the corresponding space cards are each marked for the period the space is occupied, with a notation as to where that particular truck is during the remaining periods.

As soon as the entry on the space card is made, the information is transferred to a truck tag (Figures 12 and 13), which has to be attached to the truck and which indicates that the space which the truck occupies is properly booked in the card file. Without a tag, no trucks are allowed in the greenhouses. This is a necessary counterpart to the card file and prevents unauthorized use of space which might lead to chaos because so many different investigators simultaneously use space in the Earhart Laboratory (usually 20-30 workers, some of them having several experiments running concurrently). The truck tags, when ready, are posted on a board in the control room where the experimentor finds them when he starts his experiments.

Each worker prepares a space application sheet (Figure 13) before an experiment is started. The person in charge of the space card file checks whether the requested conditions are available for the expected duration of the experiment, and if so, prepares the truck tags. When the laboratory

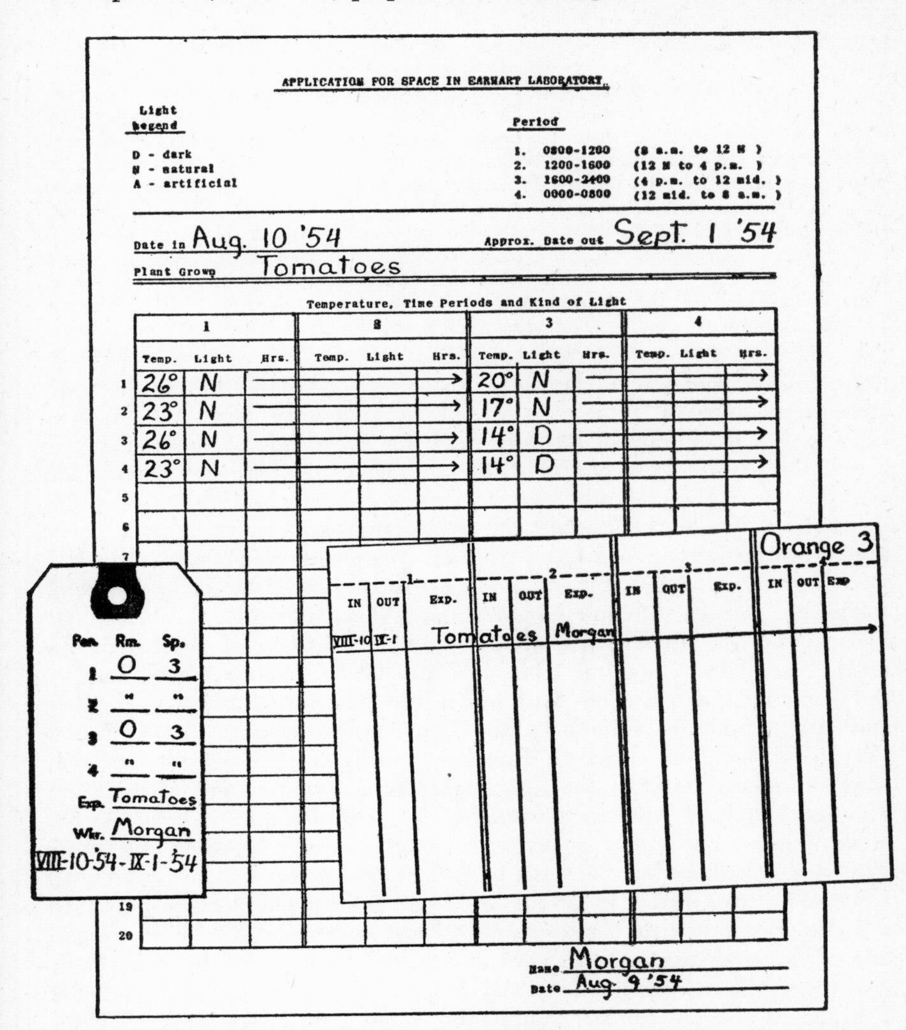

APPLICATION FOR SPACE IN EARHART LABORATORY

Light Legend

D - dark
N - natural
A - artificial

Period

1. 0800-1200 (8 a.m. to 12 N)
2. 1200-1600 (12 N to 4 p.m.)
3. 1600-2400 (4 p.m. to 12 mid.)
4. 0000-0800 (12 mid. to 8 a.m.)

Date in Aug. 10 '54 Approx. Date out Sept. 1 '54

Plant Grown Tomatoes

Temperature, Time Periods and Kind of Light

	1			2			3			4		
	Temp.	Light	Hrs.	Temp.	Light	Hrs.	Temp.	Light	Hrs.	Temp.	Light	Hrs.
1	26°	N	→	→	→	→	20°	N	→	→	→	→
2	23°	N	→	→	→	→	17°	N	→	→	→	→
3	26°	N	→	→	→	→	14°	D	→	→	→	→
4	23°	N	→	→	→	→	14°	D	→	→	→	→
5												
6												
7												
19												
20												

Name Morgan

Date Aug. 9 '54

Per.	Rm.	Sp.
1	O	3
2	"	"
3	O	3
4	"	"

Exp. Tomatoes

Wkr. Morgan

VIII-10-'54-IX-1-'54

Orange 3

1			2			3			4		
IN	OUT	Exp.	IN	OUT	Exp.	IN	OUT	Exp.	IN	OUT	Exp.
VIII-10	IX-1	Tomatoes Morgan →									

FIGURE 13.— Cards and records used in bookkeeping of laboratory space assignments. *Center:* application blank for space, requesting 4 truck spaces. *Right:* bookkeeping space card for space number 3 in orange greenhouse. *Left:* truck tag, authorizing one truck space in the orange greenhouse.

is only partly occupied, space usually is available as requested. However, at other times it may be impossible to assign the requested space to the worker. Then one of the following measures is taken:

1) The administrator discusses with the worker the space available. In many cases an experiment can be carried out by using other temperatures or photoperiods over the range to be investigated.

2) It may be possible to postpone the experiment until space is available, as indicated by the file cards.

3) Sometimes another experiment can be discontinued, freeing the necessary space.

4) If none of these methods works, it is up to the person in charge of the laboratory to judge the relative importance of the various experiments, and devise methods by which the necessary space can be made available, *e.g.*, by temporarily converting space allotted to other uses (rain room, gas room) to normal growing space. Or other experiments may be terminated earlier than expected, or a smaller experimental plant can be suggested, needing less space. Thus far, no serious conflicts in requests for growing space have occurred, due to the coöperative attitude of all workers, and no important experiment was left undone because of lack of space. Yet, the trend is towards smaller plants of which more can be accommodated in the same space. This is indicated by the continuing demand for more and more small containers instead of the 1, 2 and 3 gallon ones. Each year another 1,000-2,000 new plastic cups have to be bought; their number in May 1955 had already grown to 9,000.

Another way in which the use of space can be balanced is by the judicious acceptance of projects. When the laboratory was built, it was made larger than immediately necessary for the needs of the workers at the California Institute of Technology. The extra space has been made available to workers of other institutions or to organizations needing the special facilities of the Earhart Plant Research Laboratory. Thus, there have been projects involving research on sugar beets, *Veratrum,* chaparral plants, grasses, smog, coffee, orchids and many other subjects, which were sponsored by such different organizations as the Sugar Beet Development Foundation, the University of California, the University of Southern California, the Riker Chemical Company, the United States Forest Service, the Carnegie Institution of Washington, the American Society of Heating and Airconditioning Engineers, the Los Angeles County Air Pollution Control District, the I.B.E.C. Research Institute, the Stanford Research Institute, U.N.E.S.C.O., the American Orchid Society and Cymbidium growers. Each of these organizations have contributed to the operation of the Earhart Laboratory in proportion to the amount of space they used. This was calculated on the basis of $16.00 per square foot per year until 1954; after this, it was increased to $24.00 per square foot per year. In the last years fewer such projects have been accepted and a larger proportion of the laboratory space is used by academic visitors and by less specific projects supported by the National Science Foundation, the Rockefeller Foundation and the Earhart Foundation, such as water relations in plants, the inheritance of quantitative physiological characters, etc. In 1955 the National Science Foundation has made a large 3-year grant to help the California Institute with the operating costs of the Earhart Plant Research Laboratory, particularly to contribute to the cost of research by visitors and students, whose fellowships do not include contributions to the running costs of the laboratory.

It is possible to reserve growing space in the laboratory in advance. In such a case the necessary entries are made on the file cards, but to indicate that the space is temporarily available until the contemplated experiment is started, a red rider is attached to the space card and this is removed at

TABLE 3: *Utilization of growing space on October 31, 1954:—*

	Temperature in C°		Truck spaces available	Truck spaces occupied during		Percent occupancy	
	Day	Night		Day	Night	Day	Night
Greenhouse:—							
Red	30	23	46	36	25	78	55
Orange	26	20	98	90	46	92	47
Yellow	23	17	98	92	57	94	58
Green	23	17	98	92	52	94	53
Blue	20	14	98	76	56	78	57
Purple	17	12	46	39	24	85	52
Total Greenhouses			484	425	260	87.8	53.8
Artificial light rooms:—							
11	30	30	8	6	8	75	100
9	26	26	24	6	22	25	92
8	23	23	24	7	24	29	100
7	20	20	24	9	24	38	100
6	17	17	24	6	23	25	96
5	17	17	24	6	21	25	88
4	14	14	24	7	23	29	96
3	10	10	24	8	17	34	71
2	7	7	16	6	7	38	44
1	4	4	8	2	3	25	38
Total light rooms			200	63	172	31.5	86.0
Dark rooms:—							
9	26	26	24	14	12	58	50
8	23	23	24	4	14	17	58
7	20	20	24	13	24	54	100
6	17	17	24	5	20	21	83
5	17	17	24	7	20	29	83
4	14	14	24	12	14	50	58
3	10	10	16	11	15	69	94
2	7	7	16	1	4	6	25
1	4	4	16	4	2	25	13
Total dark rooms			192	71	125	37.0	65.2

the time the space is no longer available. Short term experiments can then be accommodated in the reserved space.

As soon as a truck is not in use any more, its tag is returned to the administrator, who cancels the reservation on the space card, puts a rider on the card and thus makes that space again available for experiments. On the space card the date of termination is stamped as a sign of cancellation.

This system of bookkeeping, done carefully, has proven fully satisfactory. It takes 3 man-hours per day to keep it up. Once monthly a check of all trucks in the laboratory is made against the space cards to discover occasional errors, which may occur when complicated sequences of treatments were requested.

To be able to find the space cards easily their edges are tinted in the color of the greenhouses they represent (Red, Orange, etc.), and each carries in the right upper corner the code designation (*e.g.*, R21, or O57, meaning space 21 in the Red greenhouse, or space 57 in the Orange one, or 4P5: space 5 in the Purple section of room 4, or 4D20: space 20 in darkroom 4).

When the space cards are filled up with entries, they are moved to the dead card file, which gives a complete record of all experiments ever carried out in the Earhart Laboratory with starting and terminating dates.

Because there are so many different rooms and conditions, it requires much planning to have most of the space occupied. To this end, a certain amount of standardization of experiments is necessary, so that in connection with temperature treatments usually 8-, 12-, 16- or 24-hour photoperiods are used.

To make use of the unassigned spaces in the artificial light rooms, often temporary experiments are placed in them. A certain number of plants of general botanical interest (*Drosera,* epiphytes, *Tradescantia paludosa, Mimosa pudica,* etc.) are grown, and these are occasionally tested under different conditions.

To give an idea about the operation of the Earhart Laboratory as far as the actual utilization of the space is concerned, TABLE 3 is included. In it the amount of space available and actually used on October 31, 1954, is shown in terms of truck spaces (4 square feet each). When the space in use is expressed as percentage of the actually available space, it can be seen that the greenhouses were as fully occupied during day as is possible under optimal management (88 per cent). During night these greenhouses are only partially used, because so many plants requiring the high intensity of daylight are at night in darkrooms or artificial light rooms, whereas the plants which are during day in darkness or artificial light are not moved to greenhouses at night. The greenhouses with intermediate temperatures (Orange, Yellow and Green) were over 90 per cent occupied; those with the lowest and highest temperatures were only 80 per cent filled. This shows the relative demand for various temperature conditions in greenhouses under normal operation in the Earhart Laboratory.

The available space in the artificial light and dark rooms is almost fully occupied during night (86 and 65 per cent). Here it is again the intermediate temperatures which are in greatest demand. Actually two sets of rooms (5 and 6) are kept at 17°C. When much work was done on the response of native plants, the lowest temperature darkrooms were completely filled. They also are necessary to establish the extreme limits within which growth is possible; therefore, they cannot be discontinued even though at one time or another they are only partly filled.

In addition to the rooms upstairs, the special rooms in the basement were occupied as follows with plants: 1B 4/8, 2B 0/8, 3B 0/8, 4B 0/8, 5B 8/8, 6B 8/8, 7B 4/8, 8B 4/8, 9B 3/8, 10 (Cold Room) 1/8, 12 (Rain Room) 0/16, 13 (Wind Room) 0/8, 14 (Gas Room) 16/16, 15 (Radioactivity Room) 8/16. This means that at the end of October 1954, a total of 613 truck spaces out of a total number of 1,012 was occupied. Of these spaces many were occupied only at one time or another, since 262 trucks were moved daily. This means that actually 778 of the 1,012 available truck spaces were being used, or 77 per cent occupancy. This is about average for autumn, winter and spring, when the largest number of students, staff members and visitors use the facilities of the Earhart Laboratory; in June, July, August and September 1954, the occupancy was 13 per cent less than in April, May and October, and amounted to 65 per cent of the approximately 1,000 available truck spaces.

The amount of bookkeeping involved in the ever-changing experimental demands for truck spaces varies between 200 and 500 truck tags processed per month. This means the average duration of an experimental treatment is 2 months.

When the space used by the different investigators is considered, we find that at one time 175 truck spaces were used in sponsored research, 285 by eight research fellows (visitors from other Universities or Institutions), 41 by six graduate students and 138 by staff members, including demonstration material, and material for future experiments.

When divided according to the type of plants, one half of all truck space was occupied by annuals (tomatoes, beans, peas, grasses, smog indicator plants, *Lemna,* etc.), 7.5 per cent by orchids (*Cattleya, Cymbidium, Cypripedium,* etc.), 25 per cent by shrubs or trees (oaks, pines, coffee, *Camellia, Yucca*), 10 per cent by other perennials (strawberries, *Veratrum,* carnations, roses), and the rest by desert and alpine plants, insectivorous plants, and other biologically interesting material. At any one time, as many as 200 different plant species may be under cultivation, practically all of them raised from seed.

When we consider that about 40 different experiments are carried out simultaneously by 25 students and research workers, then the effectiveness of the 4,000 square feet of growing space becomes apparent, and the operating cost of the Earhart Plant Research Laboratory does not seem excessive.

Personnel:— To make the Earhart Plant Research Laboratory continuously working, both operation and maintenance personnel are employed. The California Institute of Technology has an excellent Maintenance Department which furnishes the personnel for maintenance of the built-in mechanical equipment such as motors, air washers, compressors, etc., for repairs when needed and for emergency standby. Because of the great variety of equipment, one general maintenance man could not take care of it, but plumbers, electricians, refrigeration and air-conditioning specialists check, oil, clean and adjust all machinery at regular intervals. Only with such continued care can the complicated machinery of a "phytotron" be kept in working condition.

The operating personnel employed at the Earhart Laboratory consists of a Superintendent, an Assistant Superintendent doubling as a gardener, a Mechanic, an Assistant Mechanic also doubling as a gardener, two regular gardeners and a secretary. Since the operation has to continue every day of the year, an arrangement has been made by which the regular gardeners, the assistant superintendent, and the assistant mechanic take turns working on Saturdays, Sundays and holidays so that every day at least two gardeners are present. During Sundays and holidays only the essential operations with the plants are carried out, whereas on week-days a number of special jobs have to be attended to. During the vacation period, the

TABLE 4: *Time required per day to perform the different functions of the gardeners in the Earhart Plant Research Laboratory, assuming full occupancy of the greenhouses and artificial light rooms:—*

FUNCTION	MAN-HOURS
Moving of trucks	6
Watering of plants	4
Bookkeeping of the truck space	3
Oiling and reconditioning of casters on trucks	3
Preparation of nutrient solution and regenerating the deionizer	1
Lamp replacement	0.5
Fumigation of mail, materials and plants entering the laboratory	0.2
	17.7

regular two-week yearly leaves for each man are staggered. During this time a temporary gardener (often a student) is usually employed, which keeps the operating personnel at the regular number. On Saturdays and Sundays when only two gardeners are present to take care of the moving and watering, one or two of the students or scientists working in the laboratory help with the moving, so that it usually takes not more than 40 minutes for plants to be moved in the morning and in the afternoon. To give an idea of the approximate time necessary for the regular operation of the laboratory, TABLE 4 gives the number of man hours per day required for the most common operations.

All this regular work requires 17 man hours per day which is furnished by two gardeners who are there on each day of the year. In addition, there are many chores which have to be taken care of, such as photographing, planting, repotting, staking of plants, washing of containers, indoctrination of new workers, cleaning of greenhouses and laboratories, maintenance of visitors' clothing and shoes, etc. Whereas in principle the photographing, planting, staking and repotting of the experimental plant material has to be taken care of by the research workers in the laboratory, the gardeners will assist them in these operations to the extent that their time permits. In addition, a certain amount of plant material is maintained in the laboratory to have experimental plants available when necessary. Their maintenance has to be taken care of by the gardeners. Occasionally a person comes on a part-time basis to help with the washing of plant containers of which there is a turnover of several hundred per week.

The operating personnel arrives slightly before 08:00 in the morning and changes its clothes so that the men are ready to start moving the plants at exactly 08:00. The moving of 250 to 300 trucks is then finished by 08:35 to 08:45, depending upon whether three or more men help with the moving. Immediately afterwards all plants are watered. At 11:30 the greenhouses are checked to see if additional watering is necessary for the largest plants. At 12:00 those trucks which require moving at noon are taken care of and then the personnel takes an hour off for lunch, which usually is taken in the basement laboratory area. Then at 14:30 the greenhouses are checked once more for the necessity of watering. At 16:00 the regular afternoon moving is done, after which the gardeners go home.

Concerning the division of labor, all operating personnel, except the mechanic, help in the morning and afternoon with the moving of plants. Thus on regular weekdays, there are always four persons taking care of this operation. The watering is done by the gardeners and assistant superintendent. The superintendent and assistant superintendent, both first-rate photographers, help the research people with their photographic work when necessary, and do the processing and specialized photography. The superintendent takes care of most outside contacts — contacting repair men, ordering supplies, communicating with Administration and Maintenance Department and general checking of all varied operations of the laboratory. He shows visitors around, obtains technical information, and is general advisor on technical matters for all scientists working in the laboratory. The assistant superintendent is in charge of the plant bookkeeping methods. He also takes care of fumigation, autoclaving, steam sterilization, etc. The mechanic takes care of the construction and maintenance of all special equipment such as recorders, control boxes, etc. He also operates the Kathabar unit when required. The assistant mechanic makes up the nutrient solution and regenerates the water de-ionizer and otherwise assists the mechanic in construction and maintenance of apparatus. The gardeners in addition to their plant work are charged with replacing of light bulbs, keeping visitors' clothes and shoes available, general cleaning up, maintenance of casters on the trucks, etc.

All these duties leave very little time for other activities so that practically all the potting, staking, measuring, etc., of experimental plants has to be taken care of by the investigators. This is rather an advantage because in this way the research persons working in the laboratory are necessarily in continuous contact with their plants, which is important if a complete picture of the life activities of plants is to be obtained.

During night there is no regular personnel in the laboratory but it has been found that air-conditioners and other machinery are very reliable and do not need continuous attention. The whole mechanical operation is automatic to such a degree that it can be attended to during daytime. A night watchman comes several times each night but checks only on major disturbances, and has to notify the Maintenance Department when any of the half dozen alarm bells are ringing.

The maintenance personnel of the California Institute of Technology is on a 24-hour standby basis so that anything going wrong during or outside laboratory hours can be taken care of. As an example of the efficiency of the Maintenance Department, it can be mentioned that when on a Sunday morning the 60 h.p. motor on the main compressor burned out, they had a standby motor installed by Sunday afternoon so that the air-conditioning of the laboratory was little affected.

The facilities of the Earhart Plant Research Laboratory maintained by the personnel just enumerated are used by four main groups of persons: (*1*) The staff of California Institute of Technology, (2) Students both from California Institute of Technology and neighboring universities, (3) Visitors, (4) Organizations requiring the special facilities of the laboratory.

Although the proportion between these groups changes, it can be said that approximately one third of the space is used by the staff and students, including fellows working on problems of a general nature such as the genetics of physiological characters and the water relations of plants. One third of the space is used by visitors who come with fellowships while on leave of absence, and the remaining space is used by sponsored research projects.

The following list (TABLE 5) includes most of the research workers who have, at one time or another, made use of the facilities of the Earhart Plant Research Laboratory.

TABLE 5: *Names* (with their institutions and years spent at Earhart Laboratory) *and subjects of investigation* (with references to chapter and bibliography) *of the investigators who used the facilities of the Earhart Plant Research Laboratory:—*

— *Staff, Research Fellows and Assistants* —

F. W. Went (Prof., C.I.T.) 1949- . — Tomatoes, strawberries, beets and various other plants, photosynthesis, variability. — *Cf.* WENT 1943-55.

W. C. Ashby (Res. Fel., C.I.T.) 1950-54. — Climatic response of Chaparral plants and water relations of plants. — *Cf.* Chapters 14, 22 & 23 and ASHBY 1955.

Mrs. **S. Bendix** (Res. Asst., C.I.T.) 1949-51. — Thermoperiodicity of tomatoes. — *Cf.* Chapter 6 and BENDIX 1956.

Mrs. **R. Morgan Behnke** (Res. Asst., C.I.T.) 1951-54. — Flowering of *Moraea,* thermoperiodicity of peas, efficiency of photosynthesis. — *Cf.* Chapters 7 & 20.

A. M. M. Berrie (Res. Fel., C.I.T.) 1953-54. — Effect of sugar sprays on plants.

Mrs. **R. Corbett** (Res. Asst., C.I.T.) 1949-53. — Garden flowers and *Veratrum* research. — *Cf.* Chapters 10 & 13.

E. Darley (Plant Pathologist, Univ. Calif.) 1949-50. — Smog investigations. — *Cf.* HAAGEN-SMIT *et al.* 1951.

E. Eichenberger (Res. Fel., C.I.T.) 1953-55. — Ecology of desert plants and water relations. —*Cf.* Chapter 22.

A. W. Galston (Assoc. Prof., C.I.T.) 1950-52. — Auxin induced growth in corn and peas. — *Cf.* Chapter 25.

A. J. Haagen-Smit (Prof., C.I.T.) 1950-51. — Smog. — *Cf.* Chapter 24 and HAAGEN-SMIT 1951.

J. Hanson (Res. Fel., C.I.T.) 1953. — Photoperiodism in tomatoes. — *Cf.* HIGHKIN *et al.* 1954.

H. Hellmers (Res. Fel. & Forest Service, C.I.T.) 1950- . — Climatic response to shrubs. — *Cf.* Chapter 14 and ASHBY *et al.* 1955.

H. R. Highkin (Res. Fel., C.I.T.) 1952- . — Genetics of temperature response and vernalization. — *Cf.* HIGHKIN 1954, 1956*a* & 1956*b*.

H. Hull (Grad. Stud. & Res. Fel., C.I.T.) 1949-53. — Effects of smog on plants, translocation. — *Cf.* Chapters 16 & 24 and HULL 1952 & 1954.

Mrs. **M. Juhrèn** (Res. Asst., C.I.T.) 1949-52. — Germination and growth of grasses, ecology of desert plants. — *Cf.* Chapters 11, 18 & 19 and JUHRÈN 1953, 1956 & WENT *et al.* 1952.

Miss **N. Jeung** (Res. Asst., Univ. Calif.) 1949-50. — Sugar beets. — *Cf.* Chapter 10.

Mrs. **H. G. Koritz** (Res. Fel., C.I.T.) 1951-52. — Effects of smog on plants. — *Cf.* Chapter 24 and KORITZ 1952.

A. Lang (Res. Fel., C.I.T.) 1951-53. — Photoperiodism of *Hyoscyamus* and tobacco. — *Cf.* LANG 1952.

Mrs. **H. F. Metzenberg** (Res. Asst., C.I.T.) 1953-55. — Coffee. — *Cf.* Chapter 12.

K. Ohki (Res. Asst., Univ. Calif.) 1949-53. — Sugar beet investigations. — *Cf.* Chapter 10.

Miss **E. Pinsker** (Res. Asst., C.I.T.) 1955-56. — Tomatoes.

G. Streisinger (Res. Fel., C.I.T.) 1953. — Tobacco.

M. Zaitlin (Res. Asst., Univ. Calif.) 1949-50. — Smog investigations. — *Cf.* HAAGEN-SMIT *et al.* 1951.

— *Visitors* —

Miss **O. M. van Andel** (Univ. Groningen, Holland) 1953-54. — Bleeding of root systems, water uptake through leaves, transpiration. — *Cf.* Chapter 24 and VAN ANDEL 1957.

R. Bandurski (Univ. Chicago) 1951-52. — Pigment formation in plants. — *Cf.* Chapter 6 and BANDURSKI 1953.

N. Barber (Univ. Tasmania) 1954. — Temperature and photoperiodic responses of peas. — *Cf.* Chapter 7 & 26.

E. Bonde (Univ. Colorado) 1953-54. — Photoperiodism in light cycles longer and shorter than 24 hours. — *Cf.* Chapter 6.

G. Camus (Sorbonne, Paris) 1949-50. — Climatic response of tobacco varieties, and flowering of *Baeria*. — *Cf.* Chapters 6 & 21 and CAMUS 1952.

L. de Capite (Univ. Perugia, Italy) 1954. — Temperature effects on tissue cultures. — *Cf.* Chapter 16 and DE CAPITE 1955.

R. Casamajor (Pasadena, Calif.) 1951- . — Growth and flowering of *Cymbidium* and *Cypripedium*. — *Cf.* Chapter 10 and CASAMAJOR 1954, 1955.

D. Dunn (Univ. Calif. at Los Angeles) 1949. — Climatic response of *Lupinus*. — *Cf.* Chapter 18.

S. Dunn (Univ. New Hampshire) 1952-53. — Photosynthesis and light quality. — *Cf.* Chapter 20 and S. DUNN 1956.

S. Duvdevani (Dew Res. Sta., Karkur, Israel) 1952-53. — Dew research. — *Cf.* Chapter 19.

R. Erickson (Univ. Pennsylvania) 1954-55. — Morphological and physiological development of the shoot apex.

M. Evenari (Hebrew Univ., Jerusalem) 1949. — Transpiration.

L. Evans (New Zealand) 1954-56. — Climatic response of *Vicia faba, Lolium perenne* and *Trifolium subterraneum*. — *Cf.* Chapter 8.

L. Gregory (Costa Rica) 1952-54. — Climatic response and tuber formation of potato. — *Cf.* Chapter 6 and Gregory 1954.

Paul Grun (Carnegie Inst. of Washington, Stanford, Calif.) 1950. — Cytology of grasses.

F. Gustafson (Univ. Michigan) 1951. — Influence of temperature and light on vitamin content of plants. — *Cf.* Gustafson 1953.

K. C. Hamner (Univ. Calif. at Los Angeles) 1950-55. — Photoperiodism of *Xanthium* and soybeans. — *Cf.* Chapter 24.

W. Hiesey (Carnegie Inst. of Washington, Stanford, Calif.) 1950. — Thermoperiodic response of *Achillea, Mimulus* and grasses. — *Cf.* Chapters 11 & 18 and Hiesey 1953.

W. S. Hillman (Yale Univ.) 1954-55. — Response of tomatoes to abnormal photo and thermo cycles. — *Cf.* Chapters 6 & 24 and Hillman 1956.

T. H. van den Honert (Univ. Leyden, Holland) 1956. — Transpiration studies.

R. Knapp (Univ. Köln, Germany) 1955-56. — Ecology of weeds.

P. Kramer (Duke Univ.) 1955. — Temperature response of trees. — *Cf.* Chapter 12.

E. Landolt (Tech. College, Zürich) 1954-55. — Temperature response of *Lemna.*

A. Lange (Univ. Hawaii) 1955-56. — Study of papaya and coffee.

D. Lewis (John Innes Hort. Inst., England) 1955-56. — Hybrid vigor in tomatoes.

H. Lewis (Univ. Calif. at Los Angeles) 1950. — *Clarkia.* — *Cf.* Chapter 18.

F. and Mrs. **L. Lona** (Univ. Parma, Italy) 1955-56. — *Chlorella.*

Miss **M. G. Mes** (Univ. Pretoria) 1954-55. — Physiology of coffee. — *Cf.* Chapter 12.

C. R. Millikan (Dept. of Agriculture, Melbourne) 1953-54. — Mineral nutrition of flax and subterranean clover. — *Cf.* Chapter 10.

S. Monselise (Rehovoth, Israel) 1955-56. — Growth of carnation, translocation.

J. Morello (Univ. Tucuman, Argentina) 1955-56. — Germination and growth of desert plants.

Mrs. **M. R. Myles** (State College, Nashville, Tenn.) 1949. — Pea test.

K. Nanda (Univ. Calif. at Los Angeles & New Delhi, India) 1955. — Photoperiodism in soybeans. — *Cf.* Chapter 24.

A. Nygren (Agric. College, Ultuna, Sweden) 1951. — Temperature response of annuals.

Miss **D. Osborne** (Univ. London) 1951-52. — Climatic and hormonal control of tomato fruit set, and pea test. — *Cf.* Chapter 6 & 16 and Osborne 1953.

P. Pilet (Univ. Lausanne, Switzerland) 1954-55. — Climatic response and root development of *Lens.* — *Cf.* Pilet 1956.

W. de Ráfols (Agric. Res. Org., Madrid) 1951-52. — Climatic response of *Taraxacum Kok-saghyz.* — *Cf.* de Ráfols 1953.

Miss **F. M. Scott** (Univ. Calif. at Los Angeles) 1950. — Leaf anatomy of tomato. — *Cf.* Chapter 6 and Bandurski *et al.* 1953.

A. Soriano (Dept. of Agriculture, Argentina) 1951-52. — Germination of desert plants and wind effects. — Chapters 18 & 19 and Soriano 1953*a* & 1953*b*.

Miss **J. Sobels** (Univ. Utrecht, Holland) 1952. — Myxomycetes.

Mrs. **M. Taylor** (Howard Univ.) 1953. — Wind effects on plants.

A. Ulrich (Univ. Calif.) 1949-53. — Sugar beet investigations. — *Cf.* Chapter 10 and Ulrich 1952 & 1955.

E. Vacin (San Marino, Calif.) 1949-51. — *Cypripedium.* — *Cf.* Chapter 10.

K. and Mrs. **W. Verkerk** (Agric. College, Netherlands) 1952-53. — Climatic response of tomatoes and Brussels sprouts. — *Cf.* Chapters 6 & 16 and Verkerk 1955.

R. Vickery (Univ. Utah) 1955. — Climatic response of *Mimulus.*

R. Weintraub (Army Chem. Corps) 1952. — Translocation of 2,4-D in beans.

Miss **K. Zarudnaya** (Univ. Missouri) 1952. — Pigment formation and growth in corn plants. — *Cf.* Chapter 25.

— Graduate Students —

H. Burroughs (C.I.T.) 1950-52. — Tobacco.
V. Burrows (C.I.T.) 1954- . — Germination.
R. Cleland (C.I.T.) 1953-54. — Growth of lettuce.
Crosby (C.I.T.) 1950-52. — Testing of plant inhibitors.
L. Eggman (C.I.T.) 1953. — Tobacco.
N. Grobbelaar (Cornell Univ. & Univ. Pretoria) 1953. — Climatic response of pea varieties. — *Cf.* Chapter 7 and GROBBELAAR 1955.
L. Jaffe (C.I.T.) 1952-53. — Algae. — *Cf.* JAFFE 1954.
L. Jansen (C.I.T.) 1949-52. — *Lycopersicum pimpinellifolium.* — *Cf.* Chapter 7 and JANSEN 1953.
Koo (C.I.T.) 1952. — Carotenoid formation.
E. Kurtz (C.I.T.) 1949-51. — Effect of environment on production of fats and waxes. — *Cf.* KURTZ 1952.
L. Labouriau (C.I.T.) 1954- . — Morphogenesis in ferns.
J. Liverman (C.I.T.) 1951-53. — Photoperiodism of many plants, including *Silene* and *Xanthium.* — *Cf.* LIVERMAN 1952.
A. Millerd (C.I.T.) 1952. — Potatoes.
H. C. Moore (Univ. Southern Calif.) 1951. — Nutrition of tomatoes. — *Cf.* Chapter 21.
R. Niemann (Univ. Southern Calif.) 1950-51. — Salt uptake by roots.
J. Nitsch (C.I.T.) 1949-50. — Strawberries, flowering of *Cucurbitaceae.* — *Cf.* NITSCH 1952.
B. Rogers (C.I.T.) 1951-54. — Germination, peach flowering. — *Cf.* Chapter 12.
R. Sachs (C.I.T.) 1953-55. — Photoperiodism of *Cestrum.* — *Cf.* Chapter 12 and SACHS 1955, 1956*a*, 1956*b*, 1956*c*.
J. Skoss (Univ. Calif. at Los Angeles) 1952-53. — Cuticular development. — *Cf.* SKOSS 1953.
T. Tomita (C.I.T.) 1954-55. — Vernalization.
D. Viglierchio (C.I.T.) 1951-55. — Thermoperiodicity of beans. — *Cf.* Chapter 15 and VIGLIERCHIO 1955.

Since the facilities of the Earhart Laboratory are now fully occupied, a restriction of its use is necessary. In the earlier years a larger number of sponsored projects such as on sugar beet, *Veratrum,* etc., were carried out, but during the last two years so many visiting research workers have been admitted that the number of sponsored projects had to be decreased. Staff members of other universities on leave of absence or on sabbatical leave and also a large number of persons supported by different fellowships have worked in the laboratory as visiting scientists. Some selection has to be made of these visitors, since the number applying for permission to work in the Earhart Laboratory is larger than the available space permits. Therefore, particularly those persons were admitted who wanted to work on a problem for which the facilities of the Earhart Laboratory were essential or highly beneficial. In addition to using the facilities of the laboratory most efficiently, the visiting investigators contribute much to the intellectual atmosphere of the laboratory and at all times discussions about botanical problems are in progress between staff and visitors. A truly international spirit reigns in the laboratory, with people of all parts of the world sharing space and experiences with each other, and in many cases collaborating in research problems.

Since with each entry of the building the chance exists of bringing in contaminations, only professional botanists and persons specifically interested in particular phases of work carried out in the Earhart Laboratory are admitted as occasional visitors. Unfortunately, it has been impossible to open the laboratory also for visits by interested laymen and by students in general. In the design of another phytotron, it might be advisable to have on one side of the greenhouses a gallery for visitors, where they could look into the greenhouses without having to go through the de-contamination procedures.

Photography:— Photography is used extensively for the recording of experiments. This is done in two ways:

1) Routine pictures of all plants grown on trucks are taken with a photo-record camera. In this way, the condition of the plants can be recorded every few weeks. In PLATES X*a* and *b*, a number of these photographs are combined showing the progress of growth in the course of time for a number of temperature treatments of tomato plants. Since the photographs are taken on 35 mm. film the fine details of the plants are lost, but it is possible to check back on certain features of development which are hard to describe or measure. The photo-record camera can be set up in the Atrium in an accurately marked position and is pre-focused so that when the trucks with plants are placed one at a time in front of the camera, held in place by a special bracket, sharp pictures can be taken. The camera itself is operated by a foot pedal which exposes one frame and then automatically moves the film one frame further. With a standard illumination, a standard exposure time is used which makes it very simple to take pictures in a routine manner.

2) When photographs are to be taken for reproduction purposes, a Grover camera is used with 4 × 5 inch film. A white or black curtain is used as a backdrop and provides an even background for pictures that are taken. To arrange plants for a picture, a set of adjustable shelves can be placed in front of the backdrop. PLATES XIII*a* and *b*, XIV, XVII, XX, and XXI show examples of the arrangements of plants on such shelves. In front of the shelves metal guides can take letters and numbers indicating the treatment of each plant.

For photographing smaller plants (*e.g.*, PLATE XVI), a studio is provided in the basement — next to this studio a dark room is available for developing, printing and enlarging (*see* FIGURE 5).

Units of Measurement and Notation:— All measurements in the Earhart Laboratory are taken in the decimal system. The only exception to this is, as yet, the time, for which the conventional minute/hour/day/month/year is used. The hours are counted from zero to 24, and are marked in four figures; the first two indicating the hours, separated from the second two, indicating minutes, by a double colon. As soon as feasible, the time recording will be converted to a continuous counting in the decimal system. The day would become unit, with fractions of a day in decimals, dividing it into 100 centidays of 14.4 minutes.

Most light measurements are given in foot-candles. This unit equals 10 Lux, and is approximately 32 erg/cm.^{2}/sec. or 3.2 microwatt/cm.^{2}. Measurements are made with a Norwood light meter, which is recalibrated at least once a year. This can be used for measuring the light intensity of fluorescent and incandescent lamps as well, by using the conversion factor supplied by the lamp manufacturer in connection with each type of lamp. By referring to the spectral distribution curve of each lamp, which can be supplied by the manufacturer, it is even possible with the one light meter reading to calculate the amount of radiant energy in each wavelength band.

To indicate the conditions under which a particular plant is grown, not only photoperiod, phototemperature and nyctotemperature have to be indicated, but also if possible the light intensity at which the plants are maintained at any time of the day or night. Since in some plants the light period coincides with the night, no differentiation is made as to day or night, but only in photoperiod and nyctoperiod. In all work reported here the dark period is referred to as nyctoperiod. Etymologically skotoperiod (such as used by BÜNNING) is more correct, but unfortunately the words photo and skoto are very similar, and could lead to confusion, especially in pronunciation. For this reason the word nyctoperiod is preferred, which is unlikely to cause misunderstanding. For each light-dark cycle the successive treatments are placed one below the other. Temperature, light intensity and duration of treatment in hours are shown as follows: 26° 1500 fc 24 hr without punctuation. This means that the plants are subjected at 26°C to a light intensity of 1500 ft.-c. for 24 hours daily. To show a 12-hour light 12-hour dark cycle the notations would be:

26°	1500 fc	12 hr
26°	dark	12 hr

When plants are grown in the greenhouse the following notation could apply:

26°	daylite	8 hr
20°	1000 fc	8 hr
20°	dark	8 hr

or

26°	daylite	8 hr
20°	natnite	16 hr

in which daylite stands for natural daylight and natnite for natural length of night supplemented with daylight from 16:00 till sunset and from sunrise till 08:00.

Cycles other than 24 hours can easily be indicated, *e.g.*:

26°	1500 fc	8 hr
26°	dark	8 hr

which would mean a 16-hour cycle, or:

17°	1500 fc	4 hr
17°	dark	4 hr
17°	1500 fc	4 hr
17°	dark	12 hr

which indicates an 8-hour cycle alternating with a 16-hour cycle. When growing under optimal conditions, the whole life cycle of a tomato plant could be shown as follows:

26 dark 24 hr 5 days;

$$\frac{\text{26 daylite 8 hr}}{\text{20 natnite 16 hr}}\text{14 days;}$$

$$\frac{\text{23 daylite 8 hr}}{\text{17 natnite 16 hr}}\text{14 days;}$$

$$\frac{\text{23 daylite 8 hr}}{\text{17 dark 16 hr}}$$

Chapter 5

GROWING METHODS, ACCURACY AND RELIABILITY OF ENVIRONMENTAL CONTROL

Root Medium:— Since the number of variables in the experiments carried out in the Earhart Laboratory is so large, all those which are not directly related to the experiment are, if possible, eliminated or kept rigorously constant. For this reason the methods of growing plants have been standardized as far as possible, and thus responses are not attributable to irregular water content of the containers, varying soil composition, differing nutritional levels, changing aeration of the roots due to packing of the soil, etc. For this reason no soil is used in the experiments. As a growing medium the following materials have been tested:

1) *Gravel* (number 5 crushed rock). — This is relatively free from soluble minerals, but cannot be used in experiments in which mineral nutrition is being investigated. It seems to supply the necessary iron, for plants never showed iron chlorosis in it even when the nutrient solution with which the plants were watered was iron deficient, as water cultures and spray-cultures proved. It does not hold very much liquid in relation to its weight but once plants are established in it, growth is normal if they are watered sufficiently often. Its low water-holding capacity makes gravel a poor medium for plants to germinate in or for the first two weeks after transplanting. When growing in gravel, a fairly large portion of the finer roots is lost in the washing out of the root system.

2) *Sand.* — Fine sand is not advisable as a growing medium in non-porous containers because of insufficient aeration. Coarse sand (washed plaster) works fairly well, yet, gravel seems to be preferable in most cases. Both sand and gravel tend to make the containers very heavy in relation to their water-holding capacity. But both materials have the great advantage that they are easy to sterilize with steam, even in large bins (holding 5 tons). Besides, they carry few diseases and pests.

3) *Vermiculite.* — We now largely use Number 2 vermiculite, either alone, or mixed with an equal volume of gravel. It comes in paper sacks, which need only superficial sterilization, which is done by leaving the sacks overnight in a methyl bromide atmosphere. The material itself is largely sterile, since it is produced by heating mica to very high temperatures in which it exfoliates. It can hold five times its weight in water, and is relatively easy to wash out from root systems without excessive loss of the finer rootlets. It contains a fair amount of available potassium and other minerals so that it cannot be used in nutrition experiments where small amounts of minerals are critical. Its major disadvantage is that in the course of time (usually in ½ to 1 year) it compacts and finally may become quite soggy with regular watering. This can be partially prevented by mixing it with gravel, which gives it "substance." For this reason vermiculite is not used over again after having served in an experiment. The vermiculite locally available can be used as it comes from the bag. In other places (*e.g.* in Australia) the local vermiculite first has to be leached with water to remove toxic materials.

4) *Sponge rok.* — This is also a light weight material, which holds a considerable amount of water, but unlike vermiculite, it does not contain available mineral nutrients and does not compact. Plants have difficulty in becoming established in it, but afterwards growth is normal.

5) *Peat moss.*—This has to be sterilized properly, since it carries diseases and pests. Overnight exposure to methyl bromide, after spreading it out in a layer not more than 5 cm. thick seems to be sufficient to have it lose its living complements.

6) *Leaf mold and other organic materials.*—After it became evident that these cannot be properly sterilized with methyl bromide fumigation, even if spread in a thin layer, these materials are now banned from the laboratory.

7) *Soil.*—Only relatively uncontaminated soils such as desert soil have occasionally been used in the Earhart Laboratory for special experiments. The heavy fumigation probably killed not only all animals but also part of the seeds contained in it.

Watering:— Although it was realized that a fully automatic watering system for all plants would be ideal, it soon became evident that this was not practical under the conditions of the Earhart Laboratory. Since for reasons of flexibility of climatic treatments plants were grown on many small trucks (600 individual trucks are often in use at the same time), each truck would have to be connected and disconnected individually with the periodic nutrient or compressed air supply. This was tried in the Clark greenhouses, but the different systems, modeled after various published accounts, were too time-consuming to set up and were too cumbersome when thousands of individual plants had to be watered (in May 1955, *e.g.*, over 10,000 individual containers were in use, and each had one or more plants growing in them in the greenhouses).

For this reason all plants are watered individually, the only improvements over ordinary greenhouse operations being that nutrient solution and water are supplied under pressure in hoses (*see* Plate III, where two such hoses can be seen suspended from the greenhouse roof), which are installed in each greenhouse and artificially lighted room, and end in an aluminum spout 60 cm. long with a hand-operated squeeze valve. Thus, all plants even in remote corners can easily be reached, which is essential when 9,000 containers have to be watered by 2 gardeners within 1½ hours. This makes a careful watering of each plant according to its individual needs impossible, but the general practice is to water all in excess. Due to the porosity of the root medium the excess liquid drains out rapidly and thus approximately the same concentration of nutrients is maintained in the containers at all times. Most plants grown in the Earhart Laboratory grow better with excess watering than when watering is restricted to only a few times per week: *e.g.*, in corn grown in sufficiently large containers so that no wilting occurred with only twice-weekly watering, growth was restricted in comparison with similar plants watered twice daily.

Only occasionally after plants have grown for a long time in the same container, the drain holes become plugged, either by roots or by algae. Poking them will restore drainage.

Nutrient Solution:— The nutrient solution is a slightly modified Hoagland solution, in which the iron is present as a chelate (sequestrene). It is made in a large 7,000 l. concrete storage tank with gauge glass calibrated in 100 l. and from there it is pumped into a pressure tank at 25 pounds per square inch pressure (about 2 atm.), from where it is distributed throughout the building in black iron pipes, without any brass or tin connections. In seven years of operation no toxicity symptoms nor excessive rust accumulation have been observed. The solution is now made by refilling the storage tank with de-ionized water (of a salt content of 10 p.p.m. or less) and adding one l. of each of the following 5 stock solutions per 400 l. of de-ionized water (*see* TABLE 6). These stock solutions are made in 200 l. steel drums, lined with plastic, with a valve in the bottom. As soon as the nutrient solution in the storage tank is nearly used up, new solution is made. This is done immediately after the morning watering at 10:30. First the pressure tank is filled with the old solution, which then is available for watering during the rest of the day. Then the nutrient supply

TABLE 6: *Composition of the Hoagland nutrient solution used in the Earhart Laboratory:—*

	MOLECULAR WEIGHT	GRAMS PER LITER IN STOCK SOLN.
1) Calcium nitrate $Ca(NO_3)_2$	164.1	364.0
2) Potassium nitrate KNO_3	101.1	221.28
3) Magnesium sulfate $MgSO_4 \cdot 7H_2O$	120.4	217.6
4) Potassium dihydro phosphate KH_2PO_4	136.1	62.08
5) Mixed micronutrients, containing		
$CuSO_4 \cdot 5H_2O$	249.7	0.0354
$MnSO_4$	151.0	0.609
$ZnSO_4$	161.4	0.0974
H_3BO_3	61.8	1.269
$H_2MoO_4 \cdot 4H_2O$	234.0	0.0398
6) Fe-Sequestrene, prepared by mixing		
KOH		6.8
Sequestrene AA		10.4
$FeSO_4 \cdot 7H_2O$		10.0

pump is disconnected, and the pressure tank is connected with the compressed air, to keep the nutrient solution lines in the laboratory under pressure. De-ionized water is then run into the nutrient solution tank at the rate of about 20 l. per minute, and some time toward the end of the run the required amounts of stock solution are added. To mix the chemicals thoroughly, the nutrient solution is pumped out of the bottom of the storage tank and re-injected at the top for 2 hours.

For most plants this Hoagland nutrient solution is perfectly satisfactory and gives excellent growth. Some plants, such as strawberries, oaks, *Phalaenopsis, Cypripedium* and some other orchids, need a lower concentration. This is easily accomplished by watering the plants part of the time with de-ionized water and giving them the regular nutrient solution once or thrice weekly. This involves no complicated mixing and is entirely satisfactory. To make such different regimes of watering simple for the gardeners, every container or truck, which requires watering other than the twice daily supply of nutrient solution, carries a colored pot label, the color indicating the type of watering. A red pot label means no water whatsoever (usually the experimenter does his own watering), a green label means only de-ionized water (*e.g.*, the orchids growing in peat moss), a green label with one yellow band means nutrient solution on Monday morning only, at all other times de-ionized water (*e.g.*, strawberries), a green label with three yellow bands means watering every Monday, Wednesday and Friday morning with nutrient solution, the rest of the time they receive de-ionized water (*e.g.*, *Cattleyas*). A container with a red label with one yellow band receives nutrient on Monday, but is not otherwise watered (*e.g.*, young pines). Other variations on this system are easily conceived, and this system makes it very simple for the gardeners to water even quite complicated experiments without errors.

During recent years the essentiality of Cl ions was shown for a number of plants. It was also known that many plants, such as sugar beets, grow better with a nutrient solution containing NaCl. Therefore, in 1955, the Hoagland solution used in the Earhart Laboratory was modified by adding NaCl to it at a concentration of 0.001 mol. During the following year a number of plants, such as oaks and *Desmodium gyrans,* showed leaf injury symptoms which made the impression of salt damage. When, after a year, the NaCl addition was omitted, no further damage to these leaves was observed. Our de-ionized water contains a few parts per million Na, and the U.S.P. or C.P. grade chemicals, which we use in making our nutrient solution, probably contain enough Cl to satisfy the plant need for this element.

When other nutrient solutions have to be used, they are made up in 20 l. bottles, or in 200 l. monel metal tanks, which are placed on casters and thus can be moved to wherever that particular nutrient solution is to be used. From the bottom of these monel metal tanks a small stainless steel centrifugal pump delivers the solution to a hose with which the solution is distributed.

The watering schedule is as follows. Immediately after the plants have been moved at 08:00 the gardeners start watering, which takes about 3 man hours. Since the plants in the dark sections of the constant temperature rooms should receive as nearly as possible their scheduled dark period without interruption, those dark sections are watered first, followed by the artificial light rooms and the greenhouses. The larger plants in the greenhouses need additional watering later in the day, usually only at 15:00 and sometimes, especially in summer, also at 12:00.

The plants are always given an excess of water or nutrient solution so that part of it runs out of the drainage holes of the containers. In this way no accumulation or depletion of salts occurs and the roots remain in the same nutrient surroundings. It also prevents underwatering and keeps all plants under exactly comparable root conditions. In early experiments, in the Clark greenhouses in 1940, automatic sub-irrigation was installed, with time clocks energizing pumps which supplied nutrient solution three times daily to plants growing in gravel. Although this was entirely feasible, the amount of work involved in setting up the sub-irrigation system was too great in comparison with ordinary watering, without affording much advantage, so that it was abandoned.

Occasionally, plants are grown in water culture when specific nutrient experiments have to be carried out. Provided part of the roots develop in these nutrient cultures above the nutrient solution, growth of the plants will be satisfactory. In comparative experiments, tomato plants grew as well under these conditions as when planted in gravel and vermiculite. In our case the technique is to use 2-gallon crocks of which the bottom hole is plugged with a cork. On top of the crock a wire basket is fitted which hangs down approximately 3 cm. in the crock, and completely fills the opening. A thin layer of glass wool is spread on the wire and then the basket is filled with vermiculite, which has to be kept damp with de-ionized water. Seedlings are planted in this medium with their tap roots protruding through the basket into the nutrient solution below. As a good root system develops the level of the nutrient solution is lowered until it fills the crock half-way. This leaves a sufficient air space for the development of roots outside the nutrient solution. Under these conditions, further aeration of the nutrient solution is unnecessary. This method of growing plants in nutrient solution works well with tomatoes (WENT 1943*b*). As long as no roots have developed outside the nutrient solution, the growth rate of the plants is slow and they are slightly chlorotic in appearance. Upon development of roots above the nutrient solution, these become covered with root hairs, the growth rate increases and the growing leaves become dark green. Whatever the stimulus coming from the root is, it travels rectilinearly up in the stem. If new roots are formed only on one side of the stem, only the leaves above these roots darken, whereas the others remain chlorotic.

Nutrient Fog Box:— Because of the importance of aerial roots in the development of plants, attempts were made to grow plants with all their roots suspended in air. In accordance with the experience of other investigators (VYVYAN and TROWELL 1953) it was found perfectly feasible to do this by atomizing a nutrient solution around their roots. Mr. G. P. KEYES has developed this technique in the Earhart Laboratory to such an extent that many plants can now be grown as well in aeroponics as in hydroponics or gravel culture. After many initial difficulties were overcome, the following technique was adopted (*see* PLATE VIII):

1) Large water- and light-tight containers, 51 cm. wide, 152 cm. long and 122 cm. deep, have removable lids 24.5 cm. square, each with a central hole in which the stem of a plant can be wedged with sponge rubber. The roots of the plant are thus suspended in the light-tight box.

2) In the bottom of each box there are two spray nozzles with which nutrient is atomized by means of compressed air. This dual injection is necessary to obtain a fairly even distribution of nutrient fog inside the box and also as a safety measure

in case of occasional plugging of an injector. PLATE VIII shows the uneven development of tomato plants with only a single spray nozzle at one end of the box. The spray nozzles have to be regularly cleaned even though the nutrient solution enters them by way of a glass wool strainer.

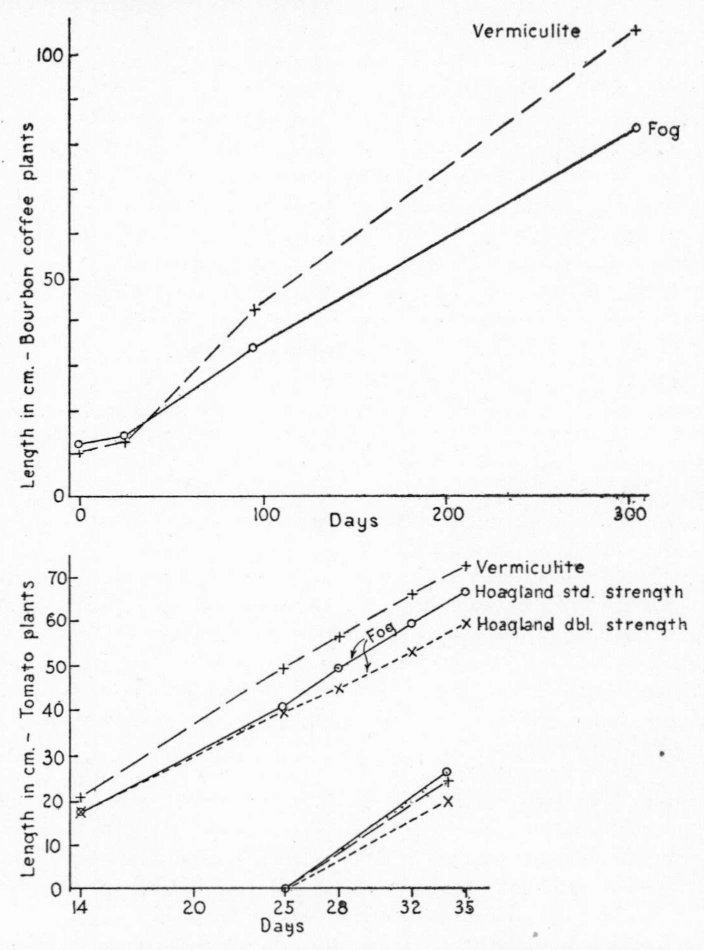

FIGURE 14.— Comparison of stem elongation of coffee and tomato plants growing with their roots either in a container with vermiculite or in a nutrient fog (*see* PLATE VIII). In all cases the fog was made with a standard Hoagland nutrient solution, except for the lower curve for tomatoes which were supplied with double strength Hoagland. Whereas the coffee plants grew somewhat better in a solid medium, the tomatoes, after an initial lag period, grew slightly better in the nutrient fog (*see also* PLATE IX).

3) The best development of plants is obtained when the amount of nutrient fog is only slightly higher than that required for a sufficient water supply for the tops. The fog droplets become attached to the root hairs and are there absorbed. Because of the very different water requirement of plants during day and night, the nutrient

fog is also produced at very different rates. The variation is obtained by varying the proportion of time that the sprays are on each minute. Whereas from 06:00 to 18:00 the spray works 15 seconds per minute, during night fog is produced only two seconds out of every minute. The spray is controlled by solenoid valves which cut off the air and nutrient supply. The solenoid valves in turn are operated by time clocks from the control room.

5) Before root hairs have been produced, more nutrient spray is needed; therefore, as long as the plants are not fully established, it is advisable to increase the rate of fog production by increasing the duration of injection per cycle. An alternative method would be to adjust the needle valve of the spray nozzle. In this way, during the first week the spray is made denser than later, when the plants have become established.

6) The nutrient fog moves up mainly along the ends of the fog box, and the closer the roots of the plants are to this rising fog stream, the better they develop (this was found for tomatoes and coffee plants).

7) Whereas in ordinary nutrient solution culture the concentration of the solution is not critical, with nutrient fogs this concentration is more important. Roots suspended in nutrient solution are able to extract from it the salts they need in the proper amounts and proportions, leaving the rest in solution. In the case of the nutrient fog the salts left behind after water and nutrients are absorbed may accumulate on the root hair surface. Such accumulations are either toxic or retard growth. Similarly an insufficient amount of nutrient will express itself in decreased growth rate, since the roots are unable to accumulate the deficient salts from a large volume of solution as they do in water-culture.

8) Root systems of different plants are highly diverse in the fog box. Tomatoes develop an intricately branched, very heavy root system which is completely covered with root hairs (*see* PLATE IX). These root hairs show a periodic difference in length which apparently is related to the day and night changes. Other plants such as lettuce, poppies (*Eschscholtzia californica*), and strawberries have thin and weak roots. The first roots of carrot plants are also thin and weak, but after they have developed a thickened primary root, the root system widens out and becomes very extensive. The date palm (*Phoenix dactylifera*) has a stiff tap root soon joined by a few adventitious roots which branch and have even stiff secondary roots without a trace of root hairs. Coffee plants develop fairly extensive root systems with root hairs.

9) In getting plants established in the fog box, it is advisable to spray them with sugar 3 days prior to transplanting. This was the only way in which strawberries could become established.

10) FIGURE 14 gives a comparison of the growth rate of tomato plants developing in the fog box and similar plants growing in gravel or nutrient solutions (*see* PLATE IX). After an initial period of adjustment when the plants in the fog box lag behind, all of them tend to grow equally well. This same figure shows how coffee plants also grow equally well in a fog spray and in vermiculite.

Water Softener:— Because the city water supply in Pasadena is very variable as far as the salt content is concerned (fluctuations between 200 and 550 p.p.m. of total salts are possible), all water used on the plants and in nutrient solution is passed through a de-ionizer of the exchange resin type. It consists of two columns of 220 cm. height and 35 and 30 cm. diameter, the first one filled with a cation and the second with an anion exchange resin. In the first one the cations are exchanged against H-ions and in the second the anions are replaced by CO_3-ions. The resulting CO_2 is removed in an air stream and the water which leaves the de-ionizer has less than 10 p.p.m. of solvents left. Since for our purpose this purity is sufficient, no special efforts have been made to improve the purity of the water beyond this point, although in some instances we have reached purity of one p.p.m.

Our water softener was designed to deliver 4,000 l. of purified water between regenerations. In the course of years the personnel in charge of the regeneration of the de-ionizer has found ways to improve its performance and now we regularly get 12,000 l. and sometimes 20,000 l. of de-ionized water between regenerations of the columns. To reach such a good performance, factory recommendations had to be followed closely; however, in addition the following improvements were necessary:

1) The 3-way Solo valves are only used during regeneration of the columns but are by-passed as long as the ionized water is delivered. Since these valves easily develop slight leaks some of the water does not pass through the columns and thus does not become de-ionized. This improvement is now installed on all de-ionizers which are delivered.

2) The acid should pass during regeneration through the cation exchanger much slower than recommended. When it takes 80 to 100 minutes the resins are much better saturated with H-ions.

3) In general, by decreasing flow rates during operation and regeneration deionization is more efficient.

Because complete removal of salts is not necessary in our operation we usually wash the resins down until the solubridge indicates a salt content of 14 p.p.m. This is accomplished usually with less than 200 l. of wash water. After the next 400 l. have passed through, the salt content has decreased to 5 p.p.m. and then remains below that value for 10 to 15 thousand l. When the solubridge indicates a rising salt content of 10 to 15 p.p.m. the de-ionizer has to be regenerated.

Difficulties encountered in the operation were: (*1*) The original pyrex pump which pumped the de-ionized water into the pressure tank had to be replaced with a stainless steel pump; (2) when the amplifier tubes in the solubridge went bad, wrong readings of the conductivity of the de-ionized water were obtained, and (3) it is very difficult to keep Solo valves without leaks.

The de-ionized water is distributed through the building in hard rubber tubing with hard rubber taps. In the beginning organic substances leaked out of the hard rubber into the water, but these have not caused damage to plants watered with it.

Staking:— The stems of many plants are not strong enough to stand up by themselves, and in many other cases the root medium is not solid enough to anchor the plants in it. In all those cases the plants have to be staked. Several handy methods have been developed in the Earhart Laboratory which deserve description.

When the root medium is solid enough, a regular stake can be inserted in it, and plants can be tied to it with, *e.g.*, Gard-n-tys (paper-covered tying wire), or raffia. Aluminum tubing was found to be ideal as stakes (*e.g.*, PLATES IX and XV). It is light, and cheaper than most other material.

It can be bent if necessary, but, best of all, it can be easily extended. The first stake placed next to the plant does not need to have the length of the mature plant, but can be approximately the size of the plant as it is staked. As the plant grows, galvanized wire is inserted in the aluminum tubing; by slightly bending the wire one can wedge it solidly in the tubing. If necessary another piece of aluminum tubing can be put over the top of the galvanized wire, so that a three-fold extension is possible.

As the plants grow taller, they may become top-heavy, and then they

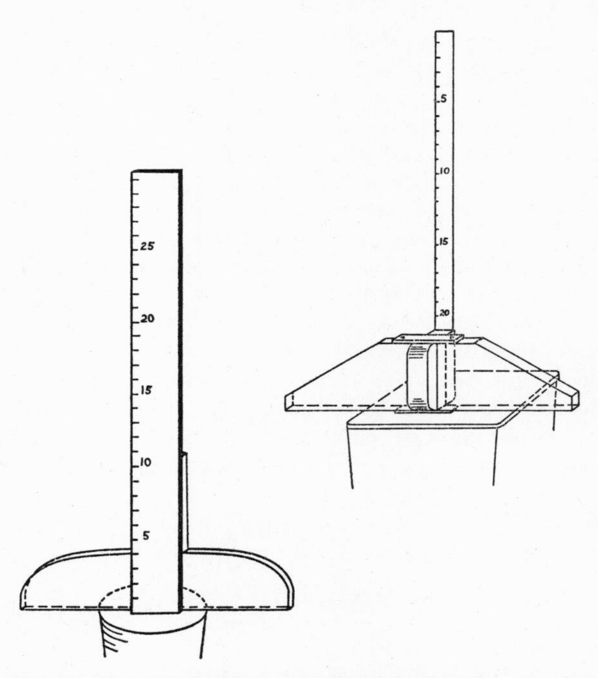

FIGURE 15.— Methods of measuring stem length. A ruler is placed by means of a crossbar on the rim of the plant container. The steel tape (*upper figure*) is pulled out until its top is even with the growing point, highest visible node or other recognizable point of reference, and is read at bottom.

are placed on adjustable trucks. The stakes are then tied to two diagonal crosswires put up between the four extended legs of the truck. Or, the stakes are tied onto the square band-iron frames attached to the upright ringpost of the fixed table trucks.

When the root medium is not solid enough to support a stake (*e.g.*, in the case of pure vermiculite), a galvanized wire, bent so as to fit the bottom of the container, is placed in the container before potting; this wire can then be extended on top with aluminum tubing.

It is also possible to attach the stakes to the containers. This is done in the case of the small containers, especially the cups. Three-legged stakes are made of wire and are cadmium-plated. The three legs clamp over the rim of the cup and hold the stake solidly upright. Extensions can be slipped over the primary stake, following the plant in its growth (*see e.g.* Plates XIII*a* and *b*). For the square plastic containers 4-legged clamps have been made.

Since the stakes often extend just to eye-level, corks or pieces of red sponge-rubber are put over their tips so as to prevent possible injuries of personnel when the plants are watered or inspected at close range.

The staking of plants is necessary not only to prevent them from becoming tangled, but also to insure even illumination to all of them, and to make length measurements possible. Of all parameters of a plant, stem length frequently is the quickest to measure with considerable accuracy, and it gives a running record of the performance of an individual plant. Unless the plant is staked from an early age on, bends in stems develop which make accurate length measurements illusory. The most convenient methods to measure the length of plants are shown in Figure 15. As reference point is always used the top of the plant container which, being of plastic, is always smooth and even. A crossbar is attached to the ruler which can thus be placed on top of the container. For short plants, up to 50 cm., stiff rulers are used, but for taller plants a flexible tape ruler is attached to the cross bar which can be pulled out so far that its top coincides with the top of the plant to be measured. In tomatoes, peas and other plants, the growing point is externally visible and is used as reference point; in grasses, such as corn, the top of the longest leaf is used.

Containers:— In the Earhart Laboratory no ordinary porous clay pots are used. Instead of these, we have (*see* Plate VII):

1) Metal containers, cans of different sizes. The largest are three-gallon, so-called egg cans with a diameter of 25 cm., and 31 cm. tall. They are covered outside with aluminum paint and inside with asphalt paint. Like the other containers, they have small holes in their bottom for drainage; if the holes are made small enough, vermiculite or gravel cannot wash through them. Smaller cans (16 or 10.5 cm. diameter and 17.5 cm. high, painted the same way) have also been used, but are now replaced with plastic containers, because no matter how well the metal cans are painted, they will rust; the plastic containers outlast them in spite of greater fragility.

2) One and two-gallon glazed earthenware crocks, with a drainage hole in the side at the bottom. If this hole is plugged with a cork, the crock can be used for nutrient-culture vessels. Their inner diameters are 17.5 and 21.6 cm. and their inside depth is 17.5 and 20 cm.

3) When working with gravel or vermiculite, plastic containers are used with drainage holes (3-4 mm.) drilled in the bottom. Sizes of containers are: 7.5 × 9 cm. cups, 10 × 10 × 6 cm. square containers (so-called ice-box dishes), 21 × 10.5 × 6.5 cm. rectangular containers, and 9.5 × 9.5 × 14 cm. square containers. All these containers are somewhat conical and can be nested together for convenient storage. They are made of molded plastic which is not in the least toxic for plants. Another plastic material turned out to be highly toxic because of the insufficiently evaporated solvent. These plastic containers are available in different colors, which allows coding of experiments (*e.g.*, each variety of experimental plant is sown in a cup of different

color). Containers without drainage holes are all of one color contrasting with those with holes.

The larger plastic containers are not too easily cracked, and are more durable than clay pots. They have the great advantage that they are easily cleaned, do not absorb nutrient, are light, take little space and look neat. For identification purposes they can be marked with grease pencil. Thus, no stakes or pot labels, so easily displaced, need be inserted in them.

All the three types of containers (cans, crocks and plastic) are non-porous. This means that the oxygen supply for the roots has to penetrate through the root medium, and, therefore, no soil or other rather non-porous root medium can be used in connection with them. Vermiculite, gravel or even coarse sand, and any mixture of them can be used. Even orchids develop good root systems under these conditions, and in not a single case did development of the plants seem impaired by the non-porous containers.

When roots are very light-sensitive, the plastic containers, which are translucent, should be painted on the outside, first black and then aluminum to keep their temperature down even in strong sunlight. This is essential when these plastic containers are used for water cultures: only when both the lids and the containers are light-tight will plants, such as tomatoes, grow well in them.

Since practically all plants are grown on wheeled tables (trucks), and since these are moved regularly (twice daily) or irregularly (when measuring or inspecting or harvesting the plants) over the slotted floors, the containers have to be supported to prevent them from tipping over or sliding off the truck. For the big cans, and one and two-gallon crocks this is not necessary, since they are stable enough.

The smaller square containers and cans are usually anchored to the truck table-surface (made of expanded metal) with springs to which hooks have been fastened on both sides, one fitting over the edge of the container, and the other hooked into a mesh of the table. Two such springs on opposite sides are usually sufficient to prevent slipping of the container.

The cups are fitted into metal racks (*see* PLATE VII), one side of which consists of 9 rings welded together in a square. In these rings 9 cups are held to about 1 cm. below their rims. Four of these metal racks fit together on a truck top, and thus 36 cups can be accommodated per truck.

These metal racks are so constructed that the side opposite the rings consists of four wire squares, in which the square plastic containers just fit. In the center, between the 4 squares, a small metal plate with perforation is welded. To this can be attached an aluminum pipe by which the rack can be carried and around which colored rings can be put, indicating in which greenhouse or darkroom this rack has to be located at different times. Thus not only whole trucks, but smaller units can be moved, too. This is important when experimental treatments are carried out with less than a truckload of plants.

The four squares of the wire racks are separated by 1 cm. wide slots so that air can circulate between the square containers. This is essential to insure uniform conditions for the plants in the containers. When *e.g.*, 16 squares of tomato plants are placed on a truck, and when these are moved close together towards the center of the truck, preventing air from moving up between them, the plants in the center 4 squares will be several cm. taller than those in the peripheral containers. This is due to deficient air circulation around the plants in the center containers, for when the squares are placed evenly over the truck top, leaving 1 cm. wide spaces between them (not enough to change the light distribution, but allowing air to move up between them), the plants in all containers have the same size. There are large enough openings between the round containers to allow sufficient air to rise between them.

From these experiences it can be concluded that to get more uniform growth of plants on greenhouse benches, it is advisable to make these benches of expanded metal and to let air rise freely between the pots. When plants are grown in plastic or glazed containers this will not increase evaporation from the containers. In the greenhouses of the Los Angeles State and County Arboretum this arrangement has given improved performance of the plants. In this case it was combined with some air-conditioning.

Accuracy and Reliability of the Environmental Control:— The accuracy of both temperature and humidity control in air-conditioned greenhouses depends on the type of thermostat and humidistat, the placement of the sensing elements, the capacity of the air-conditioning units, the rate of air turn-over, and the method of air injection into the controlled spaces. Contrary to common belief, the accurate measurement of temperature is very difficult, especially in the presence of much radiation, such as in a greenhouse. A properly calibrated thermometer or thermocouple gives an accurate measure of the average temperature of the mercury or metallic junction. This temperature depends on radiation and heat exchange at the surface of the sensing element. When a thermometer can be inserted in a space with equal temperature all around, a temperature equilibrium will be reached when as much long-wave radiation is received as is emitted, when the temperature of all surfaces and of the thermometer is the same. But, whenever the radiation of an object with a different temperature, such as the sun or a lamp, can reach a thermometer, radiation equilibrium will be reached only when the sensing element has the average temperature of its surroundings, which means a temperature considerably higher than that of the surrounding walls. Even though the sun occupies only a very small section of the sky, its radiation temperature is so high that a thermometer reads several degrees higher than the air temperature when exposed to it. The actual reading of a thermometer exposed to radiation depends on the amount of radiation and the heat loss of the thermometer through convection and conduction to the surrounding air.

In experiments with plants, it would be desirable to control accurately the temperature of the whole plant. This is only possible for plants submerged in water. The temperature of a leaf depends upon: (*1*) radiation, (*2*) heat exchange through convection and conduction, (*3*) transpiration, and (*4*) heat production by metabolism. In comparison with the other three factors the last one is insignificant and can be neglected, but the others are all of the same order of magnitude in their effectiveness. Thus, heat absorption from the sun may well be balanced by heat extraction through evaporative cooling. Since the amount of incoming and outgoing radiation differs from leaf to leaf, according to color and exposure, since the transpiration varies from edge to center of leaf, and differs according to stomatal width and rate of air movement past the leaf, and since the circulation of air controlling the heat exchange between leaf and air is quite different at different parts of the plant, it is utterly impossible to produce an even temperature throughout a land plant exposed to light. Even in darkness, transpiration makes temperature control of a plant to within less than 1° difficult.

Because of all these practically insurmountable difficulties in the control of the temperature of a plant, it was decided rather to control the air temperature of the greenhouse, and that the leaves, stems and other plant organs would be left to adjust themselves to the ambient temperature. In general, leaf temperatures are rather close to air temperature, because on the one hand radiation and transpiration hold each other more or less in check, and because on the other hand the leaves are so thin that through conduction and convection they exchange heat easily with the surrounding air.

Measurement of the leaf temperature can be done with a thermocouple inserted in or held between two leaves. Or a leaf can be wrapped around a thermometer. Theoretically, the best method is to measure leaf temperature by their long-wave length infra-red radiation. This can be done by using a pyrometer operating in wave lengths of about 100,000 Å. Trials with a commercially available pyrometer constructed for a measuring range of 50°-500°C was tried but the accuracy was too low for our purposes. However, preliminary tests with a radiation thermometer constructed by Strong (1939) gave very encouraging results. With a concave mirror the image of a leaf is thrown on a thermopile. Before reaching the thermopile the light is passed through a residual ray monochromator, which isolates a narrow wave band at about 90,000 Å. The deflection of the galvanometer connected with this thermopile can be calibrated in degrees. Thus, the surface temperature of a leaf can be measured by pointing the radiation thermometer at it.

The root temperature can more easily be controlled than the leaf temperature. This is done in the Earhart Laboratory by circulating thermostatically controlled water through coils buried inside the vermiculite in which the root system develops. Since these coils also cover the surface of the root medium, and since the crocks inside which the coils are wound are insulated on the outside, a very constant temperature can be maintained throughout the whole root system.

When pots or plant containers are exposed to full sun radiation, the contents will attain a considerably higher temperature than the surrounding air, dependent upon their color and consequently upon the absorption of radiation at their surface. Dry surfaces may have a temperature more than 20° higher than the air. For this reason it is important to have containers as reflectant as possible, painted white or aluminum, and to use a light-colored root medium as well.

Measurement of the air temperature has to be done with a completely shielded thermometer or a radiation-insensitive thermocouple. To shield a thermometer a double aluminum tube, through which air is drawn at a fast rate, is most desirable. Air movement past the thermometer bulb is essential, otherwise the shielded enclosure will attain a higher temperature than the surrounding air. It also insures a more rapid equilibrium between thermometer and air temperature.

A very simple and effective radiation-insensitive thermocouple can be made by mounting a thin-wire thermocouple junction (with as small a surface as possible) on a vibrator. This junction will absorb little radiation but can easily reach temperature equilibrium with the surrounding air since the vibration acts like a strong wind.

The air temperature in the greenhouses can best be measured in the exhaust air duct, where no radiation, but a strong wind exists. In these ducts the temperature readings are usually lower than in the greenhouse, which either means that the temperature measurement in the open greenhouse is too high or that poor mixing of the air occurs inside the greenhouse. The latter is not the case as indicated by smoke injection in the air stream. Therefore, one has to take many precautions in the measurement of greenhouse air temperature.

In the artificial light rooms the air circulation near the light panels is not sufficient to prevent a rise in temperature. This amounts to approximately 2°C within 10 cm. of the light panel. In all descriptions of experiments in the following chapters this fact should be taken into consideration. Air circulation could be improved by: (*1*) having exhaust ducts all along the side walls of the lighted compartments, (*2*) having these exhaust ducts extend to near the light panels, and (3) increasing the rate of air movement in these light rooms from 30 to 60 air changes per hour (this latter rate has recently been reached in all artificially lighted rooms).

Any interference with the rate of air movement past plants will increase their temperature in light, and, therefore, in the Earhart Laboratory, where the air enters from the floors, plant containers never should be placed so close that no air can pass between them to reach the tops of the plants. If they are placed too close, a pocket of stagnant air is formed, and the plants in the center will grow taller and spindlier than those along the edge. For this reason it is advisable to grow plants in the smallest containers which will allow sufficient root development.

When plants are grown in test tubes or flasks, they will be subjected to much higher temperatures: about 6° at 1,000 ft.-c. This was measured by DE CAPITE (1955) for his tissue cultures; it is due to the very slow dissipation of heat from the tissues of plants in the stagnant air of the tube and the low conductivity of glass for heat. To keep such tissue cultures in a light-dark succession at constant temperature, they have to be moved from a room at lower temperature in the light to a higher temperature in the dark.

Not only are there temperature differences between plants and air on account of imperfections in the air distribution in the growing rooms, due

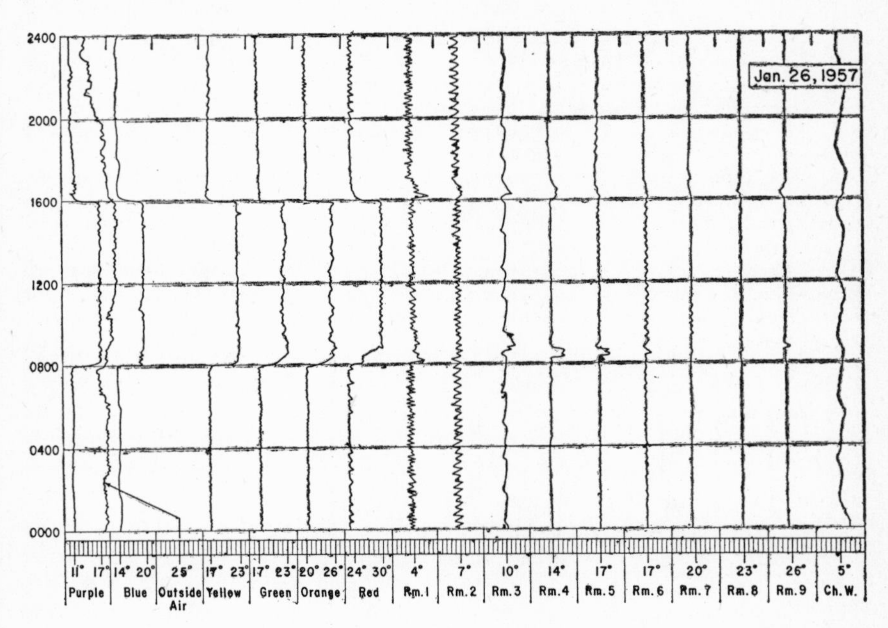

FIGURE 16.— Temperature record for January 26, 1957. For each thermocouple in greenhouse or constant temperature room its temperature range is indicated on the scale below. The record reads from bottom to top from 00:00-24:00. The 08:00 and 16:00 lines are clearly indicated by the temperature shift in the greenhouses. The outside air temperature line starts at 9°C at 00:00, drops then to 6.5° at 07:00 from where it rises to 11.5°C at 15:00. Ordinarily, this line crosses over the temperature curve of the blue greenhouse. On warm summer days it may cut across the record of the yellow greenhouse. The right hand curve marked Ch.W. indicates the temperature of the chilled water in the tank.

to differential absorption of light and due to uneven transpiration, but there are also occasionally aberrations of the room temperature from the thermostatic setting. These are due to a number of different causes:

1) The modulating thermostat reduces the fluctuations in temperature only when the lag period of the thermostat and of the heating and cooling mechanism are not the same. If they both have the same period a condition of "hunting" appears in which no equilibrium position of the valves is attained. By reducing the heat supply to the radiators this hunting can be prevented.

2) The average temperature of a greenhouse differs about 1°C with the same thermostat setting, according to whether heating or cooling is needed. This is due to the fact that the modulating thermostat does not start to call for cooling until the temperature is measurably higher than that for which it is set, and only as the temperature of the room rises, will the thermostat call for more cooling. In the same manner the average room temperature has to be lower before the heating will come on, and has to become still lower to open the heating valve fully. Therefore, in warm weather the greenhouses are about 1°C warmer than in cold weather. But rapid fluctuations in temperature as produced by the off-on type of thermoregulator are practically eliminated. This can be seen from a comparison of the temperature records of FIGURE 16. Rooms 1, 2 and 3 have the off-on type of thermoregulator, whereas the other rooms and greenhouses have the modulating type of thermoregulator.

3) Very rarely the bleeding valve of a thermostat becomes clogged, which keeps the cooling on continuously. This can be prevented by careful drying and filtering of the compressed air entering the pneumatic control system.

4) When the air circulation is stopped by failure of the fan motor the room or greenhouse air is not cooled or heated any more.

5) When the temperature of the cold circulating water needed for cooling rises to within 6°C of the set room temperature, or when the circulating warm water becomes too cool due to failure of the gas boilers or of the hot water circulating pumps, temperature control becomes impossible.

6) When the doors to the basement air-conditioning equipment rooms are left open when the upstairs room doors are open at the same time, the capacity of the air-conditioning equipment is insufficient to adjust the temperature of the rooms.

FIGURE 16 shows a temperature record for a 24-hour period for all greenhouses, the upstairs air-conditioned light rooms, the outside temperature and the temperature of the water in the chilled water tank. In this figure the charts of two ten-point type 153 Brown Electronik Recorders are combined. These recorders have as a special feature ten separate potentiometers mounted on them, each one connected with another thermocouple. Thus the zero-point can be set individually for the recording of each thermocouple temperature, and the record for each of the rooms and greenhouses can be separated on the chart. This is essential if one wants to see at a glance whether the temperatures are accurately controlled. In ordinary recorders the temperature records of, *e.g.*, the yellow and green greenhouses and of rooms 5, 6 and 8 would be all overlapping, but here they are neatly separated, the range being indicated on the scale below.

This record shows typical imperfections in the temperature control for the sake of discussion. It can be seen that in most of the greenhouses and in the temperature-controlled rooms no. 4-9 the temperature curves are smooth due to the modulating controls. In room 1 the temperature becomes 8° or 9°C just after 08:00 and 16:00 because the cooling coils are unable to supply sufficient cold to counterbalance the influx of warm air from the atrium. On the other hand, the temperature in rooms 8 and 9 becomes lower at those times because the atrium air is cooler. The irregularities in the temperature of rooms 1, 2 and 3, amounting to fluctuations of almost 1° above and 1° below the set temperature, are due to the different thermostats in those rooms which are of the off-on type. Thus, either a full load of refrigerant is supplied to the cooling coils, or this is cut off completely. This causes an overshoot in the temperature during the cooling cycle, but the temperature remains around the average for which the thermostat is set. In the red greenhouse the contact of the night thermostat was slightly sticking and this caused the irregularities. The fluctuations were less after cleaning of the thermostat. It takes the greenhouses approximately one-half

hour each morning to heat up to the set day temperature. In the afternoon the cooling is achieved quickly during winter, but in the warmer season it may take approximately one hour for the blue and purple greenhouses to cool down to their night temperatures.

In most cases the temperatures in the rooms, with the exceptions mentioned above, remain within 0.5 degree of the set temperatures. If closer control is desired, not only are more expensive thermostats needed, but also the volume of air passing through the rooms has to be increased.

Control of the relative humidity is not so essential as discussed in the chapter on water relations, but it is kept within reasonable limits, so much so that transpiration measurements on successive days agree to within 10 per cent.

In the greenhouses it is impossible to maintain during daytime humidities above 80 per cent. For even if the air which enters the greenhouse were fully saturated, the heating by radiation of the air inside the greenhouse at a renewal rate of 2 air changes per minute will reduce the relative humidity to 75 per cent. Only by injection of fine water droplets into the air inside the greenhouse could a higher relative humidity be maintained, at least under the conditions of our greenhouses. By reducing the radiation or by increasing the rate of air turnover higher humidities are possible.

For the operator of a phytotron the question of the degree of control required for efficient operation is always present. Doubling of the accuracy of control may roughly double the operating costs, because of larger volumes of air which require so much more cooling or heating. Therefore, one has to be realistic and weigh the advantages gained through closer control against its costs. In the Earhart Laboratory we have arbitrarily set a range of 1°C (0.5 degree deviation from the set temperature) as the desirable goal. Since the temperature differential between successive rooms and greenhouses is 3° or 4°C, there is no overlap in their temperature.

Since each day at moving time the temperature in most of the rooms and greenhouses shows aberrations because of opening of all doors, it also seemed unnecessary to go to a closer control than 1°C. It is very likely that the individual phenotypic variability of the plants could be further reduced by keeping a closer temperature control, but to do this the operation of the greenhouses would have to be radically changed. To obtain minimal phenotypic variability periodic moving of plants should be avoided, and the flexibility of climatic treatments as described for the Earhart Laboratory would have to be sacrificed.

PART II

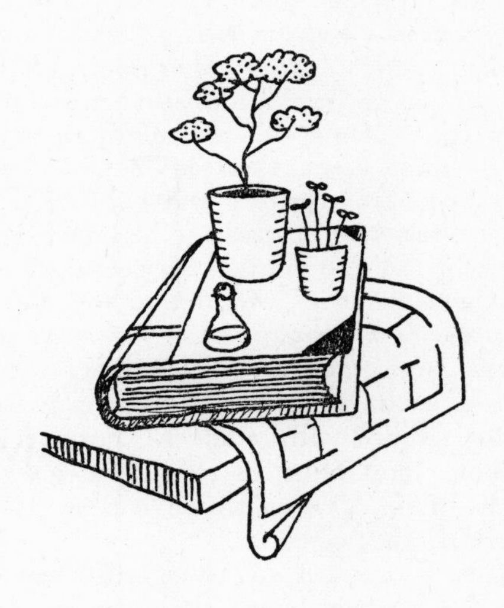

CLIMATIC RESPONSE of INDIVIDUAL PLANTS

Introduction:— In the following chapters the behavior of a number of plant species and varieties is described as determined in experiments in the Clark and Earhart greenhouses, where in the course of the last fifteen years, approximately 150 different kinds of plants have been investigated. The selection of these plants was based on several different considerations. In the first place the reaction of specific plants to environment was studied in connection with their practical growing. The tomato was originally selected as the best experimental plant for this purpose. The sugar beet, *Vicia faba, Pisum sativum, Veratrum viride, Cymbidium,* chaparral plants, *Taraxacum kok-saghyz, Coffea arabica* are examples of plants whose laboratory behavior was studied to gain information applicable to field-growing problems. Most of these plants are, potentially or actually, of economic importance, and, in most cases, their investigation was made possible through financial support from private and public organizations.

In the second place, selection of plants to be grown in the laboratory was based on their suitability for the solution of specific problems. For investigations of photoperiodic behavior, *Xanthium,* tomato, strawberry, *Baeria, Hyoscyamus, Chenopodium amaranticolor, Cestrum nocturnum, Silene,* and *Pisum sativum* were used. For germination problems, primarily desert plants, California annuals, and some common weeds were selected. Tuber formation was studied with potatoes. For the investigation of the effects of smog, plants most sensitive to it were grown, such as endive, spinach, barley and alfalfa. Vernalization was studied with peas, *Vicia faba,* rye (*Secale*) and other cereals.

In the third place, a number of biologically interesting plants such as *Mimosa pudica, Desmodium gyrans,* many succulents, several insectivorous plants, epiphytes, alpine annuals, etc., were grown in the expectation that at some time their behavior would attract the attention of an investigator.

In the fourth place, plants were grown under completely controlled conditions to study their phenotypic and genotypic variability. Since until recently it had been impossible to grow higher plants under exactly known conditions no reliable information was available as to the degree to which the environment influences not only the expression of its genes, but also the genetic composition itself. This work is at present carried out by Dr. H. Highkin with a grant from the National Science Foundation, but final results of this long-range experiment are not as yet available so that this aspect of the work in the Earhart Laboratory will not be discussed.

In the fifth place, the behavior of ecotypes was studied, supplementing transplanting experiments in the field. The distribution of plants in nature may depend on so many factors, such as temperature in all its aspects (daily and seasonal variations, extremes), light (as far as duration, intensity and color are concerned), different forms of water supply (mist, dew, rain, irrigation), and transpiration, wind etc., that usually only laboratory experiments can establish the basis for their distribution. Plants used for such ecological studies were *Poa* species and hybrids, *Achillea, Lupinus, Clarkia* and *Mimulus.*

In general, there is a trend towards growing smaller plants in the Earhart Laboratory. As the space becomes more fully occupied either the number of experiments has to become limited, or the size of the experiments has to be reduced. This can be achieved either by using fewer plants per treatment or by using smaller plants. A shift from tomatoes to peas allows a 9-fold increase in the number of plants which can be grown to maturity per unit area. Further increases in the number of plants are possible by selecting the smallest possible annual plants, the so-called belly plants (only visible while crawling on your belly over the ground; it is a translation of the term "Bauchpflanzen," coined by C. SCHRÖTER). A deliberate search for such "botanical *Drosophila's*" was started in 1940 and has been going on ever since (*see, e.g.,* LEWIS and WENT 1945); some of the best experimental plants which were discovered in this search are *Baeria chrysostoma* and *Phacelia parryae* (seeds are available by writing to the Rancho Santa Ana Botanic Garden, Claremont, California; prospective investigators should be warned, however, that some persons develop an allergy against *Phacelia* species, and cannot handle them without having skin trouble).

Perhaps the most important ultimate aim in studying plants in the Earhart Plant Research Laboratory is to get an overall picture of basic plant behavior. It is essential to gain a general understanding of which factors are of greatest importance in the development of a plant. Is, for instance, photoperiod as universal a controlling factor in growth and flowering as assumed; is thermoperiodicity widespread; how do plants differ in their light requirements? These and other questions are of special significance in guiding future work and in designing research facilities. They have to be taken into account in considerations about evolution, distribution of plants over the world, breeding programs, etc. To accomplish this aim a large number of different plants have to be investigated and their selection should be as much as possible at random. Among plants selected for such a survey were a group of garden annuals which flowered at different times of the year, and a group of 100 native California plants, obtained from the Rancho Santa Ana Botanic Garden as seed. Very poorly represented in the experiments are perennial plants, particularly trees and shrubs.

Since so many different species have been grown in the air-conditioned greenhouses, for a description of their behavior a selection had to be made. Plants about which most information is available, and those which are particularly interesting for one or another reason will be discussed. In addition to describing experimental results, an attempt has been made to give hints as to the optimal growing conditions for each one, which may make it easier for other investigators to decide which plants could, and which could not, be grown together in the same greenhouse. For instance, both *Bellis perennis* and *Baeria chrysostoma* will die under the optimal growing conditions for *Saintpaulia* and *vice versa*. Under conditions that

FIGURE 17.— Aluminum shield adjusted around plastic square with young tomato plants, containing the leaves in an area of 10.5 × 10.5 cm. As the plants grow the shield can be slipped upwards. It is held in position with a rubber band.

tomatoes produce most fruit, potato tuberization is practically impossible, whereas in a greenhouse in which potatoes grow well, no normal tomato fruits will develop.

Chapter 6

THE TOMATO AND OTHER SOLANACEAE

The Tomato (*Lycopersicon esculentum*):— The tomato plant has always been a favorite experimental plant in physiological research. When the first work was started in the Clark greenhouses, a number of plants were compared as to their suitability for studying growth responses, and from these (tobacco, sunflower, cotton, corn, *Mimosa, Bryophyllum, Cosmos* and others) the tomato was chosen. Its growth is indeterminate in most varieties and after a certain size is reached (about 50 cm.) its growth rate under controlled growing conditions becomes approximately constant. It is not photoperiodic as far as flowering is concerned and its leaves are light saturated at 1,000 ft.-c., which makes it grow well both in summer and winter when natural daylight is used. It has a strong root system which will grow even under adverse conditions, and except for viruses, it is easy to keep free from diseases. From a physiological standpoint the tomato plant is also desirable. It is easy to measure: the rate of stem elongation is very reproducible if all lateral shoots are kept trimmed off; when these reach a size of more than a few cm., they start to interfere with the growth of the main stem. The tomato plant does not store photosynthates, and after 30-40 hours in darkness stops growing because of a lack of sugars; sugar application can prolong its growth in darkness for about five days. Therefore, the plants respond with changes in growth rate within 1-2 days after the growing conditions have been changed and they soon adjust their growth rate to the new conditions. Several times I noticed deviations from the set temperatures of greenhouses or darkrooms by aberrations in the growth rate of tomato plants or by differences in their color or shape, before these deviations had been noticed in the temperature records. Flower size and fruiting are very sensitive to the environment. Stomata are easily observable with the Ultrapak microscope and the growing point is easily accessible. Finally, since the tomato has been used so extensively as an experimental plant, much is known about its physiology, such as its nutrition, mineral and hormone relationships, and about its genetics, pathology, morphology and taxonomy. On the other hand its complex leaf form makes leaf area measurement difficult and its small sieve tubes and bi-collateral vascular bundles complicate studies of its food translocation.

Dr. W. C. Ashby has developed a simple method of measuring the leaf area in tomato plants. Total leaf weight is determined and also the weight of 10 leaf discs stamped out of the leaves with a cork borer. The total leaf surface is then found by multiplying the leaf disc surface with the proportion of leaf/disc weight.

During germination, the optimum temperature of the tomato is fairly high, around 26°C. At that temperature, seeds, when planted 1 cm.

deep, will appear above the surface 4-5 days after sowing (*see* FIGURE 51). Darkness is best for germination; in light, emergence of the seedlings is delayed. Therefore, our standard practice is to plant tomato seeds in vermiculite and place the containers in a dark room at 26°C. Five days later the containers with emerging seedlings are placed in a greenhouse. Fastest development is obtained at 26°C day and 20°C (or even higher) night temperature. Under those conditions the hypocotyls elongate quite well, and light colored, slightly spindly young plants are obtained. If one wants to have much shorter, stockier plants, the containers with seedlings can be placed in a cooler greenhouse, but then their development is much slower. One can also transplant the seedlings 5-7 days after emergence, burying the hypocotyls as far as the cotyledons. Transplanting causes the plants to reach maximal growth rates in a shorter time.

When the tomatoes are planted in a porous medium, like vermiculite or gravel or a mixture of equal volumes of both, growth is perfectly normal even when the containers are small. The volume of root medium is of importance only in connection with its water holding capacity. Full-grown tomato plants can be raised in less than one liter of root medium, but under those conditions need frequent watering. As a practical size we use one or two-gallon containers for mature tomato plants; they then need two waterings per day.

Several methods of automatic watering have worked well with tomatoes, but the most convenient and requiring least over-all time is the regular slop-method, pouring enough nutrient solution on the root medium twice daily so that some of it runs out through the drainage holes in the bottom of the containers. None of the other methods has given higher growth rates or superior plants; under all different conditions the same optimal growth rate is reached, indicating that nutrition or conditions of the root system do not limit tomato growth, if the root medium is porous and sufficient nutrient solution is available at all times (compare FIGURE 14). On PLATE IX three representative tomato plants are shown; the one on the left was grown in a mixture of gravel and vermiculite and watered with the slop-method. This plant is as tall and vigorous as the plants on the right which were grown with their roots in the nutrient fog box.

If tomato plants have to be grown to maturity, the seedlings, at almost any size from 5 to 40 cm., are transplanted from the seedling flat, with or without an intermediate transplanting, individually into one or two-gallon crocks filled with a mixture of equal volumes of vermiculite and gravel. The vermiculite provides the water-holding capacity and the gravel serves to give the plant better support. When transplanted into pure gravel, the plants take about one week longer to become well established. By transplanting them out of vermiculite, one can accomplish the transfer with very little damage to the root system, which means quick establishment and rapid resumption of growth. To reduce the set-back of transplanting still further, seedlings can be sprayed one to three days beforehand with a 10 per cent sugar solution.

To insure uniformity among the tomato plants, the following precautions are taken. A good uniform variety is chosen. For sturdiest plants a *ponderosa* variety like Beefsteak can be used; for plants growing best under greenhouse conditions of low light intensity and low or high temperature, varieties like Michigan State, Ailsa Craig or Essex Wonder do best, whereas almost any other variety can be used for general purposes. Fruit production without pruning is best in determinate varieties such as Pearson. About four times more seeds are sown than plants are required. In transplanting, only uniform plants are used and about 30 per cent more than are needed are transplanted. Then, when the experiment is started, the tallest and shortest plants are discarded, and very likely the rest will grow very uniformly. Occasionally, through injury or otherwise, the growing point of a plant does not grow normally, but when four plants per treatment are used, the abnormal plant can be detected and discarded. Every few days plants are inspected, and all axillary buds more than 1 cm. long are removed to insure maximum growth of the apical bud.

When young tomato plants are used to measure photosynthesis (*see* Chapter 20), they are sown rather thickly (25-35 per container) in the square, plastic containers, and a few days before they are to be used they are thinned to 20 or 15 plants. They are used when the first 2 leaves are fully developed. Since these are approximately opposite, all leaves in the containers are then at the same height, and cover the surface evenly. By placing an aluminum shield around a square container to the same height as the leaves, these are confined within a known area, and the total amount of incident light can be calculated (*see* FIGURE 17).

According to the variety, an inflorescence is formed between the 8*th* and the 18*th* node. In the San Jose Canner it has been impossible to change the position of the first inflorescence by any experimental means: photoperiod, temperature treatment, defoliation, etc. It has been reported that tri-iodobenzoic acid causes premature inflorescence formation; from microscopic observations, it is conceivable that this treatment suppresses leaf formation to an extent that both leaves and internodes are hardly visible. This condition is occasionally observed without chemical treatment as a teratological phenomenon (WENT 1944c). In *Lycopersicon esculentum* the axillary bud of the leaf immediately below the inflorescence develops in an early stage, and pushes aside the inflorescence, which then seems to emerge laterally. In *Lycopersicon pimpinellifolium* the inflorescence seems to be truly lateral (JANSEN 1953). Therefore, in the cultivated tomato, the plant is a sympodium after the first inflorescence. Again, according to the variety, each lateral shoot ends in an inflorescence after 2-4 leaves.

The bracts subtending the flowers in the inflorescence are usually strongly reduced, but under certain conditions, such as high night temperatures, they may develop into full grown leaves, and thus the inflorescence becomes leafy. Usually, vegetative buds develop in the axils of these leaves. The number of flowers per inflorescence varies over a wide range. When the plants have been grown at 26°C nyctotemperature often not more than 2 or 3 flowers develop per inflorescence. At night temperatures of 10°C and below, the inflorescences are much branched and may carry up to 50 flowers.

The growth rate of tomatoes under any set of constant conditions gradually increases until a steady rate is attained. This rate depends on the temperature, and is seen for the San Jose Canner variety in FIGURE 40. In this figure, two curves are given — one when each plant is kept continuously at the same temperature; the other curve refers to the growth rate when the plants are kept during day at 26°C, and during night at various temperatures ranging from 4°C to 30°C. From this figure, it is obvious that optimal elongation occurs when the day temperature is higher than the night temperature.

The response of the four rigidly selected tomato plants grown per truck is usually very uniform. Therefore, a single plant from each truck gives a good impression of the behavior of all plants under those growing conditions, as seen in PLATES X*a* and *b*. When a series of plants kept at different temperatures is placed in a row, a very nice curve is produced by the tops of the plants as shown on PLATE XI. These tomato plants were grown in artificial light exclusively at an 8-hour photoperiod. From left to right they were exposed to 10°, 14°, 17°, 20°, 23°, 26° and 30°C constant. At 10°C the plant had hardly grown beyond its original size when placed in that condition. The other plants have grown very much during their stay at the different temperatures. At the highest temperature, the plant is spindly, has a thin stem and small leaves. With decreasing temperature, the leaves become larger and darker green and the stems become thicker. On PLATES X*a* and *b*, the behavior of the plants is shown in photographs taken at two intervals: 8 and 49 days after start of the experiment. All plants in the top row were subjected to a nyctotemperature of 30°C, in the row below that at 23°C, below that 17°C and on the two lowest rows they were subjected to 10° and 3°C nyctotemperature. All plants in the left hand vertical row were kept in an ordinary greenhouse during the 8-hour photoperiod at 26°C. The other plants were kept in artificial light at about 1500 ft.-c. for a 16-hour photoperiod. From left to right they were subjected to 30°, 23°, 17°, 10° and 3°C phototemperature. Each individual picture shows the four plants growing together on a single truck, and it can be seen that all plants under one treatment look much alike in habit and size. From these pictures a number of conclusions can be drawn. At the lowest phototemperature plants will grow for some time, but when the temperature differential between day and night is too high they ultimately die without reaching the fruiting stage. At the lowest nyctotemperature the plants grow very slowly but look healthy and sturdy. Although the growth in the greenhouse in daylight is slightly better than in artificial light, the difference is rather slight and lies mainly in the earlier dying back of the lower leaves in the plants under artificial light. In daylight, the fruit set also is much heavier.

That in the tomato the growth rates really are a reflection of the total growth of the tomato plant is seen from FIGURE 18, in which the total weight of tomato plants is recorded after they had been grown for 53 days in different combinations of photo- and nyctotemperature. At a phototemperature of 20° combined with a nyctotemperature of 10° the highest weights were produced in artificial light, in 8-hour photoperiods. When

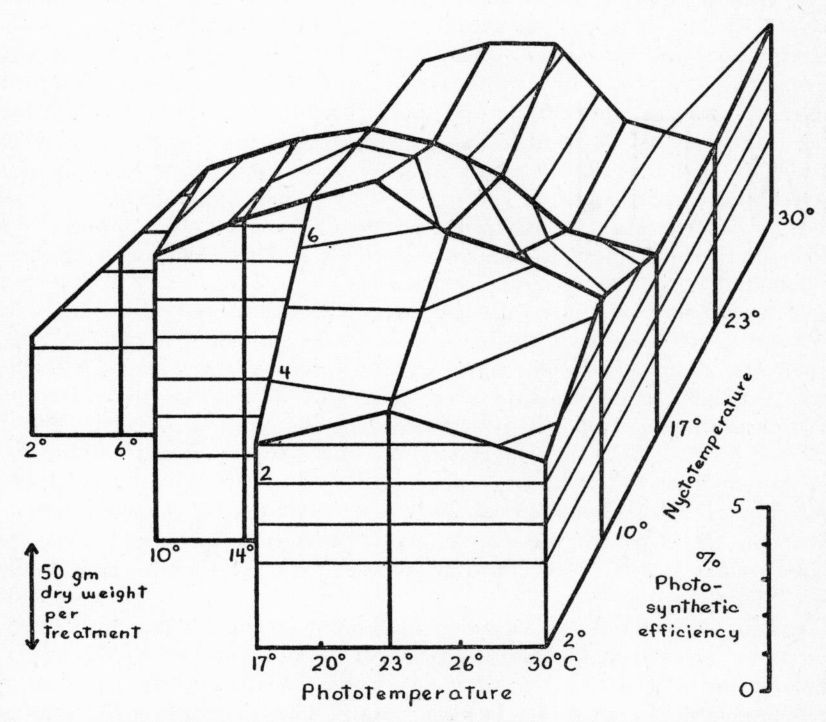

FIGURE 18.— Total weight of 4 Essex Wonder tomato plants grown for 53 days in 8-hour photoperiods in 1500 ft.-c. in different photo- and nyctotemperatures. Starting weight 40 g. At 2° photo- and 17° nyctotemperature almost no growth took place; in 30° photo- and 2° nyctotemperature and 6° photo- and 17° nyctotemperature weight was more than doubled, and in 20° photo- and 10° nyctotemperature weight was more than quadrupled. For each 19 gram increase in weight 1 per cent of the light energy had been transformed into chemical energy, which is indicated by contour lines. Only the plants growing at 14°, 17° and 20° photo- and 10° nyctotemperature had more than 6 per cent efficiency of light transformation, but the plants at 10°-10°, 23°-10°, 26°-10°, 14°-17°, 17°-17°, 20°-17°, 17°-23°, 20°-23° and 23°-23° had all an efficiency of over 5 per cent.

a similar graph is prepared using the growth rates of the same plants, its shape is almost identical, with the peak shifted slightly toward the higher temperatures. Similar experiments were carried out in the Earhart Laboratory in daylight by Dr. K. VERKERK (1955), who found an optimal temperature fluctuation between 23° day and 17° night for several different varieties. In general it can be said that the lower the light intensity, the lower the optimal temperatures for growth, until at 250 ft.-c. in an 8-hour photoperiod no growth can be sustained for longer periods. FIGURE 7 from WENT (1945) shows the relationship between light intensity and optimal temperature for growth.

When the growth rate of tomato plants grown under different conditions is calculated, then a gradual shift of the optimal growing temperature is found. Whereas in the young plants the greatest rate of stem elongation occurs at the highest temperatures, especially the optimal nyctotemperature decreases with age from 30° or 26° to 17° or 14°C. This is depicted for peas in FIGURE 21, in which the growth rate in millimeters per day is plotted for the same set of plants in successive 6-day periods. Tomatoes behave in the same way (*see* FIGURE 47). Whereas originally the highest growth rates are found at the front right hand corner of the graph, in the later periods the highest growth rates shift towards the rear left-hand side — that is to say to lower temperatures.

As the tomato plant grows up, the lower leaves die back. This die-back is caused either by lack of nutrients or by insufficient light intensity. But even when there is sufficient nitrogen and light the lower leaves will die back, especially in plants with heavy fruit set. This seems to be largely due to a drain upon the food in the leaves by the fruits.

When tomato plants have very vigorous root systems, and when vegetative growth is restricted by removal of all lateral shoots, adventitious buds develop on the leaf rachis especially near the insertion of leaflets. These shoots can develop into full grown plants bearing fruits, while being attached to the mother plant through a petiole, which shows considerable growth in thickness.

Fruiting.— Not only the number of flowers in the inflorescence is affected by temperature, but also the size and form of the flower. At nyctotemperatures of 4°-10°C, there is a strong development of the calyx, and often the corolla is practically lacking. At 17°C nyctotemperature, corolla development is optimal, and completely normal flowers are found. As the nyctotemperatures become higher, both corolla and calyx development is reduced.

Whereas flowering in the tomato occurs regardless of the external conditions, fruit development is very strongly dependent upon temperature and light intensity. At high night temperatures, the flowers remain small and often are abscised before fertilization has occurred. This is one of the main reasons why fruit set at high temperatures is so poor, for once the fruit has set, even at night temperatures of 26°C, they continue to grow and eventually ripen. In earlier work it was shown that the limitation in fruit set at high nyctotemperatures is due to a reduced carbohydrate supply (*cf.* Chapter 16). Since there is in a tomato plant a competition between vegetative and fruit growth in which the vegetative shoots gain the upper hand, fruit set at high temperatures can be improved by removal of the vegetative growing points, or by the reduction of the vegetative strength of the plant (root pruning). Since under these conditions the sugar supply limits fruit growth, hormone sprays at high temperatures do not increase fruit production (OSBORNE and WENT 1953). When fruit production is plotted as a function of night temperature (FIGURE 19) a steep curve appears with a much narrower range than for vegetative growth.

The decreased production at low night temperature is in the first place due to a lack of fertilization. Mrs. LESLIE found that whereas above 13°C nyctotemperature pollen formation was normal and that even at 30°C still 50 per cent of the pollen was viable, below 13°C most or all pollen grains were abnormal or empty. Therefore, no fertilization can occur at low nyctotemperatures; this can be overcome by auxin applications which leads to parthenocarpic fruit development. Therefore, hormone sprays are particularly effective when the night temperatures are low; that is to say, early in the season. The better carbohydrate supply at lower nyctotemperatures is not only reflected in better fruit set, but also in heavier fruits. The average fruit weight increases from a very low figure at 26°C to a 3 times higher figure at 14°C nyctotemperature.

There are large differences in growth and fruiting of the different tomato varieties. A study of the behavior of 15 tomato varieties was made in the Clark greenhouses (WENT 1945) and it was found that although they all reacted in the same way to climatic differences, in general greenhouse varieties grew fastest and had the lowest optimal night temperatures for both vegetative growth and fruit set. Western varieties, used in the interior California Valley, had the highest optimal nyctotemperature, and Eastern varieties were intermediate. These plants, however, were only grown until the early fruiting stage, when the optimal night temperature for fruit set was high (*see, e.g.*, FIGURE 19, where through January the optimal temperature was 20°-23°C, it was 14°-17°C through February, and between 10° and 20°C in March).

To find whether these differences in tomato production due especially to night temperature persist when the plants are older, at a size and age as generally used in commercial greenhouses, VERKERK (1955) investigated 6 varieties and placed them in natural light under different temperature treatments when they had formed the first flower cluster. Then they were grown for 4½ months, and cut back above the 5*th* flower cluster because otherwise the plants became too tall to move them back and forth between the different greenhouses. The heaviest production was found in the Michigan State Forcing tomato with a 23°C day and 12°C night temperature; the plants produced 3500 g. fruit per plant in 4½ months. The varieties Tuckqueen and Essex Wonder produced 2700 and 2800 g. ripe fruit during that period under the same conditions. These three are typical greenhouse varieties. Rutgers did best at a 20°-14°C day-night temperature fluctuation, but produced only 1900 g. fruit, whereas Beefsteak was very low in fruit production with a maximum of 1200 g. In all varieties production dropped strongly with nights above 17°C and days above 23°C. Whereas at the lower nyctotemperatures fruit production was very heavy,

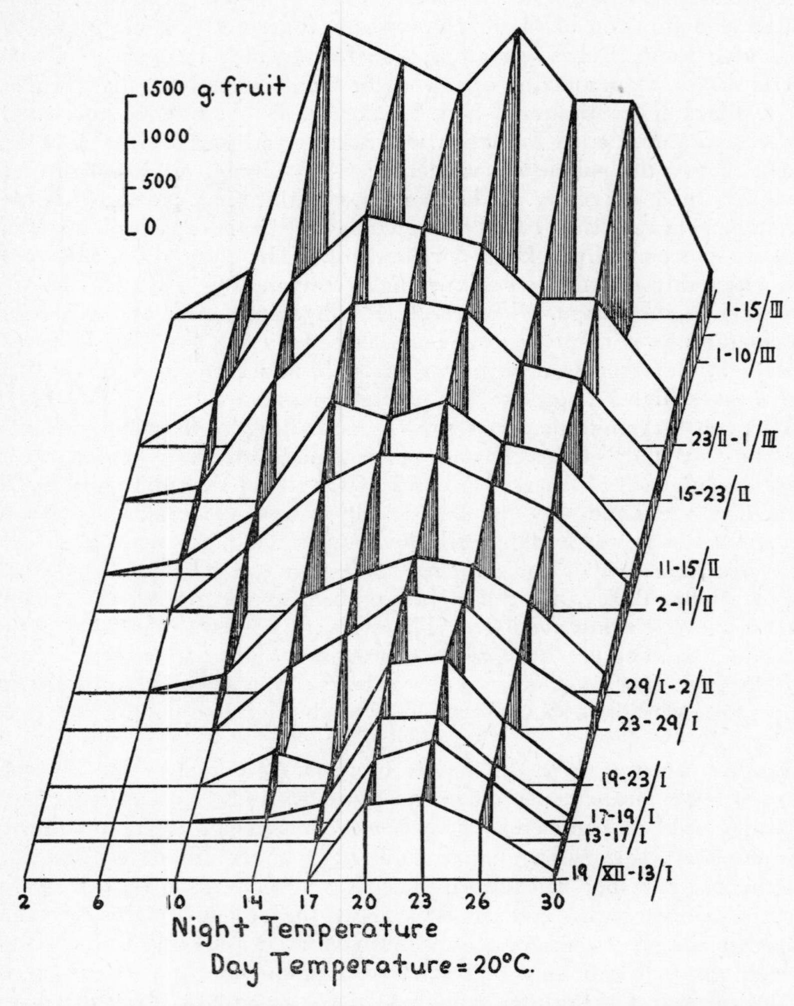

FIGURE 19.— Tomato (Essex Wonder, sister plants of those in FIGURE 18) production in grams of ripe fruit (*ordinate*) picked per plant. All plants receiving 8 hours of daylight at 20°C and 16 hours of darkness at the different temperatures marked on *abscissa*. *Third axis* shows progress in ripening with time for fruits picked per 4 plants, starting on December 19, 1949, and ending on March 15, 1950.

it was rather slow, and the first 500 grams were usually picked 1 month earlier at 22° than at 12°C night temperature. But early production was always correlated with low total yield.

The greenhouse varieties Tuckqueen and Michigan State produced on the average 1000 g. of fruit both at the lowest (17°-12°C) and at the highest (30°-23°C) temperatures at which the outdoor varieties (Rutgers, Pearson and Beefsteak) did not produce at all.

When comparing these data with commercial greenhouse production, it has to be borne in mind that in this experiment each plant had a growing area of 25 × 25 cm., with an extra 20 per cent for aisle space, that through topping the plant could not continue to produce, and that fruiting occurred largely in October and November. Assuming that only 10 plants pruned to a single stem (as in the described experiments) were grown per $m.^2$ (in this work there were about $13/m.^2$), then a production of 350 tons/Ha. or 150 tons/acre could be obtained for a 5-months growing period. It is obvious that this is only possible under ideal growing conditions: optimal temperature and lack of diseases and pests. But it shows that regular greenhouse tomato production (usually 40 tons/acre for a 6-months growing period in England and Holland) is far removed from the theoretically possible yield. As a rough estimation it could be suggested that by using optimal growing methods, greenhouse tomato production could be doubled to about 80 tons per acre, as is regularly done by Plant Protection Ltd. in their greenhouses at Fernhurst in England. By introducing air-conditioning this production could probably again be doubled. Increases beyond 160 tons/acre in one growing season are not likely to be achieved unless the photosynthetic efficiency of the plants can be improved.

The tomato plant is obviously strongly thermoperiodic in its environmental response, and photoperiod is of little importance in its fruiting behavior. This can be seen *e.g.* in FIGURE 48. As shown earlier, photoperiodic experiments in which the nyctotemperature is not controlled may simulate a response like that of short-day plants (WENT 1946), but this is only the case when they are growing in too cool a climate and the photoperiod is shortened by covering the plants in the afternoon. This extends the too cool night with a dark period at higher (afternoon) temperatures, and greatly increases both growth and fruit set (total fresh weight up to four times that of uncovered plants, total fruit weight more than ten times increased through the months of April, May and June).

Photoperiod is very important in the vegetative development of the tomato plant. The growth drops sharply at less than 8 hours of illumination per day (*see* FIGURE 59), growth also is less in continuous light. The growth decrease and the curious etiolation which occurs in tomatoes growing in continuous light has been investigated by Dr. W. S. HILLMAN (1956).

When tomato plants are grown in photocycles of other than 24-hour duration, growth rates decrease (*see* FIGURE 65), and etiolation and injury to leaves may develop. This has been investigated by Dr. E. BONDE in the Earhart Laboratory. All these phenomena show that basically tomato plants are adjusted to a 24-hour autonomic cycle (the so-called Bünning cycle).

In all work in the Clark and Earhart greenhouses plants are subjected to a constant photo- and constant nyctotemperature. Theoretically, this is the most logical and practically it is the simplest set-up. It is questionable, however, whether on the basis of results obtained under constant nycto- or phototemperatures conclusions can be drawn concerning the behavior of such plants in the field, where temperatures are continuously changing. Therefore, a set of experiments was performed in which tomato plants were subjected to two or more different nyctotemperatures. Without going into details, it can be said that when the temperature fluctuation during the night was 7°C or less, almost complete summation of effects occurred, so that the response to the two temperatures was the same as to that at the average temperature. When the differences were larger, the response was somewhat less than at the average temperature, but when 4°C and 30°C nyctotemperature were combined, the plants staying for 8 hours in each, then growth was not only much less than at the optimal 17°C nyctotemperature, but it was even less than at either 4° or 30°C nyctotemperature.

Mrs. Selina Bendix (1956) has carried out many experiments along these lines, and she found that with temperature differences of 13°C, either below or above the optimal temperature, plants exposed for more than one hour to the extreme temperature always grew less than when kept continuously at the extreme temperature. This, however, holds only for the nyctoperiod: the effects in light were very nicely additive.

An experiment was carried out in which the plants were not suddenly, but gradually, changed from one extreme to the other extreme nyctotemperature (½ hour steps of 3°C temperature intervals). The results were not clear-cut, but the effect of extreme nyctotemperature is certainly not one of shock.

More information on temperature and light responses of tomato plants can be found in Chapters 16, 18, 19, 20, 21, 22, 23 and 24. In Figure 41 the top/root ratio is shown as a function of photo- and nyctotemperature; only the latter considerably affects root growth in that the root system becomes heavier as the nyctotemperature is lower.

In Figures 54, 58, 59, 62, 63, 64 and 65 and Tables 15 and 16 the dry matter production of tomato plants as a function of light intensity, duration of illumination, and light quality is shown in considerable detail. Actual CO_2 uptake by the tomato plant in relation to time of day is shown in Figures 55 and 57; in Figures 60 and 61 their sucrose production and response to sucrose is recorded, and in Figures 67, 68 and 69 and Table 18 their transpiration rate is shown.

Chili Pepper (*Capsicum annuum*):— In an earlier publication (Dorland and Went 1947) the climatic response of the chili pepper was discussed based on experiments in the Clark greenhouses. In general, these plants behave very much like tomatoes. As seedlings, the optimal temperature is 26°-30°C, but soon afterwards it decreases. At a phototemperature of 18°C, the optimal nyctotemperature decreased after half a month from 30° to 26°C, after one month to 21°C, and after 3 months to 16°C. At a phototemperature of 27°C, growth rates were about double those at the lower phototemperature, and the optimal nyctotemperature of 16°C was already reached after 1½ months. In 3 to 4 months, a curious two-topped curve for the optimal nyctotemperature for stem elongation developed which was largely due to a decrease in growth through heavy fruit set at the 21° and 16°C nyctotemperatures. This fruit production interfered with vegetative growth. The decrease in optimum temperature is not a function of age of the plant, but is correlated with its size. This would be expected if the lowering of the optimal temperature were due to the increased importance of translocation in the top of the plant. A sliding optimum was also found for fruit formation; that is to say, that 3 months after sowing, the most fruit developed at 21°C; after 3½ months at 16°C; after 4 months at 12°C; and after 5 months a 9°C optimal nyctotemperature was reached (*see* FIGURE 47). This explains why the harvest of chili peppers continues later into autumn than that of tomatoes in which the optimal nyctotemperature does not drop below 12°C.

A number of experiments were carried out to study the nutrition of chili peppers. They were grown in sand, and watered with nutrient solutions containing the nutrient elements in different proportions. Hoagland's solution was close to optimal. Growth was decreased when any one of the major elements was applied in concentrations well below those in the Hoagland solution. With increased nitrate supply, fruit set and total fruit weight were significantly decreased which is contrary to the findings with tomatoes, where no such decrease was found.

The Potato (*Solanum tuberosum*):— Because of the continued vegetative propagation of the potato, it is very difficult to get virus-free tubers from one of the widely-grown potato varieties. We received, however, in 1951 three tubers of the Kennebec variety. They had been tested and were guaranteed free of all diseases, including *virus* X. All further experiments in the Earhart Laboratory were carried out with the progeny of these 3 tubers, and never has disease or virus been found on any of the potato plants.

In all experiments the plants were grown in one or two-gallon crocks in vermiculite. This allows unimpaired expansion of the tubers during their development, and under optimal growing conditions sometimes ¼ of the volume of the container could become occupied by tubers. Except in the lowest phototemperature (17°C), the stems are too weak to stand erect and they have to be staked. In most cases 2 to 5 stems per plant were allowed to develop. The tubers were easy to harvest and could be cleaned by simple rinsing since the vermiculite does not stick to the smooth ivory surface of the tubers.

From 1952-1954 most experiments with potatoes in the Earhart Laboratory were carried out by Dr. Luis Gregory (1954), who investigated tuber formation as a function of temperature, photoperiod and hormone production.

As Plate XII shows, when grown in the different greenhouses, top development in terms of weight produced was almost equal under all conditions, except in 17°C day, 12°C night, where the plants remained small. At the higher day and night temperatures (30°-23°C, 26°-20°C, and 23°-17°C) the plants became spindly and had relatively small leaves, but at 20°C day, 14°C night nice sturdy shoots were formed, with big, dark green leaves, and relatively short stem internodes. Under this condition, also the greatest weight of tubers per plant was produced.

In one experiment a series of plants was grown in daylight at the natural daylength at a constant day temperature (20°C) and night temperatures ranging from 6°-26°C, and at a constant night temperature of 14°C and day temperatures ranging from 17°-30°C. It was then found that potato production was largely controlled by the night temperature, and that at 10°-14°C the largest total production occurred. This experiment was carried out in summer. Above 20°C, no tubers were formed at all, in spite of a good top development. In winter some tubers were formed even at a 23°C nyctotemperature. Good potato growing conditions were indicated both by more and larger potatoes. Lack of potato production at the high nyctotemperatures was not due to insufficient underground stolon formation. At high temperatures even more stolons were formed, but their tips failed to swell. At a 30°C day temperature, regardless of nyctotemperature, typical damage symptoms were found on the leaves of potatoes. The tips of the leaflets dried out in the early stages of development, so that all leaves had shrivelled brown tips and margins. This is a reversible phenomenon, since when plants were transferred to lower temperatures, the newly developing leaves were completely normal, whereas transfer from low to high temperature resulted in the heat-damage symptoms within a few days.

To find out whether the temperature effect on tuber formation was localized in the under- or above-ground parts of the plant, Gregory (1954) grew a series of potato plants under two temperature conditions, 12°C and 23°C at night. Under each of these two conditions, the root medium in 4 crocks each was kept at the following temperatures: 10°, 20° and 30°C. It was found that regardless of the root temperature, potatoes were found in profusion when the tops were kept at a 12°C night temperature, whereas practically no potatoes were formed at all when the tops received a 23°C night temperature, even when the root temperature was 10°C. This suggests two possibilities: (*1*) translocation of carbohydrates from tops towards stolons occurs only at low nyctotemperatures, or (2) a tuber forming stimulus is produced in the tops of potato plants which are kept in a cool night temperature.

Grafting experiments have shown that the tuber-forming potentialities persist for some time in such tops after removal from cool temperatures, and therefore, it seems likely that we are dealing with a tuber-forming hormone which is formed only at night temperatures below 20°C. The cooler the nights, the more of this tuber-forming substance is formed, but at the lowest night temperatures, total growth of the potatoes is strongly reduced so that also the total yield decreases again. If we express, however, the tuber-top ratio, then a straight-line relationship is found when this ratio is

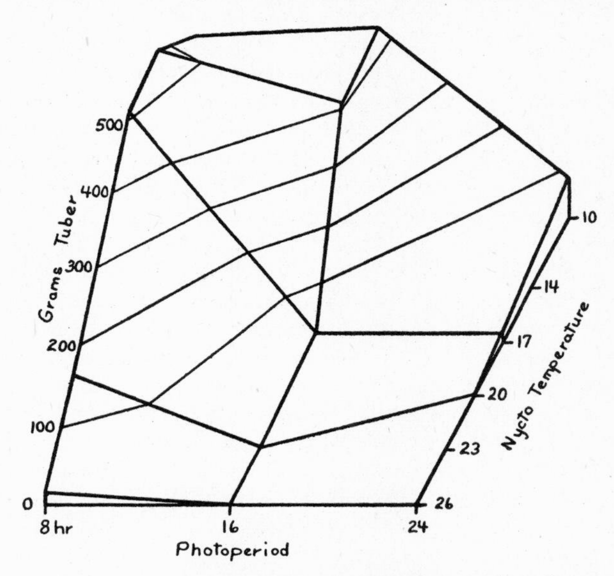

FIGURE 20.— Weight of potatoes formed in 90 days (*vertical axis*) as a function of nyctotemperature (*abscissa*) and photoperiod for the Kennebec potato, grown from 08:00 - 16:00 in daylight. Combined data of plants grown in 17°, 20° and 23°C phototemperature. Data of L. GREGORY.

plotted against the night temperature, starting at 70 per cent at a night temperature of 6°C and decreasing to zero per cent at a 20°C night temperature. In FIGURE 41 the top/root-and-tuber ratio is plotted, showing a rapid increase with increasing temperature. Although for other potatoes it is claimed that they are short-day plants as far as tuber formation is concerned, this is not the case in the Kennebec variety. As FIGURE 20 shows, at 10°C and 14°C nyctotemperature almost as many potatoes are formed in 8 as in 16 hours. Only at the higher nyctotemperature is a 16-hour photoperiod inhibitory for tuber growth. Even in continuous light some potatoes are formed at low nyctotemperatures. This behavior very much resembles the interaction between photoperiod and temperature in the inflorescence initiation of the strawberry (*see* FIGURE 28).

Since the previous work on the photoperiodic response of the potato was carried out in greenhouses at higher temperatures, it is understandable that the potato was considered a short-day plant. But in cool climates it will produce excellently also in the long days of summer, as FIGURE 20 shows, and these experiments make it clear how potato culture in summer in northern regions (Ireland, Netherlands) with harvest in August or September is possible: with cool nights the potato is not a short-day plant with regard to tuber formation.

When tubers are stored at different temperatures they lose their dormancy at different rates. Optimal and most rapid sprouting occurs in tubers which are kept at 20°C, whereas at lower temperatures sprouting is very much retarded. In preliminary experiments, no clear-cut differences were found in the dormancy of potatoes that were grown under different temperature conditions, but then stored under identical conditions.

The potato which is so closely related to the tomato thus behaves in its tuber formation very much like the tomato in its fruit production, in that both phenomena are controlled largely by the night temperature. However, the absolute temperatures at which these processes occur are quite different: at 17°C potato tuber formation is poor, whereas tomato fruit set is optimal; at 12°C, tomato fruit set is very poor, but potato tuber production is highest. In tomatoes it was found that in different varieties the optimal temperature for fruit set would vary a few degrees, but the range never extends to the optimal growing conditions for potato tuber formation.

No other varieties of potato have been tested, but it is likely that the optimum temperature for tuber formation does not differ very much from variety to variety. No potato varieties are known which will produce well during a warm summer, when tomato production is optimal; on the other hand, tomatoes do not produce well out-of-doors in climates where potato production is optimal. This behavior of the potatoes also explains why only at higher altitudes in the tropics can potatoes be produced successfully. It usually is found that an altitude of 2000 m. is necessary where the average night temperature is 12°C or lower.

Because there had been some discussion as to whether the starch grains in potatoes showed layering due to the daily light-dark cycle (*see, e.g.,* HESS 1955), Kennebec potatoes were grown in continuous artificial light at constant (7°, 10° and 17°C) or fluctuating temperatures (10°-17°C), or in constant temperature (7°C) and a daily light-dark cycle, or with both light and temperature fluctuating (17° photo- and 12°C nyctotemperature). In all conditions tubers were formed, and in all cases the large starch grains were clearly layered, with equally sharp rings. Therefore, the layering is due to an autonomous rhythm, and is not related to fluctuations in the environment, as BAILEY and KERR (1935) found for the cellulose layers in the cell wall of cotton fibers.

Egg Plant (*Solanum melongena*):— A number of plants were kept for over half a year in 26°C day and 20°C night temperature. During that time the plants grew vigorously and were cut back repeatedly. Although they flowered abundantly, not a single fruit set.

Soon after the plants were divided among the different greenhouses, fruits started to develop at 20° day and 14°C night temperature, whereas at all higher temperatures the flowers continued to drop off; at an early stage of development in 23°C, and when fully open at 17° and 20°C nyctotemperature. After 3 months in these conditions, all plants were transferred to the 20° day 14°C night temperature greenhouse. Soon after the transfer, fruits started to develop on all plants, and 37 days later the fruits were harvested and weighed. On the plants left at 20°-14°C the heaviest fruits had developed (821 gr./10 fruits). The plants originating from the 30°-23°C greenhouse had 16 gr./7 fruits, those from 26°-20°C had 510 gr./20 fruits and from 23°-17°C had only 20 gr./7 fruits. This seems to indicate that best eggplant fruit production can be expected when a warm season precedes cooler weather, and that night temperatures as experienced in summer in Pasadena (*see* FIGURE 44) should be satisfactory for their growth.

Tobacco (*Nicotiana tabacum*):— Several species of the genus *Nicotiana* have been grown in the Earhart Laboratory. *Nicotiana glauca, N. glutinosa* and *N. alata* were less thoroughly investigated, but *N. tabacum* was studied in detail by Dr. G. C. CAMUS (CAMUS and WENT 1952). Three varieties, Cuba White, Trujillo and Turkish Samsun were grown. They differ very much in their growth rates, optimal temperatures and flowering behavior. As in tomato and chili pepper, the nyctotemperature is the most critical environmental factor and largely controls the growth rate. Both Trujillo and the Turkish Samsun reach growth rates of 40 mm./day, but the Cuba White seldom exceeds 20 mm./day.

When the plants are very young, the optimal nyctotemperature is 30°C, as in the tomato and many other plants. It then gradually shifts to lower temperatures: to 23°C for Trujillo, to 17°C for Turkish and to 6°-14°C for Cuba White when the latter is growing at a high phototemperature (26°C). However, these responses are not as simple as in the tomato or pea where the growth rate of the plants under different temperature conditions continues at a constant or only gradually changing rate, since the internodes are all of the same length. When the tobacco plant is in the proper photoperiod and temperature, the stems will start to elongate at a greater rate prior to the development of the inflorescence. These sudden spurts of growth are clearly seen, *e.g.*, in Figure 2 of CAMUS and WENT (1952) for the Cuba White plants on a 30°C nyctotemperature in the week of December 18-26, and for those at 10°C and 14°C in the last week of January. Leaf development in these tobacco plants is very rapid: in the Cuba White variety a new leaf is formed every 1.12 or 1.14 days at 30°C nyctotemperature, every 1.44 or 1.48 days at 20°C, and 1.78 or 2.10 days at 10°C nyctotemperature; the first figures refer to a 26°C, the second to a 20°C phototemperature. This means that at the higher temperatures and at high light intensities (full daylight) the morphological development of the tobacco stem tip is mainly controlled by the night conditions. But the light intensity has a big effect on the initiation of leaves: at 20° and 10°C in ±500 ft.-c. artificial light there are 1.74 and 3.03 days between formation of successive leaves. Therefore, it seems as if during the photoperiod a condition is established or a factor is formed, which is essential for leaf initiation during the night. In the other varieties at 2°-10°C nyctotemperature the rate of leaf formation was the same as for the Cuba White, but it did not increase much with increasing temperature. The Q_{10} of leaf formation for Trujillo was 1.1, for Turkish Samsun 1.2 and for Cuba White 1.3.

At the different nyctotemperatures the shape of the leaves differs: as the temperature increases, the leaves become wider. This is clearly expressed in the angle the lateral veins make with the midrib. This increases from 54° at 2°C nyctotemperature to 75° at 30° C temperature. The total surface of the leaves is greatest at 26°C phototemperature and 14°-20°C nyctotemperature; the optimum differs for the 3 varieties.

As far as flowering is concerned, the tobacco varieties tested did not show differences in the length of time required to flower when grown in 8 or 14-hour photoperiods. Temperature, on the other hand, was controlling flowering in these indeterminate plants. In Trujillo the plants at a 20°-30°C nyctotemperature flowered in 18 days after the differential temperature treatments were started, whereas at 2°C nyctotemperature it took 36 days. In Turkish tobacco 20°-26°C was optimal for flowering (20 days), but at 2°, 6° and 30°C nyctotemperature the plants flowered after 36, 35 and 32 days. In Cuba White there were two ranges of nyctotemperature at which the plants flowered earliest (less than 75 days): 10°-14°C and 26°-30°C, whereas at 2° and 17°C it took 100 or more days.

It is obvious, therefore, that there are considerable differences in growth, flowering, leaf development and other characteristics of tobacco varieties as far as temperature response is concerned. In this respect it is interesting that tobacco is grown over a very wide range of climates: from the lowlands to mountain regions of the tropics, to over 50° N. latitude, from the highest light intensities in the tropics to shade in temperate regions, and from very moist to relatively dry. It seems that a further analysis of the behavior of tobacco varieties under the known conditions of a phytotron could furnish valuable data for the tobacco grower in different climates.

Tobacco is also a valuable plant for a smog survey (*see* Chapter 24). Most species (such as *Nicotiana glutinosa* and *N. tabacum*) are very sensitive to smog, particularly when the young leaves are expanding most rapidly. Thus it is possible to judge at what period of development of the plant damaging smog concentrations have occurred. Since in most large cities University greenhouses are found in which tobacco is grown on a year-around basis, the older plants in these greenhouses give a record of phytotoxic air pollutants during the preceding months.

In FIGURE 41 it is shown how the top-root ratio in the tobacco plant is lower than that of any other cultivated plant, and that it rises linearly with increasing temperature.

Chapter 7

THE PEA

Of all experimental plants used in the Earhart Laboratory, peas (*Pisum sativum*) are probably the best all-around material. Because of their self-fertilization it is easy to obtain inbred homozygous strains, and the commercially available seed gives rise to remarkably uniform phenotypes. The plants can easily be grown in individual cups, 36 to a truck, and when properly tied up, are a very neat experimental plant, of which the growth and development can be followed over long periods. By growing long-day varieties on short days, the plants will remain vegetative for several months (FIGURE 23), and grow at a very uniform rate provided occasional lateral shoots are removed. Growth is satisfactory in artificial light, especially of the bushy varieties, like Vinco, Unica, Kronberg and Green Feast, which will flower and set fruit in intensities of 1000-1500 ft.-c. Under the proper photoperiod and at intermediate temperatures they will ripen fruit from

TABLE 7: *Size and flowering behavior of different pea varieties (node number above the cotyledons which carries the first flower)*:—

VARIETY	FLOWERING UNDER 40 cm.	FLOWERING OVER 40 cm.	NODES TO 1*st* FLOWER UNVERNALIZED	NODES TO 1*st* FLOWER VERNALIZED AT 4-10°
Telephone		+	18	16
Alaska		+	10	10
Massey	+		9	9
Kronberg	+		9	9
Vinco	+		9	9
Unica	+		18	15

5-15 weeks after sowing, and the seeds will germinate immediately after (or even shortly before) ripening. This makes it possible to get 4-6 generations per year in the laboratory.

Peas can easily be grafted; both etiolated (WENT 1938, 1943*c*) and green plants have been used for this and take 5-10 days after grafting; 90-100 per cent of the grafts may succeed. The seeds contain so much storage material that seedlings will grow for a long time in darkness, where they will even produce flower primordia. Some varieties are vernalizable, others are heat tolerant or heat sensitive, and many are long-day as far as photoperiodic response is concerned (*see* TABLE 7). Both stem elongation and morphological development are easy to follow, and the orderly architecture of the plant which is a monopodium, with regular and continued flowering at each node once the critical number of nodes is reached, makes scoring of their responses a simple matter.

The reason why peas are not more generally used in experiments probably lies in the fact that they are cool-temperature plants, and require about 20° day and 14°C night temperatures in the greenhouses and 17°-14°C in

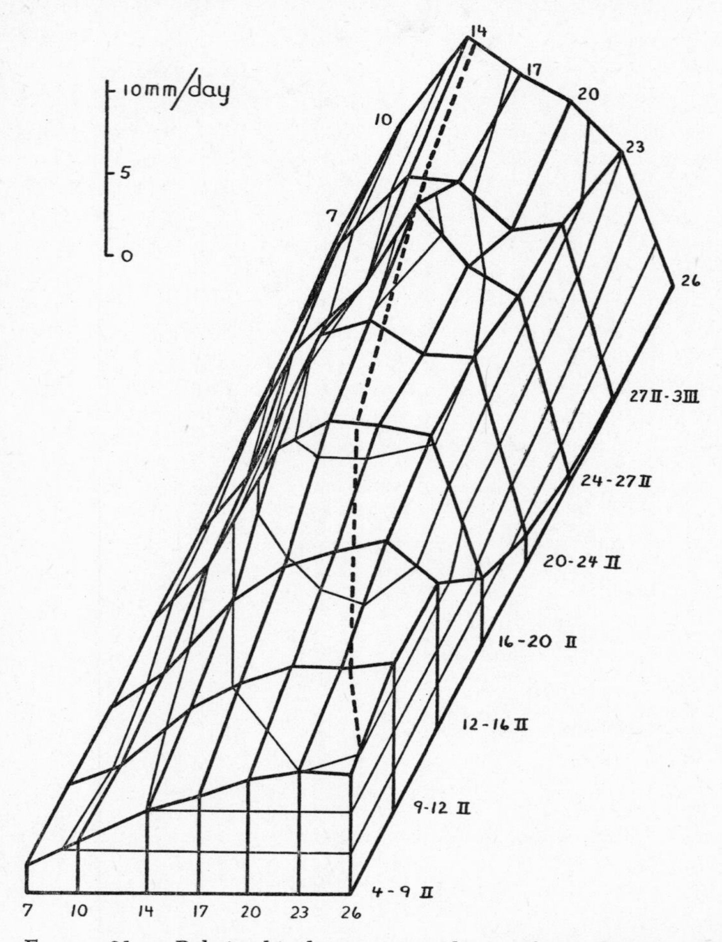

FIGURE 21.— Relationship between growth rate (*vertical axis*), different constant temperatures (*abscissa*) and age of Vinco pea plants, all of same length at beginning of temperature treatments on February 4. All plants in 16-hour photoperiod at 1200 ft.-c. Shift of optimal growth rate indicated by dotted line. The contour lines indicate equal growth rates at 2.5 mm./day intervals.

artificial light for optimal development. This is cooler than most greenhouses are kept; when the temperature regularly surpasses 30°C in the light most varieties die (*see* FIGURE 21 and PLATE XIII*a*).

Because among all easily available seeds peas are genotypically most uniform and can be grown to perfect phenotypic uniformity (*see* PLATE XX), they are ideal as experimental material for work on quantitative inheritance, and for studies on the genetics of physiological responses. This is at present being pursued at the Earhart Plant Research Laboratory by Dr. HARRY HIGHKIN. Because of the long-range nature of this work no results can be presented concerning these problems as yet.

To obtain most uniform plants, pea seeds are soaked 4-6 hours in water,

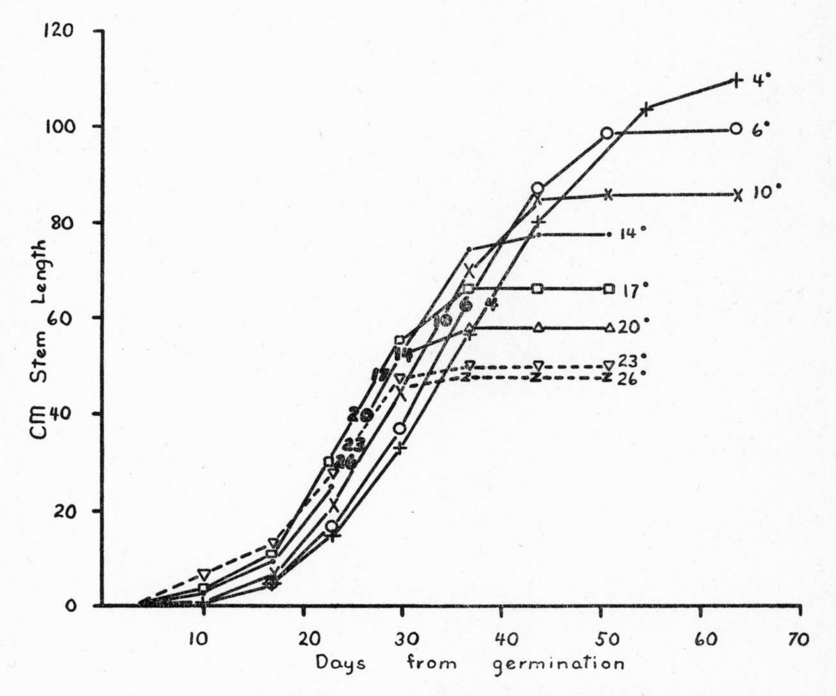

FIGURE 22.— Length of Alaska pea stems (*ordinate*) as a function of age, when the plants were grown in a 12-hour photoperiod in daylight at 20°C, with 12-hour nyctoperiods at the indicated temperatures. In each growth curve the time that the first flower opened is indicated with a bold number corresponding with the nyctotemperature.

and then individually planted in plastic cups in vermiculite watered with nutrient solution. By eliminating the smaller and larger seeds the initial growth rate will be more uniform, since the seedlings from the largest seeds start to grow slower, and from the smallest seeds faster than the average. Later these differences may reverse, and, therefore, the average weight seeds are preferable. Germination at higher temperatures (26°C) is faster, but the plants will be less uniform than when germinated at 23° or 20°C. Under average growing conditions in artificial light, the coefficient of variability of length and growth rate will be about 10 per cent at 14°-20°C, and

20 per cent at 7° and 26°C. When special care is taken to give all plants equal light (preventing differential shading of each other), the coefficient of variability can be reduced to 3 per cent at 17°-20°C. For dry matter production the variability is slightly higher but with a reasonable number of plants differences between groups of 2 per cent in weight or length can be established with certainty. Thus, peas belong to the most uniform experimental plant material available.

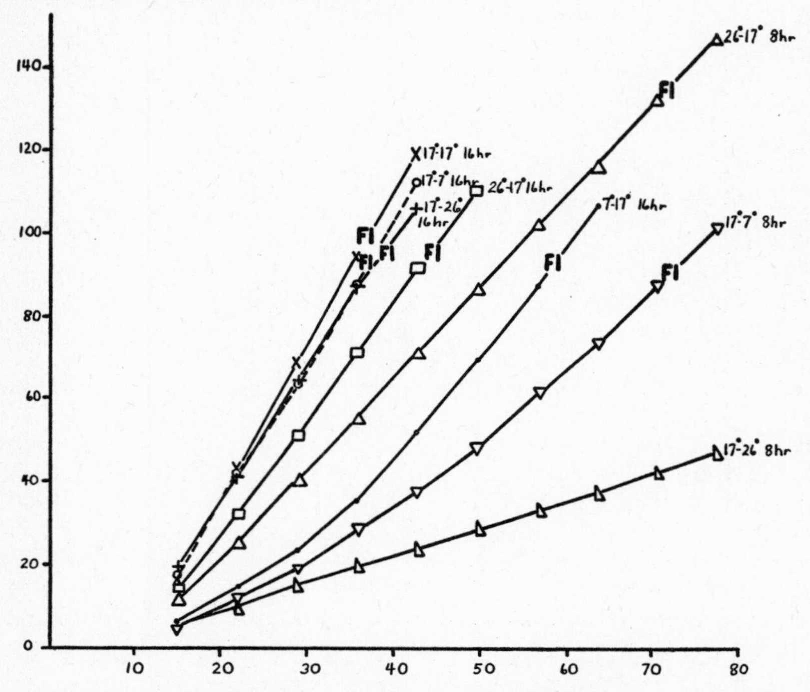

FIGURE 23.— Length (in cm.: *ordinate*) of Swartbekkie peas, as a function of their age in days (*abscissa*). They were grown in different temperatures (photo- and nyctotemperature indicated with each curve), and 8 or 16-hour photoperiods. Opening of first flower indicated by Fl on each curve. Data from N. GROBBELAAR.

As in tomatoes, the optimal rate of stem elongation shifts from higher to lower temperatures in the course of development. FIGURE 21 shows this behavior. For the Vinco pea the greatest rate of stem elongation is found at 26°C 9 days, at 23°C 13 days, at 20°C 18 days, at 17°C 27 days, and at 14°C 40 days after germination. This shift is partly due to injury of the older plants at 26°C, and the earlier reaching of the flowering stage at the higher temperatures.

Depending on the variety the lowest node at which a flower forms is number 9 or higher (*see* TABLE 7). The varieties which do not flower below the 15*th* node are usually long-day plants and are vernalizable. By growing, *e.g.*, Swartbekkie on an 8-hour photoperiod it will not flower until the 30*th* node or higher. Until there are a number of flowers opening, the rate of stem elongation remains constant, but the opening of flowers and especially the setting of pods interferes with further growth, particularly when few leaves are present or at high temperatures. This can be seen from FIGURE 22 in which the stem length of Alaska pea plants grown at different nyctotemperatures is shown. The heavy number in the middle of each curve indicates when the first flower opened at the indicated temperature, and at all temperatures the growth rate, which had been increasing or was constant up to that time, suddenly or gradually decreased two days after the beginning of flowering. The difference between the growth curves of an early flowering pea like the Alaska or a late flowering one like the Swartbekkie lies in the intermediate growth period, when the growth rate remains constant for a long period (*see* FIGURE 23). Mrs. RACHEL MORGAN BEHNKE has carried out many experiments with Alaska peas; her results are summarized in the following discussion.

From FIGURE 22 it can be seen that about one month after germination the stem length of the Alaska pea shows an optimum curve in relation to temperature, with a peak at 17°C, and that this peak has shifted to 4°C nyctotemperature after two months of growth. This shift is not due to differences in growth rate, but only in differential growth cessation in connection with the onset of flowering and fruiting. When the maximal daily growth rates at the different nyctotemperatures are compared (FIGURE 24), the values vary between 37 and 39 mm./day over the range of 7°-20°C, with 34 mm./day at 4°C, and 29 and 27 mm./day at 23° and 26°C. These last two values are low, because the plants never reached their maximal growth rate before they started to flower (FIGURE 22). Over the range of 17°-30°C phototemperature the maximal growth rates were 33, 37, 39, 33 and 26 mm./day (all figures with a 2-4 per cent standard deviation). This shows that over a 13°C range of phototemperatures considerable variation in the maximal daily growth rate occurs, whereas over a similar range of nyctotemperatures this maximal rate of elongation does not change. With this indication of the importance of the light period on the growth of peas, it is not surprising that the photoperiod influences the maximal growth rate very much. At 17°C the Alaska peas grew 29, 37, 37 and 44 mm./day at 8, 12, 16 and 24-hour photoperiods (FIGURE 24). Similarly, the light intensity greatly influences the growth rate. Since Alaska peas grow very tall, the absolute light intensity to which the different leaves of a plant are subjected under artificial light varies very much. It was attempted in three groups to keep the upper leaves and growing point at the same light intensities of 1400, 700 and 350 ft.-c.; under those conditions it was found that, regardless of photoperiod, the plants in the medium light intensity maximally grew 82 per cent, and those in the low light intensity only 72 per cent as fast as those in strong light. From all these determinations it is clear that the growth rate of Alaska (and other) peas is most strongly influenced by light intensity and photoperiod, somewhat less by phototemperature, and least by nyctotemperature (*see* PLATES XIII*a* and *b*). Their optimal temperature is quite low, 20°-23°C in their early growth, and 10°-17°C one month after germination, and even lower after 1½ months.

Fruiting responds very much like vegetative growth to temperature and light: at high temperature (23°C) hardly any seeds are set, and the weight per pea is small in the same way as shown for the strawberry in FIGURE 31. Wet and dry weight of the whole plant is affected by the environment exactly like stem elongation.

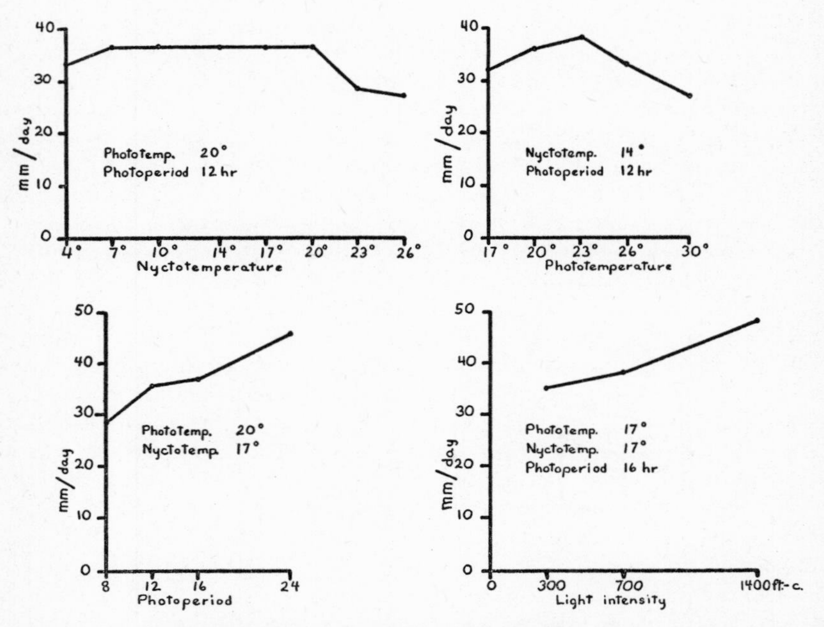

FIGURE 24.— Maximal growth rate in mm./day (*ordinate*) of a group of Alaska pea plants grown in daylight (*upper 2 curves*) or in artificial light at 700 ft.-c. (*lower curves*).

THORNTHWAITE (1952) and HIGGINS (1952) are using Alaska peas to measure the effect of climate as a whole on plants. They use a different method of scoring the development of the pea plant. This same scoring was also used in our experiments, which makes it possible to compare our results, and to interpret their results in terms of temperature and light response. Instead of using a physiological index in terms of size or weight, HIGGINS (1952) employs a morphological index. The development of the pea plant is expressed in terms of the number of internodes which are visible. Then intermediate stages are recognized by the size of the developing leaf on the highest visible node, and these are added as decimals to the internode number. HIGGINS' ten stages are not equivalent as far as length of time it takes the plants to pass them is concerned. By changing his stage 0.2 to 0.1, 0.4 to 0.2, 0.6 to 0.4, and leaving 0.8 the same, the intermediate stages are passed through in equal time intervals, and when plotted graphically with time as abscissa, a smooth line is obtained for the leaf index. In FIGURE 26 the two methods of scoring of growth are compared for Alaska peas grown in a 17° photo- and 23°C nyctotemperature. HIGGINS' leaf index, which equals the number of developed internodes, is shown in the upper curve, which approximates a straight line. When the corrections previously mentioned are made, the deviations from a straight

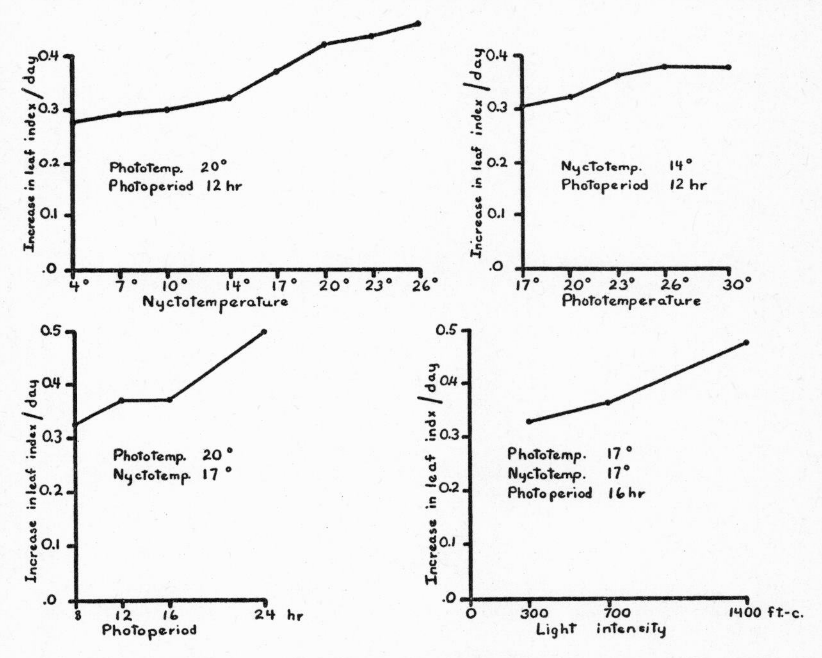

FIGURE 25.— Same plants as in FIGURE 24, except that the ordinate shows the rate of morphological development. Averages of 9 plants.

line disappear, which means that under constant growing conditions the morphological development of the pea plant has an absolutely constant rate. At the same time, the curve for the growth rate gradually rises, as seen in FIGURE 22 for the period up to 25 days after sowing. In this case also, the length of the individual internodes on each day is shown; the summation of their length gives the total length as presented in the broken line. The growth curve of each internode has a typical S-shape, and since the rate of unfolding of new internodes is constant and from the *7th* node on the final length of the internodes becomes constant, the growth rate of the whole pea plant becomes constant.

As FIGURE 25 shows, the morphological development of the pea has a very different temperature relationship when compared with its physiological development. It increases steadily with temperature, the phototemperature being as effective as the nyctotemperature, and causing an increase of 0.01/12 hour/degree centigrade. By extrapolating we find that the leaf index would not change at a constant zero degree centigrade temperature.

The effects of photoperiod and light intensity on the leaf index are even more pronounced than those of temperature. The daily increase in leaf index is smaller the lower the light intensity (for full daylight, 1400, 700 and 350 ft.-c. the relative values are 100, 100, 83 and 65), and it decreases also with length of photoperiod (at 24, 16 and 8 hours light daily the proportion is 100, 85 and 59).

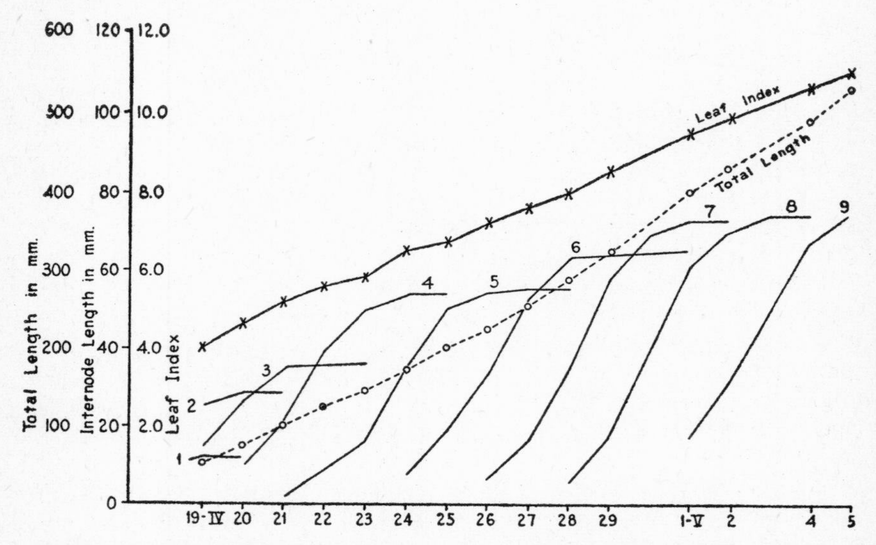

FIGURE 26.— Progression of leaf index and increase in length of internodes and whole stem of Alaska pea plants grown in 12-hour photoperiods at 17° and 12-hour nyctoperiods at 23°C. Numbers with the S-shaped curves refer to the internode number.

From these data it can be seen that at a constant light intensity and photoperiod the morphological development of the Alaska pea can be used as an integrating thermometer, with its zero point at freezing. This is, however, strongly modified by light intensity and photoperiod; in fact, so much so that below 1000 ft.-c. the leaf index of peas is a better radiation meter than thermometer.

Pea varieties differ much in morphological respects, but all have in common that they are very sensitive to high phototemperatures. At the same time they are all able to grow at very low temperatures, and even in a constant 4°C with an 8 or 16-hour photoperiod the plants do grow, although very slowly. In one year's time they had produced about 30 nodes, which bore flowers which opened but did not produce pods (with very few exceptions). The leaves and stipules on those plants became very large, and the stems were very thick and vigorous. Also at 7° and 10°C the pea plants became very strong and vigorous, with dark green foliage and large flowers. Whereas at the higher temperatures only one or a few seeds developed per pod, and one-to-two pods per plant, at the lower temperatures all ovules grew into seeds, and at 7°C all flowers produced pods.

At low temperatures, plants flower at the lowest possible node, similar to when they are grown in long photoperiods. This is an expression of vernalization. Dr. N. BARBER found a complete correlation between the long-day character in peas and ability of the pea to be vernalizable. Dr. H. HIGHKIN (1956) studied vernalization in peas. They are ideal for such a study, because of the almost absolute uniformity in the node at which the first flower forms, so that a lowering of only one node is statistically highly significant. In Unica full vernalization lowers the first flowering node from the 18*th* to the 14*th*; in other varieties this may be a lowering of only 3 nodes, but in all instances the phenomenon can be measured quantitatively. Since full vernalization may take as little as 12 days, and the effect can be measured one month later, peas can be used for a quantitative study of vernalization. A high-temperature treatment immediately after the low temperatures will completely de-vernalize the plants.

When peas are grown at 4°C or other relatively unfavorable temperatures, the main shoot often dies, and then vigorous lateral shoots take over. It is typical for peas that, once they have been subjected to unfavorable conditions, the growing shoot decreases its growth rate, and after transferring them to favorable conditions again, they will not regain their original vigor. Whereas tomatoes almost immediately adapt themselves to new growing conditions, pea shoots lack this adaptability. It is possible that this is due to the very limited amount of secondary growth of which the stems are capable; there is practically no cambial activity. In this respect peas resemble monocotyledons. Recovery of a plant from unfavorable growing conditions is only possible when axillary buds near the roots start to develop. Several other leguminous plants behave the same way, such as *Lathyrus* and *Vicia*.

In FIGURES 36, 37, 38 and 39 the rate of stem elongation and of morphological development of two pea varieties (Unica and Vinco) is shown as a function of age, light intensity, photoperiod and temperature. This multifactorial experiment shows that both for physiological and morphological development the promotive effect of light intensity and duration becomes more pronounced when the plants become older; as long as they depend on the food reserves in their cotyledons light influences them much less (in complete darkness even the opposite effect is found: etiolation with excessive elongation). An almost infinite number of other interrelationships and interactions in the response of peas to the environment can be deduced from these four figures.

The relationship between temperature and response to adenine is shown in FIGURE 71.

Chapter 8

THE BROAD BEAN

by Lloyd Evans

Div. of Plant Industry, C.S.I.R.O., Canberra, Australia

For both growth and development *Vicia faba* is similar to *Pisum* in its uni formity and environmental requirements, but the greater height and longer period of growth of the bean make it a less convenient plant with which to work. Even when grown in small cups, 18 per truck, broad bean plants may exceed 300 cm. in height before the pods have ripened.

Growth temperature effects.— The seeds germinate readily at all the temperatures available in the Earhart Laboratory, the percentage germination being highest between 10° and 20°C and lowest at 30°C. Shoot growth is approximately exponential up to a length of about 5 cms. which is reached by Bullock's winter bean about 9 days after germination at 26°C, 14 days at 17°C, 27 days at 10°C, and 73 days at 4°C. The time taken to reach the highest rate of growth in shoot length increases as the temperature falls, from 15 days at 26°C to about 70 days at 7°C for Bullock's winter bean.

Fast growing spring beans, such as the Dutch Weir and Suffolk Red varieties, attain their highest growth rates at 30°-23°C (up to 32.6 mm./day), the rates attained in the cooler greenhouses decreasing progressively with temperature (29.8, 26.2, 25.1 and 19.6 mm./day at 26°-20°C, 23°-17°C, 20°-14°C, and 17°-11°C respectively, for Dutch Weir beans). For such varieties both the exponentially increasing rates of early shoot growth and the maximum growth rates achieved seem to be fairly strictly proportional to the temperature above 0°C. With the slower-growing winter varieties, such as Garton's Giant Winter, the maximal growth rate (26.6 mm./day) seems to occur at 26°-20°C (Plate XV). At the highest temperatures most varieties maintain their maximal growth rates for a short period only, whereas at 20°-14°C and 17°-11°C, the maximum rates may be maintained in linear growth for over 60 days. Nevertheless, even winter beans will continue to grow relatively rapidly for several months at the highest temperatures, even in short days, which indicates that it is not high temperatures *per se* that cause cessation of growth of beans in the field in hot, dry weather. High temperatures affect the growth of broad beans rather less adversely than the growth of peas but, like *Pisum,* even spring varieties of *Vicia faba* grow well at relatively low temperatures. Thus the Suffolk Red Spring variety under artificial light for 16 hour photoperiods at 23°, 17° and 10°C maintained linear rates of growth of 23.8, 28.3, 17.0 mm./day respectively for over three months. At 10°C a heavy yield of seed may be obtained in seven months, whereas at 23°C a generation may be completed in about four months.

Effect of nyctotemperature.— Under 16-hour photoperiods increase in shoot length proceeds at a relatively constant rate throughout the night, is almost completely inhibited during the first two hours in the light, but then gains rapidly, declining again in the late afternoon. The nyctotemperature might, therefore, be expected to affect growth considerably. At a phototemperature of 17°C, with 16 hours of light, a California Spring bean variety initially grew most rapidly (41.9 mm./day) at a nyctotemperature of 20°C, but as with peas and tomatoes the optimum nyctotemperature subsequently fell to 17°, 14° and finally to 10°C, although the plants grown at 17°, 20° and 23°C nyctotemperature remained the tallest. At a phototemperature of 26°C the maximum growth rate was highest (42.0 mm./day) at a nyctotemperature of 26°C initially, but all growth at nyctotemperatures of 30°, 26° and 23°C eventually ceased, and plants with nyctotemperatures of 10° to 20°C were fairly uniformly the tallest when pod setting occurred.

Effect of photoperiod.— In artificial light, at intensities of 700-900 ft.-c., *Vicia* will grow more rapidly than in natural light, but the plants tend to have smaller leaves and to be more attenuated. Fast growing bean varieties, like Dutch Weir, initially increase in height almost as rapidly under 12-hour as under 16-hour photoperiods, but in 8-hour photoperiods their growth is noticeably less. French Winter, a slower-growing bean, at 23°-17°C had linear growth rates of 33.3, 23.3, 21.3, and 19.2 mm./day under photoperiods of 24, 16, 12 and 8 hours. Most varieties grow extremely well under continuous light.

The linear rate of increase in length of *Vicia* under favorable conditions is accompanied by a linear rate of node formation, and by constancy in the length of internodes. Three to four nodes are visible in most embryos. Like the growth rate, the rate at which new nodes are exposed may not reach a maximum for several weeks at the lower temperatures; in most varieties the rate of node formation increases with light intensity, but does not increase markedly with temperatures of growth above 17°C.

During the period of linear growth, most commercial bean varieties show great uniformity, even in sub-optimal temperature conditions (but not in artificial light), and the coefficient of variability of height measurements is usually about 5 per cent. However, if pods are set, especially under low light intensities, shoot growth may be suddenly reduced. Similarly, if lateral shoots (which tend to develop very abundantly at the two lowest nodes, especially in winter varieties, under short photoperiods, and at low temperatures) are not removed, growth of the main shoots may cease; as each new shoot reaches its maximal growth rate the previous shoot tends to stop growing, and the plants become compact bushes.

For plants grown in the glasshouses, robustness of stems and size of leaves and ligules increase as the temperature of growth falls, especially below 23°C, and as the photoperiod increases. The number of leaflets at a given node also increases in striking manner as the temperature decreases, or as the photoperiod increases. With Bullock's winter beans for example a leaflet index of 4.0 was reached at the 40*th*, 33*rd*, 26*th*, 20*th*, 15*th* and 11*th* nodes, by plants grown in 8-hour photoperiods at 23°, 20°, 17°, 14°, 10° and 7°C respectively. This is noted because the number of leaflets bears a marked relationship to apparent ripeness to flower. Varieties differ considerably in this respect; with Bullock's winter beans the first node to flower is very frequently the first node with five leaflets.

Flowering response to temperature.— Some spring beans, such as Dutch Weir and a California variety, flower at the 7*th* or 8*th* node regardless of the temperature at which they are grown. In other varieties, the temperature at which the seeds develop in the pods, the temperature of germination, the temperature of growth, and the photoperiod all interact to affect the node of first flowering.

A factorial experiment with three levels of seed-set temperature, three germination, and three growth temperatures was made with Suffolk Red Spring bean in short days to determine the relative importance of the three factors in hastening flowering. Low temperatures during seed setting and pod growth (10°C) or during germination (4°C) gave early flowering plants regardless of the subsequent temperatures to which they were exposed. Moreover, high temperatures during both germination (23°C) and growth (26°-20°C) could not delay flowering if the seeds had been vernalized in the pod (at 10°C). Similarly, even if the seeds had developed at high temperatures (26°-20°C), a low germination temperature could still lead to early flowering. On the one hand, plants from seeds set at 10°C, germinated at 4°C, and grown at 17°-10°C flowered at an average node number of 6.5; on the other hand, plants from seeds set at 26°-20°C, germinated at 23°C, and grown at 26°-20°C, flowered at an average node number of 36.6.

In another experiment, Bullock's winter beans were grown for 1, 2, 4, 8 and 16 weeks at all the temperatures available in the Earhart Laboratory, under 8-hour photoperiods, and were then transferred to 23°-17°C, under 8 hours of natural light, until they flowered. The control plants and the plants germinated at 20°C, flowered at about the 31*st* node. Plants kept above 20°C flowered at progressively later nodes the longer they were kept at such de-vernalizing temperatures. Temperatures below 17°C may be regarded as vernalizing temperatures for *Vicia faba,* and at each such temperature the lowering of the node to first flower increased with the period of vernalization. After one week of vernalization the lowering of the node to first flower was most marked at 10°C (27.7), after two weeks at 7°C (24.0), and after eight weeks at 4°C (14.8). The lower the temperature of germination, the longer is the period required to obtain the maximal effect in hastening flowering. Vernalization did not affect the subsequent growth rates of the plants at high temperatures.

Cold treatment is effective not only at germination, but at any time during the growth of the plant: thus plants from 23°-17°C given 1, 2 and 4 weeks at 4°C when 1, 2, 4 and 8 weeks old, all showed a lowering of the node to first flower. Similarly, seeds germinated at temperatures up to 30°C for as long as 12 days still retained the capacity to respond to low temperature treatment.

Response to photoperiod.— The effect of temperature of growth on the node of first flowering is especially noticeable with plants grown in 8-hour photoperiods. Thus, French Winter beans grown in 8-hour photoperiods at 17°-10°, 20°-14°, 23°-17°, 26°-20° and 30°-23°C had an average node of first flowering of 17.2, 20.6, 25.7, 27.5 and 41.0 respectively. In continuous light at these temperatures the range was reduced, from an average of 12.3 at 17°-10°C to 19.5 at 30°-23°C.

Most varieties of *Vicia faba* are quantitative long-day plants. For example, French Winter beans grown at 23°-17°C in 8, 12, 16 and 24-hour photoperiods flowered at an average node number of 25.7, 24.0, 21.6 and 13.8 respectively, whereas Dutch Weir spring beans, under the same conditions, all flowered at the 7*th* or 8*th* nodes. Thus low temperatures, at any stage during growth, and long photoperiods both operate to reduce the node of first flower initiation in *Vicia faba,* except in the very early flowering varieties such as the Dutch Weir spring bean. In some of the later flowering varieties, such as Bullock's winter bean, low temperatures seem to be more effective than long photoperiods; in others, such as the French Winter bean, the response to long photoperiods is greater. In this latter variety the node of first flowering of plants in continuous light at 30°-23°C is approximately the same as for plants in 8-hour photoperiods at 17°-10°C: with Bullock's winter beans it is by no means so.

The initiation of flowers, which appear in fully differentiated microscopic inflorescences, less than 3 mm. in length, in the axils of the leaves, alone is not sufficient. The major field problem of bean production in Europe is the low proportion (10-25 per cent) of flowers setting pods, and in the Earhart Laboratory also, floral initiation may take place without floral expansion, and floral expansion without pod setting. This is very prominent at the higher temperatures, and in short photoperiods, when all the microscopic flowers formed may abort. In several varieties at least floral expansion seems to have an absolute requirement for long days, even when floral initiation does not. At 23°-17°C 12-hour photoperiods are barely sufficient for floral expansion, while 16-hour photoperiods are adequate at all temperatures. Even then, if the night temperature is above 17°C or so, the young pods may still fail to develop, and provision of nyctotemperatures of 4°-10°C may be necessary. At these cooler night temperatures the young pods (whose vascular supply is initially tenuous) seem to establish themselves more adequately. However, although five or more pods may begin to develop at each node, it is seldom that more than three reach full size, even under optimal conditions. Lowering the temperature of growth not only increases the number of mature pods per plant, but also tends to increase the number and size of seeds in each pod. (For Suffolk

Red Spring beans the average number of seeds per pod increased from 1.50 to 2.72 as the growing temperature decreased from 26°-20°C to 17°-11°C.)

From the preceding discussion it is clear that many European varieties of *Vicia faba,* although tolerant of heat during their growth (as might be expected from their geographical origin), would give reasonable yields of seed only in relatively cool climates. Comparison of the climatic data from Cambridge and Mildenhall, in one of the main bean growing areas of England, with the results obtained in the Earhart Laboratory indicates that the natural photoperiod and the average course of day and night temperatures of the area from May to July are excellently suited to bean production, although limitations may be imposed by other factors such as light intensity and frost incidence.

Chapter 9

THE STRAWBERRY

The cultivated strawberry (*Fragaria virginiana* × *chiloensis*) is considered to be a short-day plant (DARROW and WALDO 1934, and VAN DEN MUYZENBERG 1942), except at low temperatures. Most work in the Earhart Laboratory was carried out on the Marshall variety, grown principally in the Pacific North-West, and some additional experiments were done with Klondyke, a widely used variety in warmer areas (southern California), and the Tennessee Beauty. Because strawberries are propagated vegetatively, the older varieties usually carry many virus diseases. Therefore, special care was taken to get disease-free stock plants, which were fumigated with methyl bromide before entering the laboratory.

Strawberry plants were prepared either by starting from runners or by breaking up old plants into divisions each with 2 or 3 crowns. These were planted in the regular mixture of gravel and vermiculite. In pure gravel the plants had a tendency to become chlorotic. As containers either Number 4 cans (11 × 11 × 17.5 cm.) or the high square plastic containers were used. Regular watering with Hoagland's nutrient solution caused salt damage to leaves (brown dead margins) and caused the roots to become brown and die, but when the plants were watered once or twice weekly with Hoagland's and the other days with de-ionized water, they remained very healthy. Optimal light intensity varied with the density of the foliage; when recently transplanted 700 ft.-c. sufficed, but older plants with dense foliage needed much more light. When the plants were kept continuously under good growing conditions, meaning cool temperatures and long days, they did not need any cold treatment to simulate winter conditions, but with occasional 3-week short-day treatments to initiate inflorescences they remained in growing and fruiting condition for many years without interruption.

When plants were grown for long periods at 6°C, they had a tendency to produce *Botrytis* rot of young inflorescences and of the growing points when afterwards transferred to higher temperatures and high humidity. Otherwise the plants were healthy.

The strawberry plant in vegetative condition is a monopodium. The axillary buds can either form a new crown, or a runner when the two lowest internodes elongate. After the plant has been kept for several weeks in short-day conditions, the apical bud, and one or more of the axillary buds transform into inflorescences. There is a direct proportionality between the number of leaves per plant and the number of inflorescences, and according to the inductive treatment there may be 0.07-0.25 inflorescence per leaf (Klondyke variety).

Flower initiation can either be measured in terms of number of inflorescences appearing two to three months after the inductive treatment, or by the number of microscopically visible flower primordia one month after treatment. Both methods give the same results, except when a critical number of inductive cycles or a critical photoperiod is given. Under those conditions, in addition to normal inflorescences a number of aborted flower primordia may be found which do not develop into visible inflorescences but die in early bud-stage. But, under conditions in which no inflorescences developed at all, no flower primordia were found either.

The dead leaves and over-ripe fruits were picked off regularly, because they were attacked by *Botrytis,* which on plants in weakened condition may spread to the living parts.

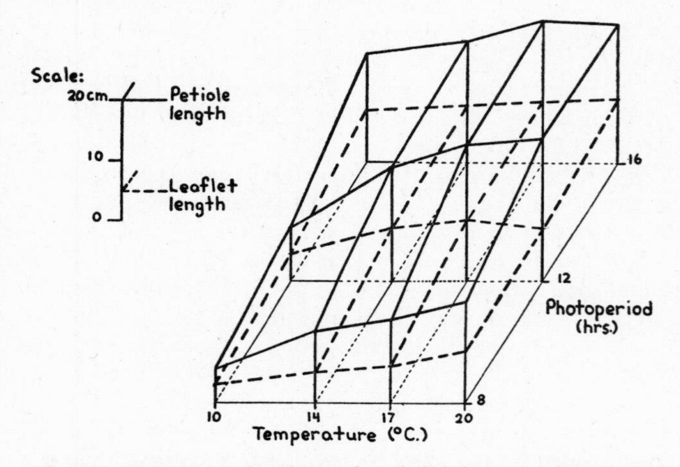

FIGURE 27.— Length of petioles (solid lines: *ordinate*) and leaflets (broken lines: *ordinate*) of Marshall strawberry plants, grown in different constant temperatures (*abscissa*) and photoperiods (*third axis*).

First the behavior of the Marshall variety will be described. The rate of new leaf development is greater at higher temperatures, but above 17°C the rate of dying of the leaves increases so much that the largest number of leaves per plant is found at 14°-17°C. Both size of the leaflets and length of petiole increase as the plants are grown at higher and higher temperatures, and with increasing photoperiods, as seen in FIGURE 27. This means that in an 8-hour photoperiod and at 10°C or below the leaves are hugging the ground, whereas either at a 16-hour photoperiod or at higher temperatures the leaves stand up well above the ground. Elongation of the peduncles is just the reverse, and is very slight at higher temperatures, but at low temperatures they become thick and elongated, raising flowers and berries above the leaves.

Another interesting temperature response is the development of an extra pair of leaflets lower down the petiole. This occurs only at temperatures above 10°C: at 14° and 17°C they are absent in an 8-hour photoperiod, but at 20°C they form at 8, 12 and 16-hour photoperiods.

Runners are only formed in long photoperiods at temperatures above 10°C, or as an after effect of such treatments. The first appear one month after beginning of the long photoperiods, and the last appear four weeks after termination of the long photoperiod treatment. A number of plants were grown in a greenhouse at 23°C for 8 hours daily, and received during night at 10°, 14°, 17° or 20°C extra light of 1,000, 500, 250 or zero ft.-c. intensity. It was found that for runner formation 1,000 ft.-c. at 14°C is equivalent to 450 ft.-c. at 17°C, and 100 ft.-c. at 20°C, in that it produces 5 runners per plant. No short-day treatment at any temperature will affect directly or indirectly runner outgrowth. At a 16-hour photoperiod no runners are formed when the night temperature is 6°C, even at a phototemperature of 20°C. At a phototemperature of 23°C, nyctotemperatures of 10° and 17°C lead to runner outgrowth, but at those same nyctotemperatures no runners are formed when coupled with phototemperatures of 14°

TABLE 8: *Inflorescences present as primordia or formed per Marshall strawberry plant over 72 days, from 47 days after beginning of photoperiodic treatments on, also total number of runners per plant (the plants were beforehand at 17°C in a 12-12 or 5-5 hour light-dark cycle):—*

	8 HOURS INFLORESCENCE		12 HOURS INFLORESCENCE		16 HOURS INFLORESCENCE		RUNNERS FORMED		
TEMPERATURE	PRIMORDIA	MACROSC. VISIBLE	PRIMORDIA	MACROSC. VISIBLE	PRIMORDIA	MACROSC. VISIBLE	8 HRS.	12 HRS.	16 HRS.
20°	3	1.5	0	0	0	0	0	2.6	12.0
17°	1	0.5	0	0	0	0.1	0	3.2	9.4
14°	2	2.6	2	0.6	1	0	0	0	2.2
10°	2	2.3	2	1.8	2	0.5	0	0	0

or 17°C. Therefore, a strong interaction between photoperiod and temperature exists in runner formation.

In a number of preliminary experiments it had been established that these Marshall strawberries were typically short-day plants for flower initiation, except at 10°C or below. When grown at 10° or 6°C in continuous light, the plants flowered without interruption for a year. FIGURE 28 shows the number of inflorescences formed per group of 7 plants, after having been subjected to the various constant temperatures at different photoperiods. They were then transferred to a condition (14°C in a 16-hour photoperiod) favorable for further growth of the inflorescences, but where they could not be initiated. All inflorescences developing over a period ranging from 1-2½ months after transfer to the new condition were counted. At all temperatures there was initiation on an 8-hour photoperiod, but on a 16-hour photoperiod inflorescences appeared only at 10° and 6°C. The same interaction between temperature and photoperiod was found in the potato (FIGURE 20).

In another experiment a 12-hour photoperiod was interposed between those of 8 and 16 hours. TABLE 8 shows that again on an 8-hour photoperiod the plants flowered. In a 12-hour photoperiod flower initiation occurred equally well in 10° and 14°C, but not in 17° and 20°C, although in 14°C the number of flowers which emerged was less, probably because of abortion of some of the primordia. Abortion seemed to have occurred at 14°C in a 16-hour photoperiod; only one questionable inflorescence was found upon dissection. The decrease in number of developing inflorescences at 10°C in a 16-hour photoperiod is due to a slowing down of the rate of development, because the number of inflorescences initiated was the same as for an 8-hour photoperiod.

Although it seems as if initiation of inflorescences is antagonistic to

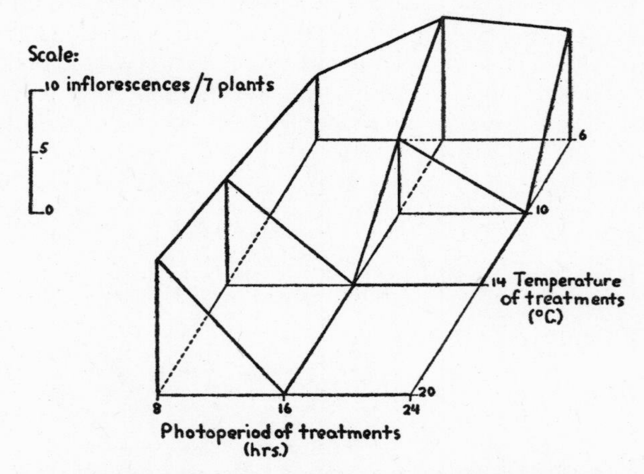

FIGURE 28.— Number of inflorescences (*ordinate*) appearing on Marshall strawberry plants from 1-2½ months after two months treatment with different photoperiods (*abscissa*) and constant temperatures (*third axis*). Average of 2 experiments. The plants on a 24-hour photoperiod at 10°, 14° and 20°, and a 16-hour photoperiod at 14° and 20°C had not produced any inflorescences.

runner formation, we find that at a 16-hour photoperiod at 17° and 20°C four times as many runners are induced as at the same temperatures and a 12-hour photoperiod; in neither case flower initiation occurs. Therefore, we must conclude that runner formation and inflorescence initiation are independent processes.

If we assume that flower initiation in strawberries is due to a low auxin concentration, as supposed to be the case in *Xanthium* (BONNER and LIVERMAN 1953), then we would expect a negative correlation between runner formation and inflorescence initiation. But, we should consider then also petiole elongation which is very likely to be controlled by auxin. Petioles of over 200 mm. length occur whenever runners are formed. Petioles ranging from 150-200 mm. occur either with maximal or slight flower initiation, and short petioles (100-150 mm.) or very short petioles (50 mm.) are found also over the whole range of slight to maximal flower initiation. Therefore, the temperature and photoperiodic effects are different for flowering, runner formation and petiole elongation, and cannot be accounted for by fluctuations in any single factor such as auxin.

In one experiment, strawberry plants were exposed to 8 hours daily of sunlight in a greenhouse at 23°C. The plants received during the remaining 16 hours artificial light at 400, 800 or 1,200 ft.-c. It is obvious from FIGURE 29 that at 14° and 17°C 800 ft.-c. completely inhibits inflorescence

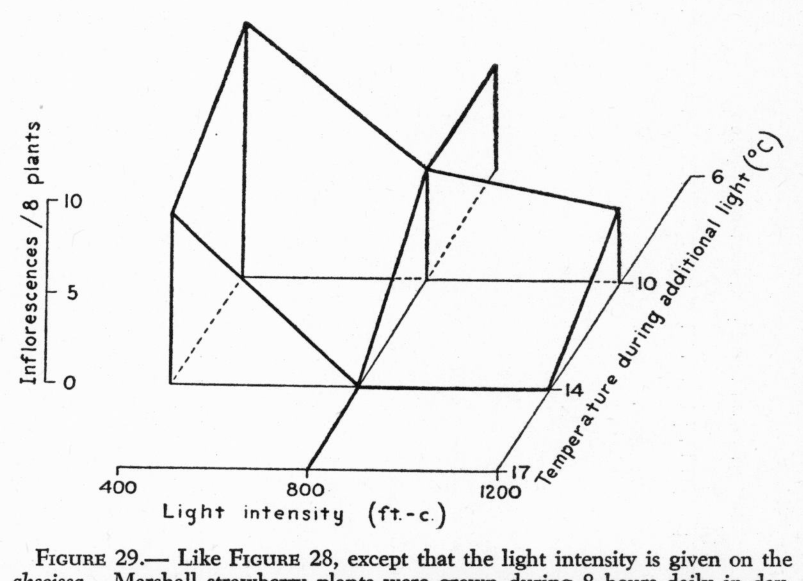

FIGURE 29.— Like FIGURE 28, except that the light intensity is given on the *abscissa*. Marshall strawberry plants were grown during 8 hours daily in daylight at 23°, and during the balance of the 24-hour day were kept in artificial light at different light intensities. At 800 ft.-c. supplementary light, no inflorescences were formed at 14° and 17°, and at 1200 ft.-c. none were formed at 14°C.

initiation. So does 1,200 ft.-c. at 14°C. At 10°C 1,200 ft.-c. cannot completely suppress flower initiation, and at 14°C and 400-ft.-c and 10° and 6°C at 800 ft.-c. flower initiation is about equal, and greater at 10° and 400 ft.-c. This can be expressed in a simple rule: the lower the temperature, the higher the light intensity has to be to suppress flower initiation. Therefore, temperature and photoperiodic response are closely linked. It might be concluded that strawberry plants seem to be indeterminate at low temperatures only because the light intensity which will suppress flower initiation is higher than can be easily attained. If the supplementary light were of an intensity of 2,000 ft.-c. it might be possible that at 10°C the Marshall strawberry would still be a short-day plant.

Another insight into the flower initiation process can be obtained by measuring the number of short-day cycles required to cause induction. Several such experiments were carried out. To get plants without inflorescence primordia Marshall strawberries were kept continuously on a (non-

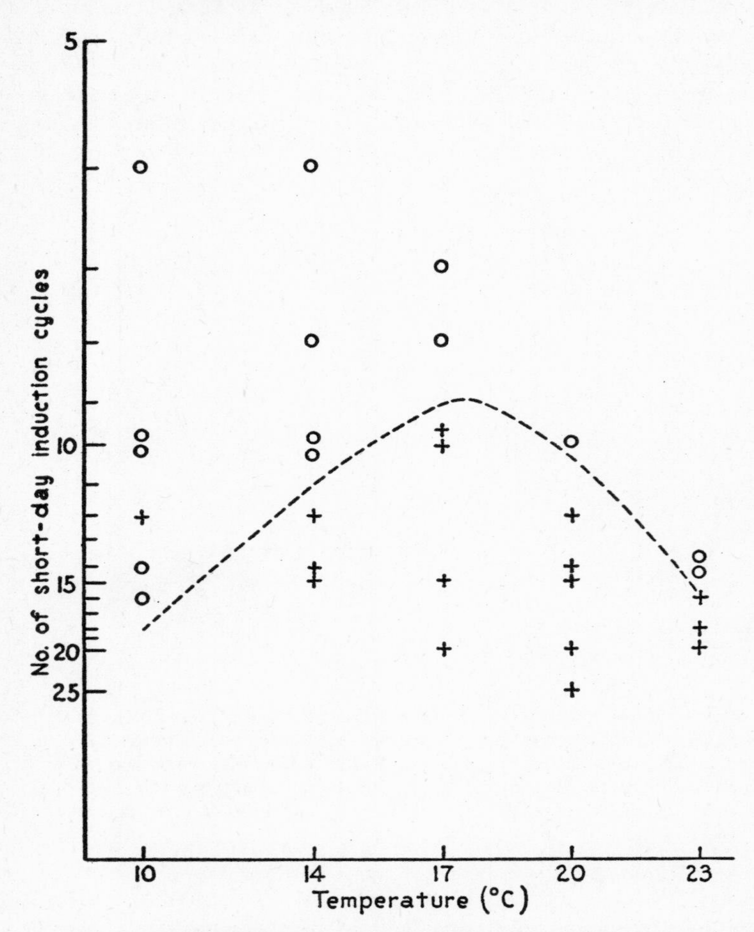

FIGURE 30.— Effectiveness in producing inflorescences (+) or none (o) after different numbers of 8-hour photoperiods (*ordinate*) at different constant temperatures (*abscissa*), when Marshall strawberry plants, after induction, were kept in 16-hour photoperiods at 14°C.

inductive) 16-hour photoperiod at 14°C; the inflorescences already present from previous inductive treatments continued to develop and were removed as soon as they became visible. When practically no inflorescences appeared any more, the treatments were started; in this case control plants indicated the level at which such pre-treatment inflorescences continued to appear. In FIGURE 30 these data for two experiments are summarized: + means that more inflorescences are formed than in the controls, 0 means no effect of the short-day cycles. It is evident that at 17°C the short days are most effective; 9 cycles are critical. At 20° and 14°C about 11 cycles are needed, at 23°C 15 cycles, and at 10°C the results are somewhat contradictory. Apparently more than 16 short-day cycles are needed, but one group flowered even after 12 days at 10°C.

The results of the experiments of FIGURE 30 can most readily be explained by assuming that induction involves two different processes. One is the true induction which process is more effective at lower temperatures. This would make one expect that the induction would be shorter as the

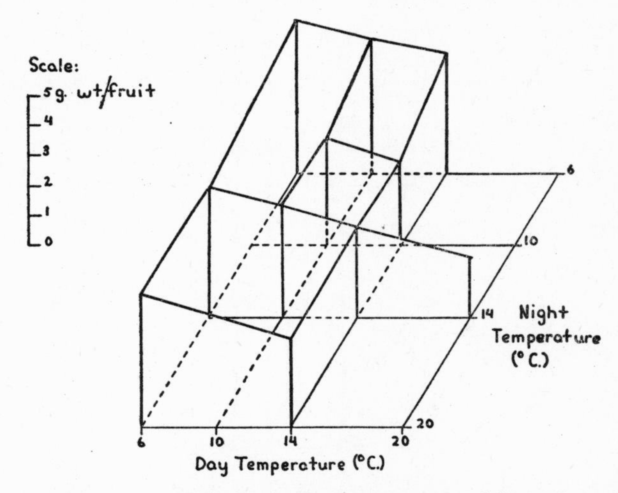

FIGURE 31.— Effect of phototemperature (*abscissa*) and nyctotemperature (*third axis*) on fruit size (*ordinate*) in Marshall strawberries. Except at 14° nyctotemperature, no fruits were produced in a 20°C phototemperature.

temperatures become lower. But then another process preceding or succeeding induction which is obviously chemical in nature, becomes so much slower, that more inductive cycles are needed. A similar dual effect of temperature was found for induction of flowering in sugar beets; STOUT (1946) for the first time proposed the above explanation for this effect. LANG (1952) working in the Earhart Laboratory, found this same phenomenon in *Hyoscyamus niger*.

Fruit production followed inflorescence outgrowth with a two-month lag, required for opening of the flowers and fruit ripening. Whenever inflorescences developed, fruits also were produced, except at the lowest temperature used (6°C), which was sufficient for opening of the flowers, but did not allow ripening of fruit. The ripening of fruit is strongly influenced by the nyctotemperature: 20°C being too high, and 6° and 10°C too low when day temperatures are low, too. Optimal fruit growth conditions were 17°C phototemperature and 12°C nyctotemperature.

Temperature has another effect on fruit growth: the size of the individual fruits is inversely proportional to the phototemperature, whereas the nyctotemperature has no effect. This can be seen from FIGURE 31. This effect is different from that in tomatoes, where nyctotemperature controls fruit size, but also at the lower temperatures the larger fruits are produced. This may be related to the increased carbohydrate transport at lower temperatures.

Strawberries seem an ideal plant to study the effects of environment on fruit taste. The berries are large enough to taste individually. Many are produced per plant, and the differences in taste are very pronounced. Therefore, a special experiment was set up to study the effect of environment on taste. A number of plants were treated for three months with a short photoperiod (8 hours) of natural light at 23°C and a 16-hour daily nyctoperiod at 17°C. This caused abundant inflorescence initiation, and by February 15, 1954, the first flowers started to appear. Then the plants were evenly divided into 28 groups of 4 each, and given 8 hours of daylight at 30°, 23° or 17°C. Seven groups received 16 hours of darkness at different temperatures; the other 21 groups were divided over 7 trucks and placed at 3 different heights on each truck. In the greenhouse all 3 groups on each truck received the same intensity daylight, but from 16:00 until 24:00 or 08:00 they received very different intensities of supplementary light. TABLE 9 shows how the number of ripening fruits varied according to temperature, photoperiod and intensity of supplementary light.

TABLE 9: *Number of fruits ripened per 4 plants for a 21-day period and the degree of taste of these strawberries* (3 = excellent, 2 = good, 1 = poor, 0 = tasteless) *grown under different temperatures and photoperiods. In each case the 8-hour day in daylight was supplemented with artificial light during night:—*

Growing conditions Phototemp. 08:00-16:00 (daylight)	Temperature 16:00-08:00 (darkness or artif. light)	Photoperiod	Fruits ripened per 4 plants from March 16 to April 6 at				Taste when fruit ripened in supplementary light at			
			1500 ft.-c.	600 ft.-c.	200 ft.-c.	0 ft.-c.	1500 ft.-c.	600 ft.-c.	200 ft.-c.	0 ft.-c.
30	10	16	3	1	2	5	2	1	0	0
23	10	16	7	4	1	0	3	1	0	
17	10	16	1	0	0	0	3			
23	6	16	4	0	0	0				
23	10	24	7	1	1	0	2	2	0	
23	14	16	6	4	4	1	1	1	0	
23	17	12				0				
23	20	16	20	9	5	5	0	0	0	0

The taste of a strawberry depends upon three different groups of compounds: sugars, acids and aromatic substances. The latter carry the typical strawberry taste; without the aromatic compounds it is impossible to distinguish strawberries from other berries by just tasting them. The sugar content is entirely a function of the light intensity to which the plants are subjected during day, and is independent of the photo- or nyctotemperature or the photoperiod. The plants at 30°, 23° or 17° phototemperature, at any nyctotemperature, were all equally sweet. The ripeness, which can be judged by the color, determines the acidity. It is possible to score for these different components of the fruit by simple taste test. This was done by a panel of two or three tasters, who scored, independently, with no prior knowledge of the conditions under which the fruits had developed. In general, agreement was good between the individual tasters.

In TABLE 9 only the aromatic content of the fruit is scored. A lack of

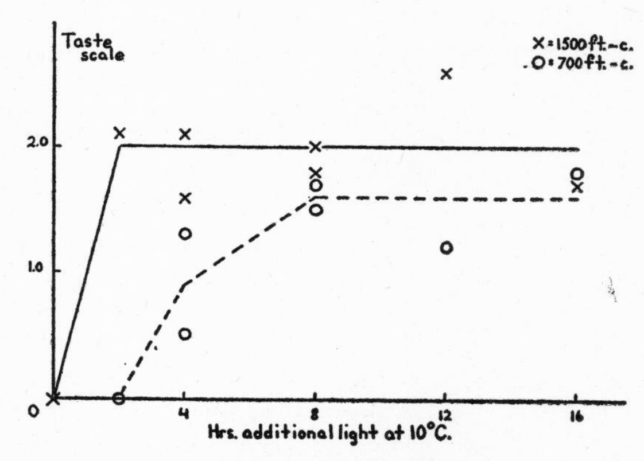

FIGURE 32.— Aromatic content (*ordinate:* o, no perceptible aromatics; 3, highly aromatic) of Marshall strawberry fruits, when the plants were kept 3 weeks long for 8 hours daily in daylight at 23°, and the rest of the time at 10° with 2, 4, 8, 12 or 16 hours of additional light at an intensity of 700 (*circles*) or 1500 (*crosses*) ft.-c.

sweetness can be corrected with the addition of sugar, acidity can be controlled by picking at the right stage of ripeness, but the aromatic content cannot be changed. This determines whether or not a strawberry tastes like a strawberry.

From TABLE 9 we see that a phototemperature of less than 15°C is necessary to produce the aromatic taste. This must be given at an intensity of over 200 ft.-c., preferably above 600 ft.-c. A period of 8 hours daily at 10°-14°C in light is sufficient to produce the aromatic content, and then the rest of the light can be given at a much higher temperature. This shows that photosynthetic sugar production and the photosynthesis of the aromatic compounds of strawberries are two different and independent processes. This was also found in strawberries grown in continuous artificial light of 700 ft.-c. at 10°C. Their fruits contained very little sugar, but were highly aromatic, whereas fruits of plants grown in continuous light of 700 ft.-c. at 23°C were utterly without taste, containing but little sugar and no aromatics.

In another experiment the aromatic content was studied as a function of the length of exposure of the plants to a low phototemperature. Fifteen groups of strawberry plants were subjected to daylight at 23°C. At night, they were all kept at 10°C, either in darkness or for different lengths of time exposed to 1,500 ft.-c. or 700 ft.-c. of light. FIGURE 32 shows the results, where the taste is expressed in a scale from zero (tasteless) to 3 (highly aromatic). When the plants were kept at 10°C in darkness, no taste developed in the fruits. But, at the high intensity a two-hour sojourn in light was sufficient to develop maximal taste, whereas at 700 ft.-c. 8 hours were required to produce approximately the same degree of taste.

Therefore, the development of the aromatic substances in the strawberry requires only a short period (not more than two hours daily) of high intensity light at low temperature, and additional light can be given at high temperatures without interfering with this low phototemperature effect.

These results explain why the first strawberries in spring taste best, when they have ripened under the lowest phototemperatures. In summer, the phototemperatures are too high for the formation of much aroma. But, high in the mountains or far North, near the Arctic Circle, phototemperatures even in summer are low, and there the best tasting strawberries are produced.

It seems likely that the taste development in several other fruits is based on the same principle as in the strawberry: the lower the phototemperature, the stronger the taste. This would explain why northern grown apples taste so much better. But, it does not hold for taste of tropical fruits. However, in many of the latter, terpenes are responsible for the taste and their synthesis is probably not increased at lower temperatures.

Other strawberry varieties behave much like the Marshall. The Klondyke and Tennessee Beauty form more runners and less inflorescences at intermediate temperatures. The Tennessee Beauty forms many runners at 17°C and a 12-hour photoperiod, whereas the Marshall forms many only at a 16-hour photoperiod, at 17°C. The Klondyke strawberry is at 200 ft.-c. supplemental light completely inhibited from flowering at 14°C, whereas the Marshall flowers; at 500 or 1,000 ft.-c., the Klondyke does not flower at 10°C, whereas the Marshall does.

Chapter 10

MISCELLANEOUS CULTIVATED PLANTS

Sugar Beet (*Beta vulgaris*):— The growing conditions of the sugar beet have been investigated in detail by Dr. ALBERT ULRICH in the Earhart Laboratory from 1949 to 1953. During this time, the Sugar Beet Development Foundation contributed ten thousand dollars annually for the experiments and twice yearly an advisory committee of this foundation met at Caltech to review the work performed and the problems to be investigated. The University of California contributed towards this project by stationing Dr. ULRICH with an assistant and a secretary at the Earhart Laboratory. The major results of this work have been published (ULRICH 1952 and 1955).

Most of the work was carried out with commercial beet varieties which have the disadvantage of being very variable because they are kept deliberately heterozygous. This increases their adaptability to different conditions as is shown in Chapter 15. Under different conditions different populations of plants will develop in which the plants germinating at higher temperatures will grow relatively better subsequently when temperatures remain higher, whereas the low temperature germinators in such a population develop best when the weather remains cool (*see* PLATE XXI). The most used varieties in the laboratory were US 22/3, GW 309 and a few inbred lines which were obtained from Kuhn and Company (Naarden, Holland) or from Dr. DEMING (Fort Collins, Colorado).

The plants were grown in vermiculite and were usually sown in place and later thinned to one, two or four plants per gallon can. To obtain more uniform plants they were sown in seed beds and were transplanted into the containers when they had developed their first leaves. Care had to be taken not to injure the tap root which afterwards developed into the beet (usually after about 20 leaves had been produced). The vermiculite allowed the expansion of the root without any hindrance and rather regularly shaped sugar beets were produced in this medium (*see* PLATE XXI).

Germination of the beets does occur at any temperature between 4° and 30°C, but at approximately 20°C vigorous young seedlings are produced in a reasonable length of time.

Growth of tops and of roots is not completely correlated; this means that under certain conditions relatively more root than top dry weight is produced. At the highest temperature the leaves die back rather rapidly and thus the size of the tops is reduced. Both day and night temperatures have a pronounced effect on beet crops, yet the effect of night temperature is more pronounced. The optimum nyctotemperature for growth lies between 20° and 23°C, whereas the optimal phototemperature is 23°C (*see* Figure 33). The sugar percentage of the beets is inversely proportional to the temperature, again nyctotemperature being slightly more effective than phototemperature: at 4°C the highest sugar percentage is reached, whereas at 30°C the sugar percentage is lowest. When the plants were watered with the Hoagland nutrient solution, the highest sugar percentage they ever reached under any environmental conditions was

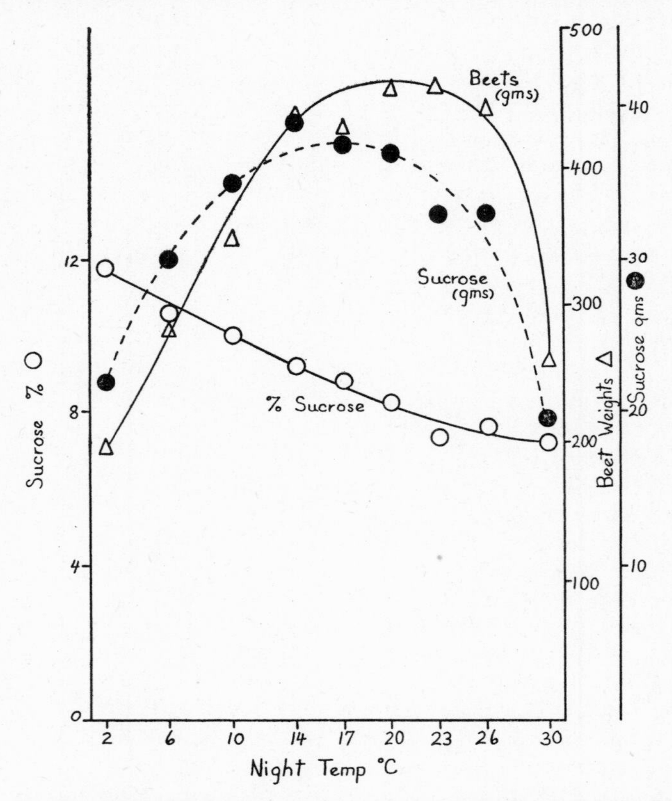

Figure 33.— **Sugar percentage, wet weight of beet roots and total amount of sugar produced in US 22/3 beet plants grown in 8-hour photoperiods in daylight (average for beets at 20°, 23°, and 26°C phototemperature) and at different nyctotemperatures (*abscissa*). Redrawn from Ulrich (1952).**

12 per cent. However, the sugar percentage could be increased by lowering the nitrate supply. By combining low temperatures and low nitrate nutrition the sugar percentage was raised to 20 per cent, which is the highest found in field experiments. This restricted the growth of the beets so that higher total sugar production is possible at somewhat higher nitrate concentrations.

When beets were kept continuously in a temperature of 23°C during day and 17°C during night, they did not become thermally induced and continued to grow vegetatively. Three or four year old plants developed stems of 1 meter length, which were swollen over their whole length similar to the tap root. Because living cells have only a limited life-span, the oldest parenchymatic tissues of these beets at the base of the stem died after 3-4 years, and the plants collapsed after that. Sugar percentage in these swollen stems was as high as that of roots grown under the same temperature conditions. Thus, the laying down of sugar is not modified by the age of the beet plants. After beet plants had been kept for a month or longer at 7° or 4°C they started to bolt and flower after bringing them to higher temperatures. When plants were growing continuously in the coolest greenhouse, which is 17°C during day and 12°C during night, several plants of U.S. varieties eventually bolted and flowered.

Other beet varieties behave essentially as the US 22/3 variety. The GW 347, a variety developed in Colorado under cooler growing conditions, did relatively better at lower temperatures whereas the US 22/3 had a slightly higher temperature optimum. Inbred strains at the same temperature responded with a slower growth rate.

A number of nutritional experiments were carried out under several temperature conditions. Whereas the response to nutrients was very similar in cool and warm temperatures, there was an interesting difference in the optimal nitrate concentration for growth. At high temperatures the highest nitrate concentration produced the heaviest plants whereas at 20° day-14°C night temperature the optimal nitrate concentration was only one quarter as high (*see* Chapter 21).

Several physiological processes were measured separately in the sugar beet. For a measurement of photosynthesis, dry weight production per plant per unit time in a known constant light intensity was measured. For this, young beets were used just before they had started to thicken their tap root. They were germinated or transplanted in containers with vermiculite. In the earlier experiments 5 plants were grown together in a 10 × 10 cm. plastic container, but because this tended to increase the individual variability, in later experiments the beets were grown singly in plastic cups of 7 cm. diameter. Before the start of the experiment all 100 or more containers with beets were lined up and visually divided into equal groups, each group containing the same proportion of heavy and light plants. One or two groups were then harvested right away, the other groups were kept for 6 or more days at different temperatures, different light intensities or different photoperiods, and then harvested. The increase in dry weight during that period of exposure can then be calculated by difference. There is a direct proportionality between duration of illumination and dry weight production. This would seem to indicate that photosynthesis is limiting. By increasing the light intensity above 1,000 ft.-c. there is no increase in dry weight. Therefore, we must conclude that the photosynthetic process cannot proceed faster than at 1,000 ft.-c. But, only the *rate* of the photosynthetic process is limiting, not the amount of dry weight which can be produced, because by increasing the duration of illumination more dry weight is produced proportional to the length of photoperiod. From this, we might conclude that at 1,000 ft.-c. intensity an equilibrium is reached between the rate of formation of photosynthates and their translocation out of the leaf cells. This limitation by the rate of translocation could either be due to the translocating system itself or to the size of the receiving end of the translocation system. If there is not enough space to store the photosynthates the translocation system will become clogged and the rate of photosynthesis will decrease.

In a coöperative experiment with Dr. JOHN SPIKES and Mr. BRUCE BURNHAM of the University of Utah at Salt Lake City, beets were grown under a number of different growing conditions. After they had been growing for 4 weeks half of the plants were harvested and this material was sent to Dr. SPIKES for biochemical analysis. The rest of the plants were divided into two groups and were subjected to light at an intensity of either 800 or 1,400 ft.-c. at 17°C in a 24-hour photoperiod. After a week, these plants were harvested and from the increase in weight during the last weekly period it was possible to get an idea of the growth potential of the beets which previously had been subjected to different temperatures and photoperiods. At 17°C approximately twice as much growth and dry weight was produced as at either 7° or 26°C. The plants which had been grown at an 8-hour photoperiod had a greater growth potential than those at 16 or 24-hour photoperiods. This seems to indicate that in short photoperiods the plants had been held back in their dry weight production by the amount of photosynthates formed. As soon as more were formed in a 24-hour photoperiod the plants gained weight at a very fast rate.

The plants which previously had been at 26°C photosynthesized better in a 1,200 ft.-c. than a 600 ft.-c. intensity, whereas the plants from 17° or 7°C were more efficient in growth at the 600 ft.-c. intensity.

Concerning correlations between individual processes and growth, the Hill reaction in beet leaves is positively correlated with length of photoperiod under which plants were grown, but there is a negative correlation with the growth potential of the beets. Therefore, it can be concluded that the photochemical reduction of water inside the chloroplasts is not the limiting process in the growth of these beets. On the other hand, there is a slight positive correlation between the respiration rate of leaf discs and subsequent increase in weight. Plants with a high respiration rate were in general those which also grew fastest when brought under the same conditions.

In another experiment three different beet varieties were grown under different temperature conditions. Under optimum temperatures slightly more growth was obtained in the 750 ft.-c. light intensity than in 1,200 ft.-c. The GW 304A was slightly better than US 22/3, especially at the lower temperatures. Variety 492 was inferior to both of the other varieties.

The high sugar percentage in beets grown at low temperatures might be explained if sugar translocation in the beet were as good or better at low than at high temperatures. This was investigated by Dr. HULL (1952) and he found with tracer techniques that sugar moved out of sugar beet leaves at a rate which is not decreased at all by low temperatures.

Corn (*Zea mays*):— Very little work with corn has been carried out in our air-conditioned greenhouses. The plants, especially hybrids, grow so large that they take too much space, and cannot be moved between conditions since the doors are too low when tasseling starts. Inbred varieties often remain small enough that they can be used in experiments requiring the moving of plants. Dr. J. LIVERMAN grew a set of corn plants in a 23° day — 17°C night temperature, in which the stems had to be marcotted repeatedly to lower the growing point in order to allow the plants to tassel. The total height they would have reached would have been about 5 m.

One interesting result is that the optimal night temperature for growth of corn is not so high as often alleged. At 23°C day temperature a sharp nyctotemperature optimum exists at 17°C, at 30°C day the optimum is shifted to 20°C night temperature. This has been found for several field corn varieties. And the optimal day temperature is either 23° or 26°C, depending on the nyctotemperature. These results were obtained in the greenhouse in winter; in summer at a higher light intensity the optimal temperatures are slightly higher. Ears were formed only at night temperatures over 12°C and optimal ear development (over two per plant) occurred at 17°-20°C nyctotemperature. At low nyctotemperatures (13°C and below) female flowers developed in the tassel.

At low phototemperatures, the leaves of corn plants remain yellow in color; in many plants also a striping of the leaves occurred, for which no satisfactory reason could be found. The plants looked as if they were iron-deficient. In continuous light some plants developed symptoms very similar to Ca-deficiency; the tips of the leaves remained rolled up around each other and only their bases separated producing a harp-like structure.

The most extensive experiment with corn was carried out with a double-hybrid. It had to be discontinued because of the size of the plants when the first tassels started to appear (only in a 26° photo and 16°-30°C nyctotemperature). In artificial light at 500 ft.-c. the plants grew reasonably well, and reached about ¼ the weight of plants in daylight. Up to a 16-hour photoperiod the weight was proportional with the length of photoperiod, but in continuous light the plants decreased in growth rate after two weeks, and after one month altogether stopped growing. Soon afterwards they died, at least at 26°C. When daylight was supplemented with artificial light to produce continuous illumination, growth was also retarded. Leaf development in this maize was slightly speeded up by temperature, with a Q_{10} of 1.3.

Flax (*Linum usitatissimum*):— Flax has been grown in the Earhart Laboratory by several investigators and since its growth requirements are rather special, our experience will be recorded. When Dr. E. Kurtz needed a supply of flax seeds grown under known conditions, he obtained best production by growing them during day in a greenhouse at 20° or 23°C and at night at 10°C, supplementing the daylight with eight or sixteen hours of high intensity artificial light. This gave good growth, flowering and heavy fruit set, and by planting batches of flax every two weeks a continuous supply of seed could be maintained.

Dr. C. R. Millikan has worked on the interaction between zinc and phosphorus nutrition in the flax-variety Sisal Crown. The plants were germinated in dishes and then transplanted into containers in which the nutrient solutions were held in plastic bags so as to avoid contamination of the nutrient solution. In other experiments the plants were sown in zinc-deficient soil. One of the latter experiments is shown in Plate XIV in which all combinations of a 10° and 23°C phototemperature with 7° and 20°C nyctotemperature, 8 and 16-hour photoperiods at high and low intensity were compared. It can be seen that only in the cool phototemperatures the flax stems grew up straight and stiff, whereas especially in the low intensities and high phototemperature the stems were weak and could not stand up by themselves. From this plate it can be seen that phototemperature is of more importance than nyctotemperature in the development of the flax plant. In dry weight production it also was found that at cooler day temperatures, about twice as much dry matter was formed than at a higher day temperature, and this difference was even more pronounced in the root systems.

Garden Flowers:— For about two years, a number of the more common garden flowers were investigated in the Clark greenhouses, under the auspices of, and with financial support of Sunset Magazine. Most of this work was carried out by Mrs. R. Corbett, whereas also Dr. M. G. Mes and Mr. R. Dorland took part in it.

Since these garden flowers are sometimes grown as greenhouse crops, a certain amount of information was available on their temperature and photoperiodic responses (Laurie and Kiplinger 1944), but we were able to get more detailed information, particularly with respect to interactions between light and temperature. In all the following experiments plants were germinated and grown to a stage where they were well established, and then the differential treatments were started. The results are summarized in Figure 44 and Plate XXII as far as the optimal photo- and nyctotemperatures are concerned.

Ageratum houstonianum (dwarf variety).— Both high photo- and high nyctotemperatures were detrimental to growth and flowering, regardless of daylength. Continuous light and cool days caused more abundant flowering, but plants grew well at an 8 hour photoperiod, a phototemperature of 18°C and nyctotemperatures of 16° and 13°C. In southern California this is an excellent spring flower; in more northern countries it flowers best during summer. Related *Ageratum* species (*e.g.*, *A. conyzoides*) grow at 1000-2000 m. altitude in the tropics. There they are subjected throughout the year to the optimal temperatures as found in the laboratory.

Begonia semperflorens.— Our variety was able to grow and flower in all temperatures (8°-30°C) and photoperiods (8, 16 and 24 hours) tried. However, a cold night retarded both growth and flowering, and continued 26° day and 30°C night was lethal regardless of daylength. When the days were cool there was very little effect of night temperature on growth in length; however, at warm phototemperatures there was a clearcut optimal nyctotemperature of 16°C. All plants flowered regardless of photoperiod, but at the longer photoperiods flowering was accelerated. This is one of the most desirable year-around garden plants in practically frost-free areas because it is flowering continuously.

During 1955 an extensive experiment was carried out with another variety of *Begonia semperflorens,* using a wider range of temperatures. At the lowest phototemperature (4°C) the new leaves were ivory yellow, but grew fairly well as long as the plants had food reserves or old green leaves, and provided the nyctotemperature was optimal (17°C). At a 7°C phototemperature the leaves were very light green, but at 10°C they had a normal green color. Similar to the tomato, and many other plants, *Begonias* growing in high nyctotemperature have light-green leaves.

Whereas at most temperatures, except the lowest, the *Begonia* flowered in an 8-hour day, only under optimal conditions (phototemperature 23-26°, nyctotemperature 17-20°) did female flowers develop, whereas the male ones grew under all conditions.

Bellis perennis (English Daisy).— In our experiments a large-flowered variety was used. It was unable to withstand higher temperatures. At 26°C phototemperature only the plants at an 8°C nyctotemperature survived, but flowered poorly, and at 13°C nyctotemperature the plants died within a few months. At an 18°C phototemperature the plants at 16° and 13°C nyctotemperature survived, but at 22° and 26°C they died. The plants kept at 18°C phototemperature and 8°C nyctotemperature were very vigorous, produced large flowers and flowered continuously. At either a higher photo- or higher nyctotemperature the flowers were very much smaller and less numerous. Of all garden plants tested this one had the lowest temperature optimum for growth and flowering. It flowers well in late winter and early spring in southern California, and becomes dormant in summer, whereas in cooler climates, it is a spring and early summer flower.

Callistephus chinensis (China Aster, variety Giant Crego Crimson).— At 26° photo- and 26°-30°C nyctotemperature the plants died early and sometimes even before flowering. Being a short-day plant, flowering was retarded in all cases where more than 8 hours of light was given, but eventually the plants would flower even in a 16-hour photoperiod. Such plants would then be very large and vigorous. This demonstrates that short-day plants will flower rapidly in short photoperiods, but because of that do not have time for sufficient vegetative development and consequently remain small and of poor quality. At 18° photo- and 8°C nyctotemperature, the largest flowers were formed, but also at higher nyctotemperatures excellent flowering occurred. As expected from its temperature and light response, this plant does best when planted in the long days of summer; it will flower in late summer and autumn.

Lathyrus odoratus (Sweet Pea, variety Early Spencer).— High temperatures were consistently deleterious to growth and flowering as indicated by slow growth, small leaves, chlorosis, stem rot and early death. At any temperature above 20°C, the flower buds died before opening. Whereas in other plants additional light usually could overcome the deleterious effects of high temperature, in the Sweet Pea lenghtening of the photoperiod would increase the harmful effects of high temperatures. Sometimes new shoots would develop at the base of a plant, subjected to high temperatures, and these showed some adaptation to the higher temperatures. Whereas in the young plants stem elongation was rapid at high temperatures, the optimum shifted downwards until the best development occurred in a 18°C phototemperature and 13° or 8°C nyctotemperature. Its temperature response makes this plant an ideal winter and spring flower in southern California. Immediately after the first series of warm days in May or June it stops flowering and soon the whole plant dies. In cooler, especially oceanic, climates *Lathyrus* is an excellent summer plant. It behaves very much like the garden pea (*see* Chapter 7).

Mathiola incana (Stock, variety California Giants).— Growth of Stocks was good at all temperatures; however, whenever either the day or the night temperature was above 20°C, the plants remained in the form of rosettes and did not flower. Even in the plants grown at 26° photo- and 8°C nyctotemperature, differentiation of flower primordia did not take place after 6 months of growth. With a phototemperature of 18° only the plants with 8°, 13° and 16°C nyctotemperature flowered in 8-hour photoperiods, whereas with a 20°C nyctotemperature flowering was possible if given long photoperiods.

At the lowest nyctotemperatures and in continuous light, the leaf edge was entire, whereas at the higher night temperatures the leaves were more or less deeply lobed. There was also a complete correlation between stem elongation and flowering as found in so many long-day plants but in this case a low night temperature could substitute for a long-day to produce flowers. Therefore, stocks are good spring flowers in southern California.

Papaver nudicaule (Iceland Poppy).— The Iceland Poppy is a typical cool long-day plant. The higher the nyctotemperature, the quicker they died, regardless of daylength. Flowerbuds developed under all conditions but they remained small or died, except in the plants receiving 16 or 24-hour photoperiods. At a 26°C phototemperature flowers were few and remained small. At 18°C phototemperature and continuous light, the plants grew well and formed abundant flowers. This was optimal for their growth. Iceland poppies are grown during winter and spring in southern California; with supplementary illumination at night it should be one of the most successful garden plants there.

Viola cornuta (Pansy, variety Blue Butterfly).— Also in these plants high temperatures were inhibitory for growth and flowering. Under all conditions flowerbuds were produced, but at the higher temperatures these would not open on an 8-hour day. They are then cleistogamous. At longer photoperiods flowering was profuse. At both cool day and night temperatures the flowers were large. The temperature and photoperiodic response of pansies make them good garden plants almost the year around.

A plant of *Viola palustris* was accidentally brought into the laboratory, and it was kept for 18 months in the Yellow greenhouse, at 23°-17°C. It grew profusely and produced large numbers of flowerbuds which never opened but cleistogamically developed ripe seeds. After this plant had been given a two-month cold treatment at 4°C in darkness, and had lost all its leaves, it sprouted from its rhizomes as soon as brought to the Blue greenhouse (20°-14°C), and then produced flowerbuds which opened normally; for several months no more cleistogamic flowers were observed.

Zinnia elegans (Zinnia, variety Miss Wilmott).— The *Zinnia* is a short-day plant which will develop vegetatively to a large size if started in long days. When later transferred to short-day conditions, flowering is speeded up and is abundant. Whereas in their early growth they have a very high optimal temperature, the optimum later decreases to a 13° or 16°C nyctotemperature. Although the largest flowers are formed at the lowest nyctotemperatures, the plants remain small and short under those conditions. To get the best *Zinnias* the plants should be sown in late spring; with the shortening of the daylength in August they will start to flower and will produce their largest flowers in autumn.

Saintpaulia ionantha (African violet).— Several varieties of this popular house-plant have been investigated in the Clark and Earhart greenhouses. Clones were established by leaf cuttings, from established plants or from seedlings raised in the laboratory. All plants showed ring spot on the leaves, even those raised from seed under insect-free conditions, suggesting that this ring spot is not a virus. It develops particularly under low-temperature conditions. *Saintpaulia* grows very well in artificial light, the optimal intensity depending on the temperature: at 23°-26°C it grows best at 500 ft.-c., at 14° at 1000 ft.-c. Such exceptional behavior of a higher optimal light intensity at lower temperatures seems to be typical of the *Saintpaulia* which also has a higher optimal nycto- than phototemperature (*see* Plates V and XVI). Both vegetative growth and flowering occur optimally at a nyctotemperature of 20°-23°C, whereas the best phototemperature is 14°. Even at a phototemperature of 10° the plants are vigorous (provided the night is warm) and form large dark-purple flowers. None of the other plants investigated thus far has shown this inverse thermoperiodic behavior. This atypic behavior, however, explains why it can be grown successfully as a house plant, whereas the outside night temperatures in the U.S. are too low to grow this plant out-of-doors, or indoors in front of open windows. When the house is well-heated, and when the heat is kept inside during night by keeping windows closed, the 20°-23°C can be realized. During day, windows should be open if possible to provide the lower phototemperature.

Coleus.— The variegated forms of this plant, propagated as cuttings, are among the most spectacular experimental objects in a phytotron. It is easy to observe the responses to temperature and light, since they are expressed not only in growth rate and leaf form and size, but also in pigment concentration and pattern. An example of this behavior can be seen in PLATE XVII, in which the effect of nyctotemperature, phototemperature and photoperiod are shown in the three rows of plants. In short photoperiods and low nyctotemperatures the leaves become narrow, and have their anthocyanin restricted to an area surrounding the midrib. Long photoperiods result in a high concentration of anthocyanin, which covers almost the whole leaf surface. At both low phototemperatures and high nyctotemperatures chlorophyll concentration is low, resulting in very pale yellowish-green edges of the leaves. From PLATE XVII it can be concluded that optimal growing conditions for this *Coleus* are: phototemperature 23°, nyctotemperature 17°, long photoperiod (16 hours).

Orchids:— Most of the work with orchids in the Earhart Plant Research Laboratory has been carried out by Mr. ROBERT CASAMAJOR. Financial support has been received from the American Orchid Society, the Cymbidium Society, and a number of individual orchid growers, who have contributed each $64.00 for the maintenance costs of one truck for one year.

Cypripedium.— A cross between *Cypripedium Octaeus Bianca* × *C. Margaret MacCaull* was sown in flasks by Mr. E. VACIN, and after they had reached sufficient size, they were transplanted to a leaf-mold mixture. While the plants were small (the longest leaves, 1-2 cm.) their optimal temperature, photoperiod, and light intensity were determined. A day temperature of 20°C and a night temperature of 14°C, a photoperiod of 16 hours and a light intensity of 700 ft.-c. were found to be best. Somewhat later, just before the first flowerbuds were laid down, growth was better at 23° day and 17°C night temperature, but during flowering itself, the optimum temperatures decreased again to 20° or 17°C phototemperature and 14°C nyctotemperature. At that time, an increase in photoperiod from 8 to 16 hours did not improve the growth or flowering. At lower nyctotemperatures, growth was much slower, the plants became yellowish green, and the flower stalks did not elongate properly, whereas at temperatures higher than the optimum, leaves died prematurely and flowers often died before opening (CASAMAJOR and WENT 1954).

As a growing medium, leaf mold or some other organic matter seems to be essential. None of the plants which were transplanted into gravel, vermiculite, or a mixture of these two, grew well, and only few of them developed open flowers. Different nutrient treatments were tried, but also none of these were effective. In the nutrient fog box, *Cypripedium* plants remained alive, but did not form new roots. Therefore, these *Cypripediums* are the only plants which we have not been able to grow successfully in an inorganic medium. Whether this is due to an actual requirement for certain organic substances, is unknown, but watering the plants grown in gravel or vermiculite with a mixture of vitamins (B_1, B_6, and niacin) did not do any good. When the plants grown in leaf mold were watered occasionally with nutrient solution, their growth improved.

We did not find any indication of photoperiodic control of flowering, for flowers were initiated and developed at both 8- and 16-hour photoperiods. In an 8-hour photoperiod, the flowers lasted much longer than in a 16-hour one.

After the plants had started to flower, they were kept for one year in ten different climates. From the behavior of these mature plants the following conclusions can be drawn; all figures are per plant and are averages of 10-13 plants.

The average number of flowers formed when plants were grown in gravel or vermiculite was 1.3, of which 0.4 had aborted before flowering. The comparable plants in leaf mold had produced 2.0 flowers in the same time without abortions. The roots in inorganic medium were much poorer, and fewer shoots were produced (8.3 against 9.7).

In long photoperiods (16 hours) 1.7 flowers were formed against 2.1 in 8-hour photoperiods. Thus increasing the length of exposure had no beneficial effect on flower formation, although the vegetative growth was slightly better. The plants continued to look good at a 700 ft.-c. light intensity.

The phototemperature did not have an appreciable effect on the number of flowers formed over the range of 14°-23°C; at the highest phototemperature the leaves were longer and slightly narrower; there were more dead leaves and fewer shoots per plant. The nyctotemperature, on the other hand, was very important for flowering; at 17°C only 1.2 flowers developed per plant, at 14°C, 2.0, and at 10°C, 2.3. At the lowest nyctotemperature the flower stalks remained short, the flowers were somewhat smaller and were slower in developing.

Therefore, the optimal growing conditions for these *Cypripediums* are about 12°C nyctotemperature and not too high phototemperatures in short days at about 700 ft.-c. Actually, these plants could be grown commercially in artificial light; in a limestone cave at 12°C electric current and lamp replacement would cost about $0.60 per plant per year; this would result in about 2 or 3 flowers. Installation costs of the light panels would amount to $3.00 per plant.

Phalaenopsis amabilis.— The plants currently grown in the Earhart Laboratory were derived from a culture flask obtained from Mr. G. Hiatt. Both in their early growth and later, they developed optimally in a 700 ft.-c. light intensity, and at a constant temperature of 20°C. There was no indication of a gradual lowering of the optimal temperature with age.

Whereas *Phalaenopsis* plants did flower at a 16-hour photoperiod, inflorescence formation was more abundant in an 8-hour photoperiod.

Excellent *Phalaenopsis* plants were grown with only artificial light. The leaves became large and dark-green, and 2-3 inflorescences developed per plant at one time, when the plants were subjected to short photoperiods. In a 700 ft.-c. intensity, the flowers were large and perfectly white, and lasted a long time. Similar plants grown in the greenhouse in daylight screened to half-full intensity had smaller leaves and smaller flowers, which had a greenish tinge, and which lasted for only a week.

In general, the plants grown in Osmunda fiber grew better than those in gravel, which was probably due to a more balanced nutrition. Occasional watering of the Osmunda fiber with nutrient solution had a beneficial effect.

Cattleya trianae.— Two clones of this *Cattleya* species were brought into the Earhart Laboratory in 1951 and 1952. They were received from the Fred A. Stewart Nursery. The single plants were separated into 20-26 clone divisions, each of 2-3 pseudobulbs. They developed very well in gravel when watered daily with nutrient solution. After the plants were well established, a first experiment was carried out in which plants were subjected to day temperatures ranging from 17° to 30°C, night temperatures ranging from 14° to 20°C, and photoperiods of 8 and 16 hours. Whereas growth was slightly faster at the higher temperatures, there was very little difference in the flowering behavior according to temperature. In all plants receiving an 8-hour photoperiod, flowers developed on the new pseudobulbs, whereas not a single flower developed on any pseudobulb which was kept under long-day conditions. This is entirely a question of development, since initiation of flower primordia occurs in both conditions.

After completion of this experiment, the plants were divided into two groups, one receiving 8 hours additional light during night (100 ft.-c.), the other getting only the 8 hours of daylight. Within 4 months the plants in long photoperiod stopped flowering, and during the next 12 months not a single flower developed. The plants in short photoperiods flowered continuously, and any new shoot would form an inflorescence with 2 or 3 flowers. After 11 months under these two conditions plants were shifted for 1, 3 or 4 months to the other condition. When the plants in long days were shifted for 1 month only to short days, 3 months later no inflorescence growth had occurred, but the sheaths were all green and in good condition in contrast with the plants kept continuously in long days, in which the sheaths dried up very soon. Another group, which had had 3 months of short days, had open flowers 1 month later, but these inflorescences carried only 1-2 flowers; of the younger inflorescences still enclosed in the sheath, each had 2 flowers developed. Plants coming from short days and having spent 3 or 4 months in long days had no inflorescences; those formed in the short days had already flowered, and no new ones were developing. Plants coming from long days, and kept for the last month in short days, showed no growth of inflorescences, but those kept for 4 months in short days had open flowers (with only 1 flower per inflorescence) and many developing inflorescences, each with 2 flowers. Plants kept for the last 3 months in short days had well-developed inflorescences but no open flowers as yet.

It is, therefore, obvious that inflorescence growth in *Cattleya* requires short days for at least 2 months, and that the first inflorescences which start growing bear only 1 flower each. Flowers in C. *trianae* will not open until 4½ months have elapsed since the short-day treatment began. One month in long days does not inhibit flowering, but after longer periods in long days inflorescence growth is completely inhibited. The inflorescences which were already growing produced good flowers under long-day conditions.

Cattleya plants can be grown in artificial light at intensities of 1,000 ft.-c. but their growth is slow, and only a few flowers develop under these conditions. In full daylight, the plants become very vigorous, and 2-3 flowers are formed per inflorescence. The leaf color may be rather light and yellowish in full daylight, but this does not impair photosynthesis or growth.

There is no indication that *Cattleya* plants need a rest-period to flower. When growing conditions are poor, for instance, in low light intensities, the actively growing new shoot completely inhibits flower development on the mother shoot, but in high light intensity, both flower development and new growth can occur on the same shoot. This makes it seem as if there is active competition for photosynthates by vegetative growth and developing flowers. When photosynthesis exceeds the demand for carbohydrates by storage organs or growing shoots, the excess sugar is excreted as liquid droplets on flower-stalks, flower-sheaths, and leaf-blades.

Cymbidium lowianum.— Toward the end of 1950, approximately 60 clone divisions of this *Cymbidium* species were received from Mr. Hertrich of the Huntington Botanical Garden. They were all planted in a leaf mold mixture. A few plants in gravel grew well also. In the course of about two years, these plants developed into sturdy individuals of flowering size, and they were transplanted into one-gallon crocks. When grown in leaf mold, they needed watering with nutrient solution only once a week, or less. The plants were all grown against the South walls of the greenhouses where they did not receive direct sunlight. In the cooler greenhouses, the plants developed very well, even when exposed to direct sunlight.

Inflorescences developed in *Cymbidium* plants as lateral buds on recently matured pseudobulbs carrying at least 10 leaves in the species used. When dissecting dormant lateral buds, it was found that each pseudobulb carried usually two buds which had differentiated approximately 10-12 nodes. All the other 6-10 buds on the same pseudobulb were very minute and had only 2-4 primordia differentiated. These latter buds did only develop when the larger buds had been removed, and when the pseudobulb itself was separated from the rest of the plant. This happens in so-called back-bulb propagation.

The larger buds present can either become vegetative shoots or inflorescences. It seems that their determination occurred only after these buds started growing. In inflorescences the first 15 nodes carry bud-scales, or sheath-leaves, which are placed in a ½ divergence (alternating in 2 stichae). Up to that point, they are indistinguishable from vegetative shoots. But after the 15*th* node, the new primordia are arranged in a 2/5 spiral, and each primordium becomes a bract carrying an axillary flower.

When these *Cymbidium* plants were kept at day temperatures of 23° or 26°C, and a night temperature of 14°C or higher, no inflorescences were formed at all, and the plants continued to form new vegetative shoots. When plants were kept for 1-3 months at a 26° day and 7°-10°C night temperatures a few inflorescences were formed. When the day temperature was lower, 20°C, night temperatures of 10° and 14°C were effective in inflorescence formation. There is no obvious effect of daylength at any time on inflorescence formation, but the plants have to come out of long photoperiods before they can be induced by the lower temperatures. Therefore, plants receiving the 20° photo- and 14°C nyctotemperature in a 16-hour photoperiod produce inflorescences continuously. Plant Number 16, for instance, had open flowers in all months of the year, except July and August, and another plant just has completed 12 months of continuous flowering (CASAMAJOR 1955).

Since flower opening is stimulated by long photoperiods, too, it now is possible to keep *Cymbidium lowianum* continuously in flower under those conditions.

This information makes it understandable why *Cymbidiums* produce inflorescences in early autumn only (usually they appear in September and October). This is when, after the long summer days, cool weather arrives. Therefore, plants which are kept out-of-doors in late summer and early autumn, where they are kept cooler than in a greenhouse, will flower more consistently. And when the long summer days are followed by long periods of 20° day and 14°C night temperature, *Cymbidiums* flower most abundantly. These conditions prevail along the southern California coast, as in Santa Barbara, where *Cymbidium* culture is particularly successful.

Chapter 11

GRASSES

by Wm. M. Hiesey

Carnegie Institution of Washington, Stanford, California

As man's major source of food, grasses have been subjected to many studies from different points of view. One needs only to scan the bulky Proceedings of the Sixth International Grassland Congress (1952), for example, to gain some inkling of the widespread efforts currently being made to improve yields, control quality and to change in various ways the characteristics of grasses to meet the demands of a multitude of economic uses.

Aside from studies on vernalization and photoperiodism, however, there is relatively little information on the responses of grasses to controlled environments. Without doubt, this is due in large measure to the lack of adequate facilities for controlling factors of the environment. Fortunately, laboratories equipped for such studies are appearing in increasing number, and we may expect that within the next decade knowledge of the specific effects of given environmental factors may be considerably extended.

Genetic as Compared with Physiological Studies:— Efforts to control the characteristics of grasses have been directed along two major lines: one is by genetic selection and recombination, and the other is through modifications brought about by manipulating the environment. These two viewpoints are represented by investigators primarily engaged in genetic studies as contrasted with those whose major interest is in physiology. This distinction, however, is breaking down under the impact of advances in both fields. The importance of hereditary factors in determining both small and large differences between and within species is established beyond question. The mode of inheritance of a given character difference may or may not be readily determined by relatively simple genetic tests. More often than not the geneticist is compelled to resort to complex hypotheses requiring the concept of several interacting genes in order to account for the baffling ratios observed in progeny tests. This becomes especially evident when such tests are conducted under several different environments.

At this point the basic physiological processes underlying the expression of inherited characters become a matter of interest to the geneticist. The physiologist, concerned primarily with mechanisms of internal processes, tends to regard these mechanisms as common to all plants regardless of species or race, and may overlook the importance of genetic factors. At the present time there is confusion regarding the interaction between genetic and physiological processes, an indication that the time is ripe for extensive experimentation under relatively strictly controlled conditions in studies specifically planned to clarify these relationships.

Flowering Responses:— Most of the studies on the *Gramineae* invoking the use of controlled or semi-controlled environments have been concerned with the development of flowering responses to varying temperatures and photoperiods. The extensive literature on vernalization and photoperiodism has been adequately covered by previous reviews, notably in the monograph by MURNEEK and WHYTE (1948) which includes summaries on special related topics by a number of outstanding investigators. GARNER (1937), GREGORY (1948), and PARKER and BORTHWICK (1950) have surveyed various aspects relating to the control of flowering, and more recently LANG (1952) has reviewed this same subject incorporating newer literature. A review by McKINNEY (1940) on vernalization includes a historical discussion of the development of the subject, and another by WENT (1953*a*) covers aspects of temperature effects in the control of development. Although the effects of light and temperature included under the terms "photoperiodism" and "vernalization" are observed in many distinct families of plants, the responses of the *Gramineae* have received special attention because many of these are striking and have economic importance. It is not intended to review the facts on these topics that already have been so well summarized, but it would be a serious omission not to emphasize the extent of the investigations in vernalization and photoperiodism and the influence of this work on current concepts.

In his pioneer work KLEBS (1918) started the precedent of attempting to break down into analyzable steps or stages the development of flowering. This approach has been followed extensively by subsequent investigators in attempting to analyze the mechanics of vernalization and of photoperiodism. As developed by KLEBS this concept, which is still largely followed by current investigators, envisions the development of flowering as being preceded by three essential and independent stages: (*1*) induction, or the capacity to produce flower primordia (Blühreife Zustand); (2) initiation, or the development of flower primordia (Blütenanlagen); and (3) elongation and further differentiation (Bildung der Infloreszenz). The bulk of evidence indicates that the primary external factors controlling development during these three stages are temperature and light, with other factors such as nutritional levels playing a secondary role. These external influences presumably affect the formation of hormones that control flowering.

This hypothesis allows a number of degrees of freedom for the varying expression of different species, varieties, strains or of individuals that differ in their genetic composition. The threshold of response of any particular grass to a given stimulus is determined by its particular genotype. Increasing genetic evidence points to the conclusion that the critical thresholds for given responses are usually determined by multiple series of genes balanced against each other. LANG (1952) points to the tendency of current investigators to subdivide the three major stages of flowering into finer steps as new evidence suggests the action of hitherto undiscovered factors. Ultimately, it may be possible to relate the action of certain genes to specific steps, but in the current state of our knowledge most reports consist primarily of a descriptive account of observed responses accompanied by the author's interpretations of possible mechanisms.

The modifications that may be induced on a given strain or clone of perennial grass by simply varying the temperature, or the photoperiod, or both, are often striking. For example, ALLARD and EVANS (1941) exposed 13 species of grasses to daylengths of 10, 12, 13, 14, 16, and 18 hours. *Poa compressa* L. remained purely vegetative and highly leafy under the shorter days but flowered freely under longer days of 16 hours or more. Early, medium, and late strains of *Poa pratensis* L. reacted in various ways: the early strain flowered at all photoperiods, but the culms became short, leafy and decumbent under a short day of 10 or 12 hours, whereas clones of the same plants became erect and stemmy under 16 and 18-hour days; the medium-late strain produced extremely decumbent stems under short days, but strictly erect stems under the longest days; and finally, a late strain responded in growth habit like the early strain but was later in flowering at all daylengths. Two tall-stemmed, early-flowering strains of a 42-chromosome form of *Phleum pratense* L., commonly used as a hay crop in the United States, flowered freely when exposed to daylengths of 13 hours or longer, but a decumbent, late-flowering 14-chromosome strain from pastures in Harpenden, England, failed to flower at any of the daylengths. Another strain of timothy from Wales flowered only when subjected to days of 16 and 18 hours. *Bromus inermis* Leyss. remained vegetative and highly leafy under short days of 10 or 12 hours, but flowered under long days, becoming stemmy.

The responses of annual cereals to varying temperatures and photoperiods are well exemplified by the extensive studies of PURVIS (1934, 1939) on winter and spring varieties of Petkus rye. The winter variety after germination requires both cold temperatures and short days to attain the first stage of floral induction. Attainment of this stage can be seen in a change in the primordia at the growing points. Normally, this stage of development takes place in the late fall or winter following fall sowing of seed. The spring variety, on the other hand, will flower freely after direct spring sowing the same season. The later stages of flowering of both winter and spring types are favored by warm temperatures and lengthening days. When winter and spring varieties are crossed, the F_1 hybrid responds as a spring type, and the F_2 progeny segregate into both winter and spring forms in a ratio that indicates that more than a single gene is involved in determining the inheritance of this difference. The factor or factors determining the difference between the spring and winter types have been shown by PURVIS to be localized in the embryo.

Studies by PETERSON and LOOMIS (1949) and GARDNER and LOOMIS (1952) demonstrate that strains of *Poa pratensis* L. and *Dactylis glomerata*

L. require both cool temperatures and short days for floral induction, a process that normally takes place during the autumn months. If kept in a warm greenhouse at 18°C during this period, *Dactylis glomerata* and *Poa pratensis* failed to flower the following spring irrespective of whether they had been exposed to short, intermediate, or long days during either the fall or spring period. The same strains kept in a cool greenhouse during the fall flowered freely during spring if, during their fall treatment, they were also subjected to short days of 12 hours; but if exposed to long days of 18 hours, they failed to flower. The effects of daylength were strictly localized to the areas receiving the light treatment in sod cultures vegetatively connected by rootstocks. After floral induction, the first stage prerequisite to flowering, these authors were unable to detect any morphological changes in the growing points of properly conditioned plants. Further development into flower primordia, the second stage, was favored by long days and inhibited by short days. The final or third stage of culm expansion was also found to be favored by long days and also by high nitrogen fertility. Both *Dactylis glomerata* and *Poa pratensis* are species that normally do not flower the first year after sowing in the spring. Other perennial grasses, however, such as *Elymus canadensis* L. and *Bouteloua curtipendula* (Michx.) Torr., do flower the same year after spring sowing. Evidently, perennial grasses differ with respect to their temperature and photoperiodic requirements in much the same way as the annual winter and spring varieties of wheat, rye, and other cereals.

The flowering of perennial grass strains held at different temperature ranges in greenhouses was investigated by Hanson and Sprague (1953) and was found to be favored by first growing them at cool temperatures and short daylengths for several months and then at higher temperatures and longer days. Species studied included *Dactylis glomerata* L., *Festuca elatior* L., *Bromus inermis* Leyss., *Phalaris arundinacea* L., and *Phleum pratense* L.

Of particular interest is a study by Olmsted (1944) on intraspecific variation among 12 native strains of *Bouteloua curtipendula* (Michx.) Torr. originating from different latitudes ranging from San Antonio, Texas, to Cannonball, North Dakota, a spread of 17° in latitude. The northernmost strain was found to consist of plants whose flowering was favored by long days, whereas the southernmost strains were composed of individuals stimulated either by short days or days of intermediate length. Forms from Nebraska, Oklahoma, Kansas and New Mexico showed a diversity of composition among individual plants ranging from long-day to intermediate-day types. A simple classification of strains of this single widespread species was, therefore, not possible, but a trend of differentiation from South to North with respect to daylength requirements was evident. Individual variability within the population samples suggests a complex genetic basis for this pattern of regional differentiation.

A series of studies on temperature and photoperiodic requirements of members of the genus *Lolium* in relation to intra- and inter-specific differentiation have been made by COOPER (1950, 1951, 1954). Species of *Lolium* are native in central Asia, the Mediterranean region, and along the northwest coast of Europe and include annual self-pollinating types such as *Lolium temulentum* L. (darnel) and *L. remotum* Schrank which are weedy species found in arable crops, and biennial and perennial outbreeding species such as *L. italicum* A. Br. and *L. perenne* L. which are common herbage ryegrasses. The summer annuals are able to flower soon after germination in the spring without special treatment with regard to temperature or photoperiod. In perennial strains of *L. perenne* flower induction or "competence" (the first stage of floral development) is dependent on treatment to low temperatures. For flower initiation (the second stage), long days are required, most rapid development taking place in continuous light; and the subsequent rate of development of the inflorescence (the third stage) is primarily determined by temperature. The annual Mediterranean species do not require cold temperatures for floral initiation and are able to initiate flower primordia at either short or long daylengths.

The annual Mediterranean species *L. italicum* and *L. rigidum* Gaud. together with the perennial northern *L. perenne* constitute a closely related group the members of which are freely interfertile when crossed, and all have the same number of chromosomes ($2n = 14$). Populations from different ecological origins show a close adaptation to local conditions of temperature and photoperiod. When grown under conditions simulating those of their natural habitat, such populations appear to be fairly homogeneous, but when exposed to a series of controlled environments different from their native environment, they display marked variation. Crosses between a form of annual *L. rigidum* from the Mediterranean area and a strongly perennial pasture strain of *L. perenne* from Wales yielded first generation hybrids some of which had the summer flowering characteristics of *L. rigidum,* and others having the temperature and photoperiodic requirements of *L. perenne.* Among the F_2 progeny, plants were segregated differing in their responses to temperature and photoperiod over a range extending between the parental types. From the complex segregations in F_2 populations and in progeny resulting from backcrosses with the parents, it is evident that the inheritance of the contrasting differences in response to temperature and to photoperiod in the parental races is governed by genes of a multiple series. Characters could not be classed as either "dominant" or "recessive" because their expression largely depended upon environmental conditioning with respect both to temperature and photoperiod. Progeny resulting from self-pollinating the parental species in both instances displayed individual variation in earliness and in response to temperature and daylength treatments thus making evident their heterozygous nature.

COOPER has succeeded notably in integrating in a broad way the complex biological patterns of variation in the various entities of *Lolium* with their ecological distribution and with their physiological and genetic characteristics. The interplay between the reasonably clear-cut physiological responses of contrasting races to differential treatments of temperature and of daylength, and their genetic characteristics, throws much light on the evolutionary development of the genus.

Seasonal Periodicity:— A quite different problem in the control of seasonal periodicity is presented by species native to areas having winter rains and summer drought. The coastal and low mountain areas of California at altitudes below 2500 feet are occupied by both annual and perennial species that are subjected to moderate winter rains at temperatures suitable for growth, and to hot dry summers resulting in drought. LAUDE (1953) has studied the seasonal periodicity of a race of *Poa scabrella* (Thurb.) Benth. ex Vasey, a perennial species particularly successful in this area. Dormancy normally takes place in early June as the days become warm and the supply of moisture becomes depleted. Active growth is resumed in the late fall during cooler weather after the first rains. Water applied to *Poa scabrella* during the summer fails to induce active growth unless, at the time, the plants are also brought to cooler temperatures. On the other hand, plants in the midst of normal winter growth can be induced to become dormant by subjecting them to warm temperature treatments at 54°C at 50% humidity for four hours on three alternate days, and then exposing them to long days of 18 hours. Plants given the heat treatment but exposed to short days do not become dormant but continue in active growth. Thus in *Poa scabrella* a combination of warm temperature and long days is sufficient to induce dormancy in active plants even when water is continually supplied in adequate amount. Plants thus made to become dormant can be induced to resume growth by subjecting them to cool temperatures having days not exceeding 24°C, but if water is withheld, they will remain dormant even at cool temperatures. Other species that become completely summer-dormant include *Poa bulbosa* L. and *P. secunda* Presl., both of which, like *P. scabrella,* are shallow-rooted plants that occur on arid range lands of the western states. More deeply rooted species such as *Poa nevadensis* Vasey ex Scribn., *Stipa cernua* Stebbins and Love, *S. pulchra* Hitchc., and *Melica californica* Scribn. may become partially summer dormant or, lacking moisture entirely, are capable of becoming fully dormant. These species are in contrast with other grasses that normally are summer-active such as *Poa ampla* Merr., *P. compressa* L., *Elymus glaucus* Buckl., *Lolium perenne* L., *Phalaris tuberosa* var. *stenoptera* (Hack.) Hitchc., and *Bromus carinatus* Hook. and Arn.

Responses in Controlled Environments in Relation to Field Performance:— A comparison of the growth of different species and hybrids of *Poa* under controlled temperatures at the Earhart Laboratory made by HIESEY (1953) revealed a number of contrasts in response-patterns that can to some extent be related to the climates of origin of the various species. A strain of *Poa ampla* Merr. originally from the vicinity of Spokane, Washington, flowered abundantly when clones were subjected to cold night temperatures of 6°C and day temperatures of either 20°, 23°, or 30°C. All the clones were otherwise treated alike and subjected to a 12-hour day. With warmer nights, but at the same day temperatures, flowering was reduced, being completely inhibited at night temperatures of 17°C. Leaf growth attained a maximum at intermediate night temperatures of 10° and 14°C, conditions under which a moderate number of culms were developed. Another race of *Poa ampla* from Kahlotus, Franklin County, Washington, in sand dune areas developed relatively better at warmer night and day temperatures than the race from Spokane. These two races have subsequently been observed to respond very differently in field tests carried on in different climates. Flowering of *Poa compressa* L. was likewise found to be markedly reduced as night temperatures were raised from 6°C to 17°C. Two strains of *P. compressa* differed in their response to day temperature, a California strain producing its greatest dry weight at a day temperature of 23°C, whereas a race from Turkey produced its maximum weight at 30°C.

A number of races of *Poa pratensis* L. showed, in general, a high range of tolerance to different combinations of day and night temperature, but races originally from extreme ecological habitats had distinctive patterns of growth. Races from middle latitudes from Central California and Oregon produced most bulk when grown at cold or cool night temperatures (*i.e.*, 6° or 10°C) and at moderate day temperatures (20° or 23°C), whereas a race originally from Lapland north of the Arctic Circle made relatively better growth at warmer night temperatures (14° and 17°C) combined with the same moderate day temperatures. The response of the Lapland race seems to indicate that it tolerates only a relatively narrow range of diurnal temperature variation. This is consistent with the continuous illumination it receives during the summer growing period in its native habitat. Hybrids between forms of *P. ampla* from southeastern Washington and this same form of *P. pratensis* from Lapland were found to have a greater range of tolerance to varying combinations of controlled day and night temperatures in the Earhart Laboratory than either parent. Field tests in contrasting climates support the laboratory data. Similar results have been obtained with hybrids between different races of *P. pratensis* and *P. ampla.*

Growth of races of *Poa scabrella* (Thurb.) Benth. ex Vasey originally from the Coast Ranges of central California was favored in the Earhart experiments by a combination of cool night temperatures (6° or 10°C) and cool days (20° or 23°C), although warmer days of 30°C when combined with cold nights of 6°C also proved to be favorable for growth. A warm night temperature of 17°C combined with the warm day of 30°C resulted in very poor growth and a tendency towards dormancy in *Poa scabrella,* a result consistent with the findings of LAUDE described above. A hybrid between *P. ampla* and *P. scabrella* proved, like its parents, to have a relatively narrow range of tolerance, both parents and hybrid being favored by the combination of cool days and cold nights. The hybrid and its parents have been tested in field experiments at different altitudes and latitudes and their relative performance is likewise consistent with the laboratory findings.

The usefulness of controlled laboratory experiments in estimating the relative performance of new strains in untried environments is quite evident. Much more investigation along similar lines is needed, however, before patterns of response can be established which can be used in predicting field performance in new environments.

Of considerable practical importance in problems in reseeding depleted ranges or establishing a grass cover on burned areas are data on the temperatures at which maximum germination for a given species or race may be expected. ASHBY and HELLMERS (1955) conducted tests on germination and seedling establishment on a number of grass species considered to be of value in erosion control in southern California at controlled day and night temperatures in the Earhart Laboratory. Three ranges of temperature corresponding approximately to summer, winter, and spring and fall conditions in southern California were tried. Three species, *Bromus marginatus* Nees, *B. rubens* L., and a form of *Poa scabrella* (Thurb.) Benth. ex Vasey were found to germinate best at the cool or winter range of temperatures (17° day, 4°C night), whereas *Oryzopsis miliacea* (L.) Benth. and Hook. ex Aschers. and Schweinf. (smilo grass) was strongly favored by summer temperatures (30° day, 17°C night). Other species favored by high summer temperatures were *Elymus triticoides* Buckl., *Muhlenbergia porteri* Scribn., *Schismus barbatus* (L.) Thell., and a late strain of *Dactylis glomerata* L. A group of species, including *Lolium multiflorum* Lam., *L. perenne* L., *Bromus mollis* L., *B. rigidus* Roth., *Agropyron cristatum* (L.) Gaertn., and a "common" strain of *Dactylis glomerata* L. germinated uniformly well at all three seasonal temperatures. Three species, *Ehrharta calycina* J. E. Smith, *Melica imperfecta* Trin. and a form of *P. scabrella* (Thurb.) Benth. ex Vasey germinated best at the intermediate spring-fall temperature range (23° day, 10°C night). Field test sowings in a burned area in the Angeles National Forest made during the winter of 1952 comparing the establishment of *Lolium multiflorum* with that of *Oryzopsis miliacea* were followed by good germination and establishment in early summer of the former species and failure of the latter. Scattered late summer germination of *Oryzopsis* was observed in local depressions where sufficient moisture persisted. The field experience, therefore, was consistent with the laboratory tests.

JUHRÈN, HIESEY and WENT (1953) subjected seeds of 14 grasses, including *Bromus carinatus* Hook. and Arn., *Agropyron dasystachyum* (Hook.) Scribn., *Poa bulbosa* L., *P. compressa* L., *P. pratensis* L., *P. ampla* Merr. and *P. scabrella* (Thurb.) Benth. ex Vasey, and various interspecific hybrids of *Poa* to germination tests at various combinations of day and night temperatures and light treatments in the Earhart Laboratory and studied their subsequent early stages of growth, including their dry weight production. Significant differences in pattern of germination and development were observed among the various species and hybrids. Forms of *Poa scabrella* from the Coast Ranges of California attained good germination over a wide range of temperatures, but subsequent development was best at cooler ranges of temperature, with a maximum at the day temperatures of 18°C and night temperatures in the range of 10° to 14°C when grown under artificial light. In summer sunlight with warm day temperatures of 26°C and nights of 10° or 20°C no germination or growth took place in this species. A form of *Poa pratensis* from near Mono Lake, California, showed relatively better germination and growth at warmer day and night temperatures under artificial light, and was also able to germinate under summer sunlight at day temperatures of 26°C and night temperatures of 20°C. The hybrid, *scabrella* × *pratensis,* although generally poorer in percentage germination than the parents, had a range of tolerance at the varying temperatures greater than either parent. A strain of *Poa ampla* from Spokane, Washington, showed a high range of tolerance in the germination tests with a maximum dry weight yield at cool day temperatures of 10° to 18°C and cold night temperatures of 4° to 10°C. A hybrid between *P. ampla* × *P. scabrella* had a considerably greater tolerance for heat than the *P. scabrella* parent, and as wide as *P. ampla. Poa compressa* and *Agropyron dasystachyum* were found to have a wide tolerance to varying temperatures during germination, but *Agropyron* grew rapidly under hot days and nights and was considerably slower in growth under a cold night of 10°C, whereas *P. compressa* was more tolerant. *Bromus carinatus,* an annual grass, germinated and flowered early under a wide range of temperature combinations. *Poa bulbosa* also grew under a wide range of temperature combinations, but responded best under cooler ranges. Grasses with the widest temperature tolerance tended to benefit most from exposure to high natural light intensities where they showed marked increases in dry weight yields over plants grown under artificial light. Field tests in plots situated at altitudes of 300, 800 and 2200 m. in southern California tended to confirm the laboratory observations in that species most tolerant in the laboratory were also the most successful in germination under extreme field conditions.

Laude and Chaugle (1953) studied the relative tolerances to heat of seedlings of different age of three species of bromegrasses, *B. marginatus* Nees. (mountain brome), *B. cartharticus* Vahl. (prairie brome) and *B. stamineus* E. Desv. (Harlan brome). Seedlings of ages ranging from 7 to 70 days were raised in a greenhouse and subjected to heat treatments in a controlled chamber at 54°C at 30% to 35% relative humidity for 4¾ hours. Injury was estimated 7 days after treatment by tabulating the percentage of dead leaf tissue. The highest level of heat tolerance was found to occur in all three species at an age of 7 or 8 days. Shortly after this period, up to 14 days, there was a rapid loss of heat tolerance which persisted up to an age of 28 days after which tolerance to heat increased with age. *Bromus cartharticus* was found to be definitely more tolerant to heat stress than the other two species which did not differ significantly from each other. By previously conditioning the seedlings by subjecting them to 30-minute exposures at 54°C every third day for 7 treatments, the heat tolerance of all three species could be increased appreciably. Seedlings kept in the dark before exposure to the heat test were injured more than comparable plants provided with light. Earlier studies by JULANDER (1945) on drought and heat resistance of pasture grasses also indicate that tolerance to heat is related to high food reserves. Hardening by drought under conditions favoring the accumulation of food reserves was found to be linked with heat tolerance. Tests on comparative seedling emergence of grasses from soils kept at controlled temperatures ranging from 42° to 53°C were reported by LAUDE, SHRUM, and BIEHLER (1952) and show that *Stipa cernua* Stebbins and Love is highly tolerant of heat, whereas *Oryzopsis miliacea* L. Benth. and Hook. and *Bromus cartharticus* Vahl. are of intermediate tolerance, and *Lolium perenne* L. relatively intolerant.

Recent studies by MITCHELL (1953*a* and *b*, 1954) on different strains of *Lolium* have been aimed at a critical comparison of growth rates as affected by controlled temperature and light. Criteria for comparing rates of growth on the basis of tillering, number of leaves, and dry weights were examined and applied to two strains of *Lolium perenne* L., one a British strain originating at Aberystwyth, and the other a New Zealand form originating as a hybrid between *L. perenne* and *L. multiflorum* Lam. The rate of appearance of successive new leaves was found to be constant so long as conditions of temperature and light were constant. The number of leaves formed, therefore, was used by MITCHELL as a physiological time scale to indicate the vegetative age of the plants independent of fluctuations in rate of growth caused by varying environmental conditions. On the same shoot, changes in environment such as altering the light by shading are quickly reflected in changed rates of growth and are readily reversible. The production of new tillers follows the maturation of subtending leaves, but for any given plant or strain rate of tiller production was found to be an independent variable. In both the British and New Zealand strains lowering the light intensity and increasing the temperature were found to reduce the rate of tillering, but the British strain was inhibited to a greater degree than the New Zealand strain by increasing temperature. The British strain when grown at 10°C at a low light intensity was found to assimilate at approximately the same rate as the New Zealand strain, but at higher light intensities at this same temperature the New Zealand form increased dry weight the faster. At 18°C, however, this difference disappeared.

General Conclusions:— On the basis of the studies made to date the relative order of importance of both hereditary factors and external influences in affecting physiological and biochemical processes is becoming clearly evident. The complex genetic make-up of most species of plants and their varying responses in differing environments, on one hand, and the as yet unknown chain of developmental processes that takes place within the individual, on the other, suggest the need for increasing precision in the isolation of factors in order to clarify these relationships. Critical investigations under controlled conditions can scarcely be said to have begun despite notable contributions by individual investigators which have brought our knowledge to the point where the need for more exact control now becomes evident. Our current imperfect knowledge is both a challenge and an opportunity to investigators of the present and the future who have at their disposal improved facilities for study as well as the benefit of a background of essential exploratory work which may serve to orient more precise investigations. The practical value of such basic scientific studies to agronomic applications cannot be predicted with certainty, but this would probably be very great.

Chapter 12

RESPONSE OF TREES AND SHRUBS

Originally, it was not intended to use the Earhart Plant Research Laboratory for the investigation of woody plants, because they take up so much more space than herbaceous plants, which exhibit most of the physiological and morphological responses of plants and, therefore, are more convenient for their investigation. Yet, perennial and woody plants must have some properties which differ from annuals, since they must synchronize their growth cycles with the yearly climatic cycle. Since some of these woody plants can be studied while they are young, and can be trimmed so as not to take up too much space, several were investigated, either in detail (coffee, *Cestrum*) or more casually (peach, orange, *Camellia,* etc.), whereas a good-scale experiment with oaks and pines has been started. In addition, the climatic responses of a good number of chaparral shrubs have been investigated (*see* Chapter 14).

Coffee (*Coffea arabica,* variety Bourbon):— Coffee is one of the tropical plants grown in the Earhart Laboratory; it was studied especially by Dr. M. G. MES and Mrs. METZENBERG, under the auspices of the I.B.E.C. Research Institute. Coffee is a small, short-lived tree, which makes an analysis of its climatic response especially interesting, in comparison to the other plants grown in the laboratory, most of which are annuals. In addition, the work with coffee is of interest because of its importance as a crop plant in the tropics. Its range of culture lies entirely within the tropics, except in southern Brazil, where it is found as far as 26° S.

Germination and early growth.— The coffee seedcoat, called "pergament," covers the actual seed or coffee bean very loosely, and is easily removed. The presence of this coat retards germination at least one week. Inside, we find the yellowish-gray endosperm covered by a thin papery membrane which is the remainder of the integuments. The embryo itself is very small, and lies embedded on one side of the endosperm. During the first weeks of germination growth is very slow. The cotyledons enlarge and grow into the endosperm, dissolving it and transforming it into cotyledonary tissue. The hypocotyl and the root break through and start to elongate, first slowly, and after 2-3 weeks more rapidly. The cotyledons are then lifted from the soil by this elongation, and soon afterwards the hypocotyledonary hook straightens. At this point, the cotyledons begin to unfold. The endosperm is then almost completely dissolved; what is left of it is sloughed off as a horny membrane. Sometimes, the embryo develops asymmetrically in the seed, and then the part of the endosperm which is opposite the embryo remains undissolved.

Germination is fastest at the highest temperatures. At 30°C constant temperature, the seedlings appear above ground 3 weeks after sowing, which is a short time compared with the 3 months needed for germination at an average temperature of 17°C. The young seedlings have still a fairly high temperature optimum and grow best at 30°C during day and 23°C during night. By the time the first lateral branches appear, 7 or 8 months after sowing, the optimal temperature is lowered to 26° day and 20°C night, and approximately one year later, the optimal temperature for general development has shifted as low as 23° day and 17°C night, where it probably remains for the rest of the life cycle of the coffee tree. PLATES XVIII and XIX give some examples of the temperature response of coffee trees.

A mixture of gravel and vermiculite has proven to be a satisfactory growing medium, for it is sufficiently porous to allow proper development of the roots. At the same time, relatively small containers can be used, for the size of the container is determined by the amount of water the root medium can hold. Thus, a 2-year-old tree, 2-3 meters high, grows well in a 2-gallon container, but must be watered twice a day to prevent wilting. The plants can be transplanted from smaller containers without injury, for the roots form a ball which is easily transferred. The coffee plants can easily be over-watered, which causes a swelling of the stem base through the development of hyperhydric tissue.

Flower initiation.— Plants grown in the greenhouse in natural daylight do not initiate flowerbuds until about November, which suggests that coffee is a short-day plant, as FRANCO (1941) had found ten years ago. Special experiments were carried out in which coffee plants were subjected to 8, 16 and 24-hour photoperiods at 30°, 26° and 23°C day temperatures, and 26°, 23° and 20°C night temperatures. Flower initiation occurred only at the 8-hour photoperiods in all of the temperature combinations tested. No flowers appeared in the 16-hour photoperiod series, but there were a few in continuous light. From observations under natural daylight, it would seem that the critical daylength is 12 hours or less, because visible flowerbuds appear towards the end of November.

Although vegetative growth is optimal at 23° day and 17°C night temperature, the greatest number of flowerbuds are initiated at the highest temperatures (30° day and 23°C night). At 20° day and 14°C night, flowerbuds are formed, but very slowly; there is no initiation and very little growth at 17° day and 12°C night.

The flowerbuds develop to a size approximately 6 mm. and then become dormant, especially at high temperatures. When kept continuously at high temperatures, only relatively few buds open; the rest eventually drops off, or develops into so-called "starlets." These are buds which remain greenish and do not elongate but unfold their corolla lobes slightly, exposing the 2 styles. They do not have any functional stamens and usually do not set fruit. If the dormant flowerbuds are exposed to lower temperatures (23° day, 17°C night for instance), they open within 13 days after the temperature shift, giving perfectly normal, white and fragrant coffee flowers.

Temperature reduction is not the only means of breaking dormancy; cutting off a branch and placing it in water is sufficient stimulus to make the buds on that branch open into flowers, even without a temperature shock. When such cut branches are placed in different temperatures, at 30° day, 23°C night the flowers open in 10 days; at 26° day, 20°C night it takes 12 days, and at 23° day, 17°C night the buds open 14 days after cutting. Therefore, the growth process after breaking of the dormancy is controlled by a chemical process with a temperature coefficient of about 2. In recent work Dr. MES has found that it is predominantly water stress which keeps the flowerbuds dormant, and any treatment which decreases the water stress inside the buds (particularly rain or submerging of buds in water) will release the inhibition.

In nature, coffee flowers are initiated when the days are shortest, but even close to the equator coffee has a pronounced yearly periodicity in flowerbud initiation. Since there the daylength does not drop below 12 hours, it is difficult to see how this can be reconciled with the short photoperiod requirements. It is suggested that in this case the shade trees, which are invariably used for coffee culture near the equator (Colombia, Surinam, Indonesia), sufficiently cut down the light intensity at dawn and dusk to shift the plants from the day to the night metabolism, increasing the length of the dark period sufficiently to cause flower initiation. It is perhaps significant that the countries where coffee is grown without shade (southern Brazil, Guatemala, Hawaii) lie sufficiently far from the equator that the critical night length could be reached even without shade.

To test this hypothesis four groups of coffee plants were placed under optimal temperature conditions for flower intiation (30° day and 23°C night), all receiving an 8-hour photoperiod in daylight. They were given extra light 4 hours after and 4 hours before this 8-hour period of daylight; to simulate dusk and dawn, the intensity of the supplementary light was 100, 10, 1 and 0 ft.-c. After 2½ months of these treatments, the plants receiving no supplementary light had well-developed flowerbuds, those with 1 ft.-c. light had also good flowerbuds, with 10 ft.-c. the buds were only barely starting to become visible, whereas those with the 100 ft.-c. dusk and dawn had no flowerbuds developed at all. Therefore, decreasing the light intensity to slightly above 10 ft.-c. is sufficient to have the coffee plants initiate flowers as if they were subjected to darkness, and these experiments show why shade trees may effectively reduce daylength for the short-day coffee plant.

In addition to the temperature shock and release of water tension there must be another factor which causes the opening of coffee flowers. For on plants grown continuously in the same greenhouse under the same temperature regime, most flowers will open on the same day, and several weeks later the buds which did not open in the first flowering period will then flower simultaneously. Yet, this unknown stimulus is much weaker than that due to increase in watersupply or to a temperature shock and can be over-shadowed by it.

Once fruit set has occurred, berries almost invariably develop regardless of the growing conditions — that is to say, both at 30°-23°C and 17°-12°C temperatures ripe berries were harvested, provided the fruit had set at a more favorable temperature. In our 3-year-old coffee trees, the rate of fruit development was strongly affected by temperature; it was very slow at 17°-12°C where the first ripe berries were harvested 9 months after transfer from the warmer temperatures, whereas this took only 4 months at the 26°-20°C temperature. The total weight of berries harvested was greatest at 20°-14°C with a total of 430 g. per tree of dry coffee beans, which corresponds to 3,000 g. wet weight of berries. Both at the higher and lower temperatures the production per tree was lower. There was a very pronounced effect of pre-treatment of the trees on coffee yield. The plants which had been at 30°-23°C and 17°-12°C during the period of flower initiation and flowering did not have any berries at all. Those coming from 20°-14°C had only 50 g. of dry beans per tree, whereas those from 26°-20°C produced 300 g. per tree, and those from 23°-17°C had 380 g. Therefore, from these experiments it seems as if heaviest production can be obtained when during the early fruiting stage the plants have been at an average temperature and during their ripening the trees were kept relatively cool. The over-all best condition was 23° day and 17°C night temperature.

Vegetative growth.— The coffee plant has a remarkable quality in its vegetative bud system. The apical bud develops into an orthotropic shoot which never bears any flowers or fruit. In its leaf axils two different types of buds are formed. The primary axillary bud gives rise to an orthotropic shoot, and usually does not develop unless the main shoot is decapitated. A larger bud, implanted some distance above the true axillary, develops into a plagiotropic shoot that never reverts to an orthotropic condition. In the proper photoperiods these plagiotropic shoots form flowerbuds on each node, and also carry axillary buds which give rise to other plagiotropic branches.

At high temperatures, the orthotropic buds grow out spontaneously which give the plant a very bushy appearance (*see* center plant in PLATE XIX). At lower temperatures, orthotropic shoots do not develop unless the main bud has been injured. However, in exceptional cases, there is a slight development of these buds at low temperatures (23° day, 17°C night only) and the resulting shoot may carry a few flowers and fruits, although it never elongates under these conditions.

All this work was carried out with the Bourbon variety of *Coffea arabica*. In further experiments also the Caturra, Mundo Novo and Semperflorens varieties were tested as to their growth responses. These varieties differ from Bourbon in only one or two Mendelian factors, and all behaved essentially alike, except for Caturra, which has at all temperatures a 30 per cent decreased rate of growth. And the Semperflorens variety would form flowers also on a 16-hour photoperiod. It is, therefore, a photoperiodically indeterminate plant, which can initiate flowers continuously and thus is ever-flowering.

Cestrum nocturnum:— The night-blooming jasmine (*Cestrum nocturnum*) is a semi-tropical shrub, native to islands in the Caribbean, which grows well out-of-doors in southern California. The plant does not have dormancy, but continues to grow the whole year long, although slowly during winter. In Pasadena, it has two flowering cycles per year, one in May and another in September and October, when a sweet aroma engulfs the shrub and its surroundings at night.

Once flower primordia have been initiated, they will develop straight through into flowers, which open during night, and simultaneously with their opening they become very fragrant. This is a direct response to the darkening, for at any time of day or night flowering *Cestrum* shrubs can be brought from light into darkness, and within 30 minutes they will be fully fragrant.

Dr. Sachs (1955, 1956*a, b,* and *c*) has studied the flower initiation of this plant in great detail. Without going into details, it can be stated here that under no single constantly maintained climatic condition did *Cestrum* flower at all; neither at high nor at low temperatures; neither in long nor in intermediate or short photoperiods. However, plants which have been growing in long days will initiate flowers soon after being transferred to short days, but not *vice versa.* This behavior had also been found in *Kalanchoë,* and is probably fairly common among perennial plants. It is likely that *Salvia apiana, Kalanchoë daigremontianum* and other species belong to this group, where a sequence of long-short or short-long photoperiods is required for flower initiation.

Camellia japonica:— Ten years ago Dr. J. Bonner (1947) investigated the flowering behavior of *Camellias* in the Clark greenhouse. He found that photoperiodic response was restricted to their vegetative development. In long days, buds grew into shoots whereas in short days, all vegetative buds remained dormant. Length of day had, however, no effect on flowering at all. At high temperatures flowerbuds were initiated and grew into large buds which did not open but dropped off; the higher the temperature, the earlier. More recently Finlandia, a semi-double white *Camellia,* has been grown in the Earhart Laboratory. Only daylight was used, and its temperature response was investigated. At 23° day and 17°C night temperature flowers were initiated, but at higher temperatures this occurred faster. Once the flower buds had a diameter of about 1 cm., the plants were transferred to cooler greenhouses. At a 23° day, 17°C night temperature flowers barely opened, but dropped off before or almost immediately afterwards; at 17° day and 12°C night temperatures, flower buds opened normally, and produced high quality flowers, which remained open on the plant for a week or more. At 20° day and 14°C night temperature only a small percentage (about 20 per cent) of the flowers opened; the other buds were shed. The petals soon developed brown spots, and the flowers lasted only two to three days. But in the lower temperatures no flower buds were initiated. Therefore, the flower-bud initiation is entirely thermoperiodic, and this behavior explains the winter flowering of *Camellias*.

Citrus aurantium (Sour-orange):— In 1950, a number of orange seeds were germinated in the Earhart Laboratory. The larger plants were selected when they were about one year old, and were then placed in different temperature conditions. After two months in these conditions, their growth rates were recorded. At 10°C night temperature and also at 17°C day temperature growth was very slow, and increased both with increasing day and night temperatures. A maximum growth rate of over 7 mm. per day was reached at 30° day and 23°C night temperature, closely followed by 23° day and 20°C night temperature. At both higher and lower night temperatures the growth rates dropped off.

Therefore, in its vegetative development the orange seems to be basically a tropical plant, and although it grows poorly, it is able to survive at low temperatures.

Prunus persica:— Peach seedlings had been investigated in the Clark greenhouses by Dr. W. Lammerts (1943). He had found that in long days the plants continued to grow vegetatively, and would flower ahead of plants grown outside in the normal sequence of high and low temperatures as found in the summer-winter cycle of the climate. Dr. B. Rogers grew more peach plants from seeds. He confirmed the necessity of subjecting them to low temperatures to have flower buds open into flowers. Upon investigating which factors were involved in the initiation of flower buds on peach trees, he found that it was necessary to subject them to low temperatures (10°C or below) for several months.

This finding was tested on a new set of peach seedlings. Flower-bearing buds can usually be recognized in that they are lateral to the main axillary bud, and are relatively wide, and more hairy than the ordinary vegetative buds. Actually, flowerbuds developed on peach seedlings less than one year old which had been subjected to 4-10°C for 2 to 3 months, and afterwards kept for 4 months or longer at higher temperatures (*e.g.*, in the 23°-17°C greenhouse). When these flowerbuds were sufficiently large, they would develop into flowers when kept for 75 days at 4°C, but not for 45 days at 4°, nor 45 or 75 days at 10°C. These peach seedlings would grow continuously when they were kept at 23°-17°C at a 16-hour photoperiod. The apical buds of the branches did not become dormant under those conditions, and continued to develop new leaves, without intervening cold treatment. But, as soon as the plants were subjected to daylengths of less than 13 hours, the buds became dormant, and the leaves present on the branches aged rapidly and after a few months dropped off. The dormant buds then needed a cold period before they started to grow anew. Therefore, dormancy is induced in peaches by subjecting them to short-days, like WAREING (1954) found for other deciduous trees. To cause flowering in peaches we, therefore, need two successive cold periods, separated by a sufficiently long warm period in which actual flower differentiation occurs. It is, therefore, the second winter before opening of its flowers that the flowering of the peach is determined by a vernalization treatment. It is likely that this same behavior is typical of other deciduous fruit trees which usually differentiate flower primordia the summer before flowering.

Oaks (*Quercus* spp.) can be grown in the Earhart Laboratory provided the plants are subjected to several months of cold treatment to bring the buds out of their dormant condition into which they lapse after a flush of growth. *Q. ruber* and *Q. alba* both become fully dormant in a thermoperiod of 30°-23°C or 23°-17°C.

Pines (*Pinus* spp.) also require cold treatments between flushes of growth as found by Dr. P. KRAMER. Northern pines (*P. strobus*) or pines from high altitudes (*P. flexilis*) require lower temperatures and longer vernalization treatments before their buds will start to grow, than southern pines (*P. taeda*). By keeping these pines or *Picea* continuously in one of the greenhouses the plants will stop growing after a few months, and in the course of time will die.

Chapter 13

MISCELLANEOUS WILD PLANTS

Desert Plants:— There can always be a question whether desert plants develop normally under conditions of daily watering, as occurs in the Earhart Laboratory. Actually, a number of seedlings of desert plants supports this treatment very poorly in the warm greenhouses and a considerable percentage dies upon daily watering. But at the lower temperatures survival even with excess water is high. Yet, by watering only once or twice weekly, survival of these desert annuals is better.

When adequate moisture in the growing medium can be provided, plants will survive for long periods without watering. This was found in the case of the smoke tree (*Dalea spinosa*). Seeds were sown on June 12, 1953, in a 34 cm. wide and 220 cm. tall cylinder, filled with sand, and soaked with nutrient solution. After another watering on June 15, 6 seedlings appeared on June 24. During the following 7 months the plants grew well, to a height of about 20 cm. and then declined, until only a few basal buds and shoots remained alive. On April 15, 1954, the sand was watered through a tube which was inserted in the sand 120 cm. below the surface. Immediately the plants started to grow again, proving that the roots of the 20 cm. tall plants penetrated at least 100 cm. deep in the same column, and had been able to exhaust the sand of water down to that depth. Towards the end of 1954 the tops of the plants started to die back again. They had then attained a height of 25 cm. On January 10, 1955, the plants were watered again, now at a depth of 180 cm., and 3 of the plants immediately recovered. Thus deep waterings 10 and 9 months apart were sufficient to keep these smoke trees growing. On November 1, 1955 they received another watering 200 cm. below the surface, and immediately buds near the base of the plants, which were dying back, grew into flourishing shoots.

The dry sand 1 cm. below the surface was heated by the sun's radiation to 20°C above the air temperature; at 4-6 cm. below the surface, at 14:45 in the middle of summer, the temperature rise was 15°C. In nature these values may be much higher: for the sunlight there is not filtered through glass and water, and the soil surface is usually much darker. Therefore, we can expect in completely dry soil top soil temperatures at least 30°C above the air temperature. Since this rises to 40°C or higher during summer, the stem bases of desert perennials must be able to withstand temperatures of at least 70°C.

The reason why these smoke trees developed so well with only 4 waterings in 2½ years' time is because they had a large volume of moist sand to extract the water from. When desert plants are grown in small containers then they must be watered at least once weekly. Dr. EICHENBERGER has grown a number of desert annuals in two-gallon crocks in sand and he found that after the sand was completely soaked with water through an artificial rain of 20 mm. the germinating seeds would develop into mature plants which flowered and set fruit without any additional water even in the high temperature greenhouses. Such plants, however, remained very small. A second watering after a few weeks made these annuals develop to normal-sized plants.

Concerning the necessity of low humidities for developing of the desert habit of plants, some early experiments of Dr. J. BONNER with guayule (*Parthenium argentatum*) showed that when plants were grown at a 26°C constant temperature the stems were thin and spindly and could not stand up by themselves and the leaves were green instead of grayish as they are in nature in the desert. This succulent growth was produced both at high (70%) and at low (40%) humidities. When another set of plants was grown at 26°C phototemperature and 8°C nyctotemperature the stems were sturdy, stood upright and carried grayish-green leaves, producing the typical desert habit. In many other desert plants it was found that the desert habit was produced only at low nyctotemperatures even at high humidities, and, therefore, the desert habit of plants is a response to low nyctotemperatures rather than to low humidities.

Much work has been carried out on the rain and temperature dependence of southern California desert plants (WENT 1948*b* and 1949; JUHRÈN, WENT and PHILLIPS 1956). It was found that the typical winter and spring annuals of the desert, such as *Gilia aurea, Eriophyllum wallacei, Chaenactis* and many others would germinate after a sufficiently strong rain at the lower temperatures, whereas the summer annuals like *Pectis papposa, Amaranthus fimbriatus, Bouteloua barbata* and *Euphorbia* only germinated in the warm greenhouses. Whereas the summer annuals would apparently flower under any photoperiod, the winter annuals were found to be long-day plants. Most shrubs such as *Franseria dumosa, Encelia farinosa* and *Larrea divaricata* usually germinated at the high temperatures, too.

Larrea was grown by Dr. E. KURTZ for investigation of the wax and fat content under different temperatures and water stress conditions, and it was found that this plant could grow under an amazingly wide range of temperature conditions although most growth was found at 26° day and 20°C night temperature. Even with daily watering the plants had a normal desert habit and grew to 2 meter high shrubs in the course of 4 years.

Because of its exceptional behavior, the Joshua Tree, *Yucca brevifolia,* will be discussed in somewhat more detail. It has a very peculiar distribution in nature. It occurs in the Mohave Desert in southern California, and North to Utah, but only at altitudes between 900 m. and 1800 m. in the eastern and above 800 m. in its western area. When this *Yucca* is grown at lower altitudes, it survives well as a young plant, but grows poorly when older. From its distribution the impression was gained that it needs a yearly period of cold for proper growth.

Seeds of *Yucca brevifolia* were germinated in the Earhart Laboratory in August, 1949. When not more than one year old, they germinated within 24 hours at 26°-30°C. For somewhat over a year the seedlings were kept at 26° during day, 20°C during night in natural daylight, and had developed about 15 leaves per plant, without showing any growth in thickness. In December, 1950, 8 plants were transplanted into two-quart cans, and two years later into one-gallon crocks. When placed in artificial light of 1,500 ft.-c. they grew very poorly especially at the lower temperatures. During 1951 and 1952 the plants were largely kept either at 30°-23°C (day and night temperature) or 17°-12°C, and under both conditions they grew fairly well to about 100 leaves, with considerable growth in thickness of the stem.

At the age of 3½ years some plants were given a two-month cold treatment at 4°C (16-hour photoperiod). During the cold period no growth took place but during the next two months more than double the number

TABLE 10: *Number of unfolding leaves per month on four-year-old plants of Yucca brevifolia (the Joshua tree):—*

Conditions during measurements:—				
Phototemperature	4°	7°	17°	30°
Nyctotemperature	4°	7°	12°	23°
Photoperiod in hours	16	24	12-14	12-14
Conditions prior to measurements:—				
4° Constant, 16-hour photoperiod	0.3	1.9	3.6	4.6
17° Phototemperature 12° nyctotemperature natural daylength	0.8	—	1.8	3.0
30° Phototemperature 23° nyctotemperature natural daylength	0.5	—	—	1.0

of new leaves developed when compared with plants which did not have the cold treatment. At the age of 6 years leaf growth and development at 30°-23°C had dropped to one leaf per month; these leaves remained short and were strongly epinastic. After 6-12 months at 4°-10°C leaf development increased to a rate of five leaves per month, and these leaves were twice as long and stood straight up. It, therefore, seems as if *Yucca brevifolia* is a plant which, after it has reached a certain age, requires a yearly succession of cold and warm weather for optimal growth. TABLE 10 shows the average number of new leaves unfolding per month, based on 42 two to six months growing periods from April, 1953, to February, 1955. This table shows very clearly that the higher the temperature, the more rapid the rate of leaf-unfolding is. But this rate is equally strongly controlled by the preceding temperature conditions. Plants coming from cool temperatures grow subsequently much faster than those which were first at high temperature.

Aloe plants were grown from cuttings and the young plants were placed at different temperatures either in artificial light or daylight. Under both these conditions, the leaves responded to temperature in a characteristic way: at 23°C or higher, they became thin and narrow, and at lower temperature, the leaves remained shorter, were thicker, and became very wide at the base. They also produced more pronounced spines at the lower temperatures.

Flowering is a short-day phenomenon in *Aloe* and requires cool temperatures during or previous to the short-day treatment. When plants with flower stalks were transferred to higher temperatures, these inflorescences died immediately, but the growth of the rosettes continued.

A number of succulents have been grown in the Earhart Laboratory. For best growth they should be subjected to high phototemperatures and low nyctotemperatures. They seem to be specifically adapted to big temperature fluctuations from day to night. For *Cereus* a 30°C phototemperature, combined with a 17°C nyctotemperature and a 16-hour photoperiod gave most rapid growth, whereas *Mesembryanthemums* (like *Lithops, Argyroderma* and *Ophthalmophyllum*) did best at a phototemperature of 23° and a nyctotemperature of 7°C. It is very likely that this is due to their acid metabolism, which requires CO_2 fixation in darkness at low temperatures.

Baeria chrysostoma belongs to the best experimental plants available. It is a small annual composite, which is very common in spring in California. It occurs in cismontane valleys and foothills and occasionally turns the floor of the West Mohave Desert yellow with billions of flowers, opening in March and April. Lewis and Went (1945) have described its growth response to environmental conditions, showing it to be a long-day plant while less than 40 days old, becoming indeterminate later. In short photoperiods the plants survive for 2 months in a 26°C nyctotemperature, but otherwise die in warm nights. At 19°, 13° and 7°C nyctotemperature the plants survive for at least 100 days. Death at a 26°C night temperature is not a succumbing to parasitic or saprophytic fungi or to pests, for under sterile conditions the plants die just the same (Loo 1946). Sivori and Went (1944) made a study of the photoperiodic behavior of *Baeria* and found that the plants became photoperiodically sensitive 5 days after germination, and that the first microscopically visible change in the apical growing point to a flower primordium could be detected 7 days after beginning of the long-day treatments. For most rapid development the plants have to be grown in daylight for 8 hours with supplementary light of more than 150 ft.-c. intensity during night. Red light is most effective as supplementary light, blue less and green is ineffective. In spite of the high light intensity required and the action spectrum the supplementary light does not exert its effect through photosynthetic carbohydrate formation, for sugar cannot substitute for this light (Loo 1946).

Dr. G. Camus has followed up this work and has grown *Baeria* under short-day conditions in sterile culture. He used the lowest light intensity under which fair growth could occur in the presence of sugar (200 ft.-c.). Thus, no flower primordia were formed in the first 40 days. All experiments were scored before the plants reached this age, when they are strictly long-day plants. Additions of different organic materials to the sterile growing medium were possible because of the sterile growing conditions. He found that adding casein hydrolysate would cause the formation of flower primordia in *Baeria* 37 days after sowing, when the plants were kept continuously in short-days. Therefore, the flowering stimulus, which normally comes from long-day treatments, could be substituted by amino-acids in the root medium.

Under the most favorable conditions for flowering (continuous light at 17°-20°C), the first flowers will open from 19 to 32 days after sowing. Curiously enough, this flowering date seems to depend on the age of the seeds; with fresh seeds, in 1941, it took only 19 days for the opening of the first flower, whereas with the same seed in 1944, it took 32 days under identical conditions. In 1950, with 5-year-old seed, flowering started 23 days after sowing.

In recent experiments, a pronounced effect of precipitation after sowing was found. In the first place the percentage germination was enhanced. After 170 hours the difference in germination between no rain and 50 mm. precipitation was 19 $\pm$ 4.5 plants. In the second place, a clear-cut effect of rain on the further development of the plants was found. When they were grown in continuous light, the length of the stem and of the flower bud, as a result of 50 mm. precipitation, was after 20 days almost double that of the rainless control; 5 and 15 mm. rain gave intermediate lengths. Also, the number of open flowers was doubled 24 days after sowing. These results are further discussed in Chapter 22, and are summarized in TABLE 19.

Baeria offers a good example of a plant in which the optimal germination and growing conditions change as the plant grows up. During the first 3 days of germination, 23°C is optimal for emergence, but the next day the optimum has shifted to 20°C, again a day later it is lowered to 17°C and the sixth day after sowing the plants develop better at 14°C. If for the first 3 days the plants were kept at 14°C, and then they were shifted to 23°C, germination was very poor. For flowering, the optimal sequence is different: most flowers appear on plants kept for the first 3 days at 14°, next 4 days at 10°-17°C, next 4 days at 17°C, and after that between 20° and 23°C. This same sequence holds for the greatest total length. The earliest flowering, however, has slightly higher optimal temperatures: first 3 days at 14°C, next 4 days at 17°C, next 4 days above 17°C, and afterwards 23°C.

Veratrum, which belongs to the *Liliaceae,* has a typical annual growth cycle. It develops ½-2 m. tall leafy shoots which sprout each year from a corm which is buried about 10 cm. deep in moist meadows, usually at high altitudes in the mountains. Its leaves are wide and plicate, with their bases forming the main body of the vegetative shoot. In the flowering shoot the leaf bases enclose the stem of the large inflorescence, which in the species studied carries either green (*V. viride*) or yellow-dotted white flowers which are delicately fringed (*V. fimbriatum*). The former species grows in the mountains of the eastern United States and at low altitudes in eastern Canada, whereas the latter occurs near the coast in northern California. The closely related *V. californicum* grows all through California at altitudes above 1500 m., and *V. eschscholtzii* occurs in the mountains of Washington and northward to Alaska.

These plants are of importance because of the veratrum-alkaloids present in their rootstocks and roots, which are effective in lowering hypertension. For this reason the Riker Chemical Company was interested in cultivating this plant, which normally is collected in the wild. In field experiments all over the United States great trouble was experienced in making the transplanted rootstocks grow again. In the hope of finding a solution for the difficulties in growing these plants, the Riker Chemical Company supported research in the Earhart Plant Research Laboratory to study their growing requirements. This work was carried out by Mrs. R. Corbett. Since it takes more than six years for a *Veratrum* plant to develop fully from seed, it was necessary to bring mature plants into the greenhouses after fumigation. To this end, whole root stocks with attached roots of *Veratrum* were dug in the field and shipped bare-rooted by air express to Pasadena. It was soon found that in most cases these rootstocks would not develop unless they had been stored at low temperatures for several months. This storage had to be done while the rootstocks were planted in crocks in vermiculite, since when they were placed between wet burlap sacks or when planted in gravel they died and rotted. Only in the case of a shipment of roots which were dug in early spring immediately after disappearance of snow from the ground could they be planted and would they grow in the greenhouses without storage at low temperatures.

All *Veratrum* species have in common that their vegetative parts consist of a short vertical rhizome, which is kept at a proper depth under the surface by a crown of contractile roots, of which there are usually 1 or 2 years' whorls alive. Above the root insertion the actual bud starts. At the time the foliage of *Veratrum* dies in autumn, the bud is of the nature of a bulb. It is surrounded by brown decaying leaf bases of previous years' growths. Within these are the fleshy white bases of the leaves of which the blades just died plus a number of white fleshy scale leaves without leaf blades. Enclosed are the foliage leaves which will grow the following season. These are recognizable by their yellowish color and corrugated leaf blades. They do not seem to expand during their actual dormancy, nor does the growing point between them develop at all during that time. The young foliage leaves in turn enclose more scale leaves immediately surrounding the growing point. The growing point usually is vegetative but occasionally it is transformed into an inflorescence with floral primordia in the axils of fleshy white leaves. In most cases a single shoot develops per corm. Only when inflorescences are present 1, 2 or, exceptionally, 3-5 axillary buds form.

When dormancy has been broken, growth of the bud is explosive. The shoot then elongates and at first looks like a big asparagus, in which the leaf sheaths surround each other and give the impression of a 30-50 cm. high stem surrounded and crowned by 5-10 leaves. The leaf blades are wide and strongly plicate. When flowering, a stem is pushed up through the center of the leaf sheaths, either simultaneously with leaf development or (*V. fimbriatum*) towards the end of the vegetative growth.

Depending on the vigor of the plant each year 5-10 mm. of new stem (rhizome) is formed, and near the periphery of this new stem, root primordia are initiated which grow out during the following growing season. Microscopically these primordia appear as yellowish meristematic areas. In *V. viride* 10-34 primordia are formed; in *V. fimbriatum*, 1-3. During storage there is no further increase in the number of primordia. These roots grow out during the growing season and form laterals either that same or the following growing season.

Removal of the roots prevented normal elongation of the leaf sheaths during the following growing season. In two groups of 36 plants the intact plants grew 23 ± 5.5 per cent more than those from which the roots were cut off. Therefore, in transplanting *Veratrum* one should be careful to transplant with the existing living roots. Rootless plants may develop into cabbage-like structures.

Many chemical treatments with auxin-like substances were tried to improve root formation or root growth, but none of the treatments tried had a consistent effect on the number or vigor of roots developing zero to one year after treatment. Indolebutyric and naphthaleneacetic acid slightly increased shoot growth, but 2,4,5-trichlorophenoxyacetic acid inhibited both shoot growth and root formation. By treating the root system with a mixture of vitamins (B_1, B_6, biotin, niacin, folic acid and Ca-pantothenate, each 10 p.p.m.) lateral root development was stimulated (516-889 laterals/plant against 98 in the untreated controls).

An attempt was made to increase the number of plants by vegetative propagation. Normally only one bud, the apical, is present, and axillary buds in the leaves or scale leaves are not visibly differentiated. Only when an inflorescence has been initiated will two or three axillary buds develop and give rise to two to three shoots in the season after flowering. Because *Veratrum viride* flowers very rarely, it was decided to test several methods of decapitation and wounding to increase lateral bud development. It was soon found that any injury to the existing shoot either inhibits or eliminates growth of the next year's shoot without the production of more growing points. None of the regular methods used by tulip or hyacinth growers to increase their stocks were effective. It finally was found that when the growing point could be injured approximately one year before it developed into a leafy shoot axillary buds were produced.

After many trials to achieve this had failed, the following method was developed accomplishing injury or destruction of the very young apical growing point. Three solid steel needles of one millimeter in diameter with rounded tips were mounted parallel in horizontal position. These three were pushed side-ways into the corm at the height where the apical bud was expected and they were pushed slightly over half-way into the corm. In this way, usually one of the three needles came close enough to the growing point to prevent its further development. Yet, not enough injury was done to the other tissues to prevent growth of the current year's bud. In a good percentage of the corms thus treated, three to five buds developed which grew out approximately one year after the treatment.

In the first experiment non-dormant corms were received in spring and were planted immediately in the different greenhouses. At the highest temperatures growth was most rapid but the leaves started to wither after a few weeks, and the corms died. Only when the plants were grown at 20° day and 14°C night temperature or cooler did the corms survive. Therefore, the length of life of a *Veratrum* leaf is inversely proportional to the temperature and only in very cool climates are these plants able to keep their leaves long enough for further corm development.

After numerous tests it was found that corms, which were collected during or after the growing season of the tops, went into a deep dormancy which only could be broken by storage at 2°-4°C, whereas practically all corms stored at 6°C or higher rotted or remained dormant. In FIGURE 34 the relationship between length of storage at 2°C and the time of digging of the corms has been shown in as far as it influences growth. To this end, the number of millimeters the plants grew during the first month after removal from storage is plotted on the vertical axis. Those plants which grew slowly during the first month either stopped growing completely or grew only very slowly during the next month, and never developed normally. On the other hand, the plants which grew 150-200 mm. during the first month continued this growth in the next and developed into normal healthy plants. FIGURE 34 then shows that dormancy could only be broken completely when the corms were harvested late in the year when the tops were dying down. Whereas three months of storage was enough to break dormancy, five months was about optimal. The failure of the plants to develop which were dug early (July) is not due to lack of differentiation since the growing point has already fully formed the leaves and sheaths. It is, therefore, more a question of failure to break dormancy which is very deep in summer and decreases in autumn. Since *Veratrum viride* grows in localities where the ground is covered with snow most of the winter, its corms are subjected to a temperature near freezing for a 6-month period, which is exactly the requirement for their starting growth next season. As soon as the dormancy has been broken completely, the shoots start to develop even at 2°-4°C, and will elongate to 50 cm. long shoots in darkness, at a fairly rapid rate. It is likely that these shoots will grow even at 0°C, and thus they can penetrate a snow cover though at a slow rate, as is seen occasionally in nature.

Plants, collected in nature, developed well in the greenhouses during the first growth cycle after proper storage. In one group of plants, whose growth was followed for 6 successive cycles, growing them at 17° day and 12°C night temperature, and storing them for 6 months at 2°-4°C, caused a gradual increase in length for the next cycles. Whereas in the first cycle they became 51 cm. tall, in the third cycle the non-flowering plants became 60 cm. tall, the flowering ones 90 cm. and in the sixth cycle they

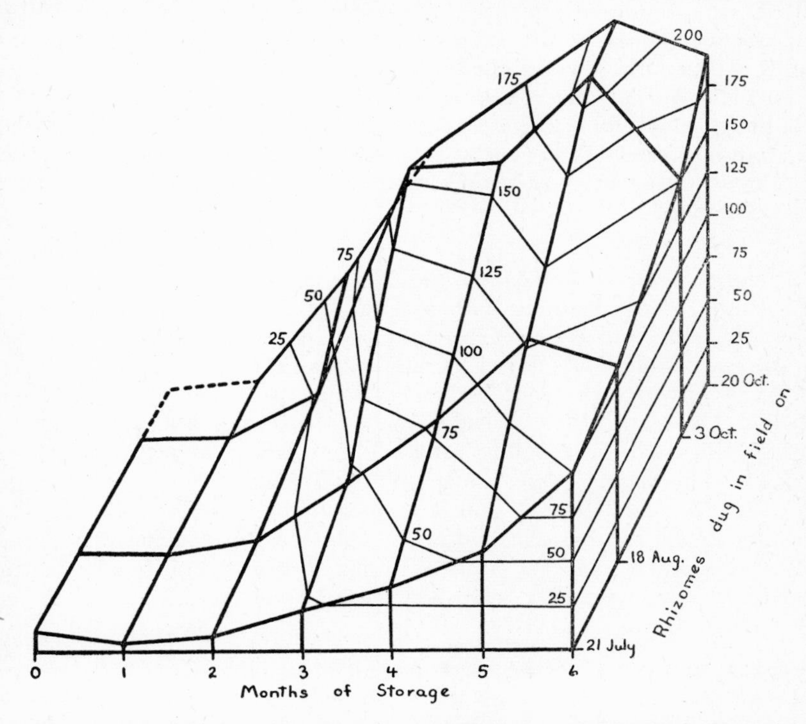

FIGURE 34.— Relationship between growth in first month after storage (*ordinate*), and length of storage at 2°C (*abscissa*) for *Veratrum viride* plants, dug from the field during (July 21 and August 18), and at the end of (October 3 and 20) growing season.

were 80 cm. These cycles do not need to coincide at all with the seasons, and we have had vigorous *Veratrum viride* plants growing at any month of the year.

Veratrum fimbriatum was largely investigated in the seedling stage. This plant grows near the coast in northern California, where its corms are never subjected to freezing temperatures. In this connection, it is interesting that storage at 6°C was as good as at 4°C, and that 2-3-month storage was optimal; both 1- and 5-month storage gave poorer growth. Optimal light intensity for the young plants was 700 ft.-c.; at 500, 900 and 1,200 ft.-c. the plants grew less vigorously. Different lengths of daily illumination (8, 12, 16 and 24-hour photoperiods) were about equally effective, except for the continuous light, in which the plants grew 20-40 per cent less. Another interesting observation was that young plants subjected to rain for 4 hours each night (and watered daily with nutrient solution), grew considerably better than when only watered with nutrient solution. Two groups without rain grew an average of 54 and 65 mm.; two groups with rain reached 86 and 96 mm.

Relatively few mature plants of *Veratrum fimbriatum* were grown; their behavior was similar to that of the seedlings. The inflorescences are very spectacular and the flowers last fairly long, which would make it an ideal house plant, except that it has to be treated just right between flowering.

Whereas of *V. fimbriatum* a large percentage of the plants flower each year, not more than 1 per cent of *V. viride* plants flower, and no treatment of storage, photoperiod or temperature was found which would increase this percentage.

Dicentra formosa:— A winter bud of this plant was accidentally brought into the Earhart Laboratory with a shipment of *Veratrum* from Virginia. After the same cold treatment as *Veratrum,* it grew and flowered in the coolest greenhouse (17° day, 12°C night temperature). After about half a year of growth, the plant became dormant as shown by dying of the leaves and the formation of a large number of resting bulbils in the axils of the basal leaves. These bulbils, which had a diameter of about 1 cm., were completely dormant. After storage at 4°, 7° and 10°C for 2-4 months, they came out of dormancy and developed normal plants as soon as they were brought to higher temperatures. Therefore, their behavior seems to be very much like that of *Veratrum* in that they also require a fairly long period at low temperatures before the dormancy of their bulbils is broken.

Alpine Annuals:— Some work was done on annuals of which seeds were collected at or near timberline in the Sierra Nevada Mountains of California. Most of these could not be germinated, but some, like *Linanthus ciliatus neglectus,* developed fairly well. At 26° or 30°C not a single one out of 1,100 seeds germinated; even if they had been only 3 days at those temperatures, there was no more germination. When kept at 23°C before being placed in the favorable temperatures of 10° or 17°C, only those left for 3 days at the high temperature germinated (2 out of 50), but none of the 150 left for 7, 14 or 28 days at that temperature developed. When left first at 4° or 7°C, 2.3 per cent germinated and when left at 10° or 17°C, 1.2 per cent germinated. This shows a predilection of the germination of this *Linanthus* for lower temperatures (17°C and below), especially when the actual germination temperature of 10° or 17°C is preceded by 4° or 7°C.

After germination these plants were placed in 4°, 10°, 14° and 17°C but only at 10°C they grew well and developed into plants considerably larger than those found in nature, probably because of the better water supply and more even temperature which remained near the optimum all the time. By subjecting them to long photoperiods they flowered abundantly and set viable seed. At 4°C growth was very slow, and at 14° and 17°C, they became etiolated and died before flowering.

Other alpine annuals which did germinate, but only at 10°C, were: *Collinsia parviflora, Gayophytum humile, Juncus bufonius, Hemizonella, Linanthus harknessii, Mimulus montioides* and *Phacelia eisenii,* each in only 1 or 2 specimens. Yet they grew excellently and flowered abundantly for many months at a 16-hour photoperiod.

Saxifraga bryophora:— This little plant is discussed because it reproduces with bulbils formed on the inflorescences. It is native in the Sierra Nevada of California and grows there at an altitude of about 3,000 m. Usually the rosettes are growing in groups together in moist places, each one sends up a raceme which is profusely branched and reaches a height of about 10 cm. The main axis, and sometimes one or two of the most vigorous lateral axes of the raceme are terminated by a perfect flower, but all other laterals develop bulbils which towards the end of the season drop off. Like bulbils of other plants, they behave in many respects as seeds and are effective in distribution of the species. Whereas the germination of seeds is usually inhibited by pre-existing vegetation, bulbils can develop within a dense plant cover. Thus, we often find that plants which propagate themselves with bulbils are the commonest annuals in an area with high rainfall. In Lapland (northern Sweden) *Polygonum viviparum, Poa alpina* and a few other grasses are all viviparous and are very common in the alpine vegetation there, where other annuals, like *Euphrasia minima* or *Koenigia islandica,* which propagate themselves with seed, are infrequent.

The behavior of the bulbils of *Saxifraga bryophora* has been studied under different temperature conditions. They were collected in 1951 and 1953 in the Sierra Nevada, and kept air-dry at ordinary room temperature. The 1951 bulbils were very much larger than the 1953 ones, and developed at constant 10°C and 16-hour photoperiod into nice big rosettes with normal inflorescences with terminal flowers and lateral bulbils. After two years storage at room temperature they had lost their viability. The 1953 bulbils were pre-treated in darkness with different temperatures (0°, 4°, 7° and 17°C) for different lengths of time (6 and 9 weeks), and then brought to 4°, 10° or 17°C in a 16-hour photoperiod at 1,000 ft.-c. They could not be kept too long in dark storage without losing viability. The results can be expressed very simply: after 0°C storage there was no germination at 4°C, but one plant grew at 10°C and several at 17°C. After 4°C storage, sprouting occurred at all 3 growing temperatures, but best at 10°C, whereas after 7° and 17°C storage best sprouting occurred at 4° growing temperature, and little or none at 17°C. For further growth of the sprouted bulbils, the optimum temperature was 10°; at 4°C there was only very slow growth, and at 17°C plants soon died.

Therefore, the temperature responses of *Saxifraga bryophora* explain its occurrence in the Sierra Nevada near timberline: at neither high nor very low temperatures will it grow.

Only the plants kept for two months at 4°C and then transferred to 10°C bolted and formed flowers and bulbils. Therefore, these bulbils seem to have a double low-temperature requirement: one to start growth after they have become dormant on the inflorescence, like the buds of peach trees, and another to make them bolt like beets and other biennial plants.

Mimosa pudica:— The sensitive plant has been tested for many years under a variety of conditions. It will grow well at a 26° photo- and 20°C nyctotemperature; it develops in artificial light of at least 500 ft.-c., and needs a dark period. If kept in continuous light, the leaves show extreme epinasty. Flowering takes place at 12-hour photoperiods and shorter, but poorly in long summer days.

The sensitivity of the plant for different stimuli varies according to its age and growing conditions. Young plants are most sensitive and a stimulus caused by burning will travel through the whole plant if it has not more than 10 leaves. In older plants the burning stimulus will not travel more than 1-2 leaves downward, and 5-6 leaves upward, except when it has recently been trimmed and has only young shoots sprouting from a woody base. Then the stimulus may still move through the whole plant, from branch to branch. The rate of movement of the stimulus is strongly dependent upon temperature. At 17°C it does not pass beyond the main pulvinus of the stimulated leaf. By plotting the rate of translocation of the burning stimulus, a direct proportionality is found with 15°C as the zero point. At 10° and 14°C the pulvini have become rigid and no stimuli, neither burning nor mechanical, can cause the slightest response. At 10°C the pulvinuli are also rigid, at 14°C these are still slightly reactive.

Whereas at those low temperatures the plants are unable to respond, they have perceived the stimulus, for when transferred to 26°C, after 40 seconds the pulvinuli start to respond, and after 1-2 minutes the pulvinus reacts, too.

Early in the morning, and also at low light intensity, downward transmission of the stimulus is more pronounced than later in the day in full sunlight. Under those conditions the stimulus moving up or down the main stem sometimes reaches the pulvinuli before the pulvinus reacts.

Also other sensitive plants were grown in the Earhart Laboratory. *Mimosa acanthocarpa* of which the seeds were collected near Medellín in Colombia, with multijugate pinnae, soon grew too big to be kept in the greenhouse (26° day and 20°C night temperature). These same temperatures were favorable for growth of the telegraph plant, *Desmodium gyrans,* which was germinated at even higher temperature. Whereas *Mimosa pu-*

dica was completely non-responsive at 10°C, the lateral leaflets of *Desmodium* continued, although very slowly, to move at 10°C. The terminal leaflets all placed themselves in the night position at that temperature. At 14° and 17°C the movements of the lateral leaflets were still very slow, but at 26°C they had a period of less than 2 minutes.

Insectivorous Plants:— Several *Nepenthes* plants were grown in the Earhart Laboratory. Although vegetative growth was very satisfactory, and inflorescences were formed from time to time, we never succeeded in having the plants produce pitchers. Only the first 1 or 2 leaves unfolding after introduction into the greenhouses developed small pitchers, but for the next 2 years none were produced, in spite of a variety of treatments: phototemperatures ranging from 23° to 30°C, nyctotemperatures between 17° and 26°C, short and long photoperiods, full sunlight or shade. In all cases the plants were watered with complete Hoagland solution; the possibility that the pitchers are formed in response to low nitrate concentrations was not investigated.

Drosera binata and *Drosera spathulata* grew excellently at a 23° photo- and 17° nyctotemperature, but developed slower at either lower or higher temperatures. They were planted in peat, and watered once with nutrient solution, and afterwards once weekly with de-ionized water. When their containers were placed in a pan with de-ionized water on the bottom, growth was less satisfactory and the plants remained much smaller.

We never succeeded in making plants of *Darlingtonia* grow, although they seemed to support the fumigation without damage. However, new leaf development was completely suspended at 23°C photo- and 17°C nyctotemperature. On the other hand, *Sarracenia* grows well under these conditions.

Chapter 14

CHAPARRAL PLANTS

by Henry Hellmers

Senior Research Fellow, California Institute of Technology, and Plant Physiologist, California Forest and Range Experiment Station, Berkeley, Calif.

The Problems:— Two problems related to the growing of vegetation for erosion control in the San Gabriel mountains of California, situated N.E. of Los Angeles, have been studied by the United States Forest Service in coöperation with the California Institute of Technology and the Los Angeles County Flood Control District. One problem was to find a plant or group of plants for use in sowing to obtain a protective cover on mountain slopes denuded by wildfire. The second problem was to find a plant or group of plants that could replace or supplement the native vegetation and thus better protect the soil on unburned slopes.

The San Gabriel mountains are very steep and geologically unstable, and consequently erosion rates normally are high (Sinclair 1954). The importance of improving the plant cover to reduce erosion in these mountains has been recognized for at least half a century. A report from the Office of Extension of the U.S. Forest Service on the subject of "Forest Conditions in Southern California," written in 1906, stated ". . . engineering works must be supplemented and reinforced by the protection and improvement of the forest and brush covers of the watersheds. . . ." Since the turn of the century the need for erosion control has been accentuated by several circumstances. First, the population on the outwash plains has grown approximately fifty-fold. Second, an extensive program of downstream channel and dam construction has been undertaken for flood control, and the capacities of these works must be protected by reducing the debris discharge from the mountains. Third, extensive fires occasionally occur, and the denuded slopes greatly increase the potential for flood and erosion damage. Fourth, most attempts to increase the density of the existing vegetative cover by planting trees or shrubs have failed.

The Environment:— The climate of the San Gabriel mountain area is classified as Mediterranean. The rainy season is mainly in the months from November through March; rarely does any rain fall in June, July, and August. Annual precipitation increases with elevation, from about 500 mm. at 300 m. altitude to 1000 mm. at 1800 m. Rainfall is erratic. During the past 75 years the annual total has ranged from less than one-half to more than twice the long-term average. Seasonal distribution of rain also varies greatly. Maximum monthly rainfall for the year has occurred in every month from October to April, and conversely, less than 0.4 mm. of rain has been recorded at least once for each of these months.

The days are warm, the nights are cool, and the diurnal variation in temperature is often large. Temperature data from a meteorological station at an elevation of 900 m. in the mountains (San Dimas Experimental Forest of the U.S. Forest Service) show that maximum day temperatures are about 40°C, whereas minimum day temperatures are at least 15°C. Minimum night temperatures have gone as low as −8°C. Diurnal differences of 10°C to 20°C are common, and a difference of as much as 28°C has been recorded.

The San Gabriel mountains are geologically young, with typically steep slopes. The crystalline metamorphic rocks of which the mountains are composed have been intensively faulted and fractured. The downcutting of streams undercuts the slopes, thus starting waves of erosion that progress up the mountain sides. Since a majority of the slopes are at or exceed the angle of repose, gravity is an active eroding force. These conditions of instability lead to average annual erosion rates in excess of 400 $m.^3$ per $Km.^2$ Removal of the vegetative cover by fire or other means accelerates the already high erosion rates to as much as 40,000 $m.^3$ per $Km.^2$

The soils on the steeper slopes are shallow, sandy, and immature. Fertility levels, particularly of nitrogen, are low. In most places the surface soil erodes too rapidly for organic material to accumulate or soil horizons to develop. Because of their depth and texture, these soils have a low water holding capacity. The underlying fractured rock supplies water to the roots of some plants but holds even less moisture per unit of depth than the soils. Therefore, once the rainy season ends, soil moisture available to plants is quickly depleted, and plant growth usually ceases by early June.

The plants on the mountain slopes are primarily evergreen sclerophyllous shrubs, collectively termed chaparral. Over much of the area, and especially on south slopes, the plants are widely spaced and the crowns do not form a closed canopy. All the shrubby species have an extensive root system and are drought resistant. During the dry season the chaparral is very inflammable and fire hazards are exceedingly high. Most of the species sprout after burning, and fire stimulates seed germination of some of them (WENT *et al.* 1952).

Cover for Burned Areas:— Plants useful for sowing after fires are required to form only a temporary cover on the denuded mountain slopes because the native shrubs occupy the area again within 5 or 10 years. The objective of sowing is to obtain a protective cover early in the first rainy season after the fire and until the native shrubs return. Therefore, the species used must germinate and grow quickly. Also, they should persist over the summer to provide protection to the soil at the start of succeeding rainy seasons. Furthermore, the irregularity of the annual rainfall pattern in fall, winter, and spring necessitates the use of species that can germinate and grow under a wide range of temperatures.

Black mustard has been recommended and used for sowing on burns in southern California for more than 20 years (GLEASON 1944). The recommendation was based on field trials with many species which showed that black mustard consistently produced the best cover. In large scale field sowings, however, the cover produced by mustard the first year has varied from excellent to practically none. Consequently other species were sought. In January 1952, for example, a burn was sown to a mixture of Italian ryegrass, perennial ryegrass, smilo, rose clover, and California com-

TABLE 11: *Germination response of grasses and forbs to southern California seasonal temperature and conditions**:—

GERMINATED UNIFORMLY WELL AT ALL SEASONAL TEMPERATURES**:—

Crested wheatgrass — *Agropyron cristatum* (L.) Gaertn.
Black mustard — *Brassica nigra* Koch.
Soft chess — *Bromus mollis* L.
Ripgut grass — *Bromus rigidus* Roth.
Harlan brome — *Bromus stamineus* Desv.
Orchard grass — *Dactylis glomerata* L.***
Russian wild-rye — *Elymus junceus*
Italian ryegrass — *Lolium multiflorum* Lam.
Perennial ryegrass — *Lolium perenne* L.
California common alfalfa — *Medicago sativa* L.
Rose clover — *Trifolium hirtum* All.

GERMINATED BEST AT HIGH (SUMMER) TEMPERATURES:—

Orchard grass (very late strain) — *Dactylis glomerata* L.***
Beardless wild-rye — *Elymus triticoides* Buckl.
Bush muhly — *Muhlenbergia porteri* Scribn.
Smilo — *Oryzopsis miliacea* (L.) Benth. and Hook. ex Aschers. and Schweinf.
Mediterranean grass — *Schismus barbatus* (L.) Thell.

GERMINATED BEST AT MODERATE (SPRING AND FALL) TEMPERATURES:—

Perennial veldtgrass — *Ehrharta calycina* J. E. Smith.
Small-flowered melicgrass — *Melica imperfecta* Trin.
Fine bluegrass — *Poa scabrella* (Thurb.) Benth. ex Vasey.***

GERMINATED BEST AT LOW (WINTER) TEMPERATURES:—

Mountain brome — *Bromus marginatus* Nees.
Red bromegrass — *Bromus rubens* L.
Fine bluegrass — *Poa scabrella* (Thurb.) Benth. ex Vasey.***

* Germination during 4 weeks (6 weeks for smilo) based upon 100 seeds per test. All tests were conducted under an 8 hour day and a 16 hour night. Source: ASHBY and HELLMERS (1955).
** Summer: 30°C. day and 17°C. night. — Spring and fall: 23°C. day and 10°C. night. — Winter: 17°C. day and 4°C. night.
*** Different seed sources.

mon alfalfa. This sowing failed to produce a cover crop sufficient to protect the soil. These results suggested that a laboratory study was needed to select species possessing the best chance for success in field sowings, and a study was undertaken in the Earhart Plant Research Laboratory.

As a first step, 20 species of grasses and forbs were tested for their germination response to temperature. Temperature conditions in the Earhart

Plant Research Laboratory corresponding to local seasonal temperatures in the mountains at an elevation of 900 m. were used in conducting the tests (ASHBY and HELLMERS 1955). Eleven of the 20 species germinated rapidly at all seasonal temperatures. These species were physiologically suitable for field use. The other species were favored by or required high or moderate or low temperatures to germinate rapidly (TABLE 11), and, therefore, were not suitable.

Of species used in previous burned-area sowings all but smilo (*Oryzopsis*) germinated well at all seasonal temperatures. Therefore, except for smilo, something other than the temperature effect must have been responsible for sowing failures. A 6-week dry period that followed a month of heavy rainfall was one of the factors contributing to the failure of the 1952 sowing. Field examinations in this instance showed a high percentage of germination of all species, except smilo, but a low percentage of plant survival. Probably most of the failures with mustard sowings in other years were also related to the rainfall pattern following seeding.

The second step in selecting species, from the 11 favorable species, was based on seed availability and cost rather than plant physiology. Because the time and size of wildfires cannot be predicted, it is necessary to have available from commercial sources a large supply of fresh and reasonably priced seed. Only two of the suitable species, Italian ryegrass and black mustard, met this requirement. Ryegrass is used extensively in pastures and lawns in southern California, and mustard is used as a cover crop in many citrus orchards. Seed of both species is available on short notice in amounts up to 25,000 Kg. at low cost.

There are advantages in using these two species in a mixture for burned area sowing. These advantages result from the different characteristics of the individual species. Mustard plants grow rapidly and have basal leaves that cover a relatively large area of soil per plant; however, the leaves wither and drop as the plant matures. Ryegrass plants, on the other hand, provide relatively little soil cover per plant in their early stages of growth but furnish better soil protection than the mustard by the time the latter loses its leaves. Also, the ryegrass leaves stay attached to the root through the dry season and furnish soil protection at the start of the second year's rainy season. Therefore the two species sown together provide better soil protection than either species sown alone.

The third step was a test of compatibility of the two species. EVENARI (1949) reported that black mustard seed contained a germination inhibitor and WENT *et al.* (1952) found evidence that mustard inhibits the germination of seeds of some shrub species native to the San Gabriel mountains. Germination tests with mixtures of ryegrass and mustard seeds sown together showed that both species germinated simultaneously under all temperatures studied and that no inhibition of either was evident.

The fourth and final step was to test the growth characteristics of mustard and ryegrass under local seasonal temperatures. For this test the range of temperatures used in the laboratory was extended beyond those used in screening the original 20 species for germination. Eight combinations of day and night temperatures were used. These combinations consisted of a day temperature of 23°C with night temperatures of 4°C, 10°C, 17°C and 26°C; and day temperatures of 30°C and 17°C with night temperatures of 4°C and 17°C. The results showed that both species grew rapidly under the entire range of temperatures.

Since the completion of these studies, a mixture of annual ryegrass and mustard has been sown on more than 20,000 Ha. of burned-over watersheds. Although most of the sowings have produced a good cover, at least one sowing and parts of others failed because of dry weather after germination. Thus, though successful establishment depends on the distribution of rainfall, the presently recommended two-species mixture offers the highest probability for success.

Possibilities remain of improving the sowing mixture, as seeds of other grass species and hybrids become available in commercial quantities. The Earhart Plant Research Laboratory and similar installations provide facilities for rapidly and accurately testing these new species for their adaptability to field use.

Cover for Rapidly Eroding Slopes:— The vegetation on the rapidly eroding, unburned, steep slopes of the San Gabriel mountains is composed mostly of shrubs. The plants are widely spaced and upright in form, allowing soil to be moved by water and gravity in the spaces between them and even under their crowns. The present cover on these slopes does not protect the soil adequately against movement.

Plants which would increase soil stability under the existing severe site conditions should have certain characteristics. They should grow rapidly in winter and early spring when soil moisture is available. They must be able to withstand the summer drought. They should be prostrate to cover the maximum area for the growth achieved, and they should root at the nodes to bind the plant and soil in place. Because low soil fertility is caused primarily by nitrogen deficiency, nitrogen fixing species would be desirable. The lack of native plants with desirable form and rooting characteristics made it necessary to look for exotic species to supplement or replace the native shrubs on these critical slopes.

Some promising exotic species were selected from descriptions found in reference literature and from examinations of exotic plants in local botanical gardens, parks, and estates. Others were recommended by botanists and ecologists in some 15 different areas of the world which possess a Mediterranean type climate. Altogether, between 75 and 100 species were to be tested for their ability to grow under southern California mountain conditions.

Field testing would be costly. The Los Angeles River Watershed covers an altitudinal range of more than 2000 m. Therefore, a series of plant nurseries would be required at various altitudes and exposures. Also, each species would have to be planted repeatedly in each nursery over a 5- to 10-

year period to sample adequately the yearly variability in rainfall and temperature.

To avoid the high cost of such an undertaking, it was decided to screen the plants in the laboratory for their ability to grow under local temperature conditions. This could be done rapidly and economically by using a range of temperature conditions in the Earhart Plant Research Laboratory that corresponded to the average and extreme conditions in the mountains. Only those species that passed the temperature screening would have to be field tested for their ability to withstand the summer drought.

Native species were included in the study so that the laboratory results could be checked against the growth of these species in the field. Plants of each species were grown under the test conditions for a 6-month period after they had been well established from seed under uniform growing conditions. Plant growth responses to temperature were appraised in terms of dry weight of the tops at the end of the test. The results of the tests, both with native and exotic plants, brought out striking differences in the growth capabilities of the several species. Detailed results obtained for 8 native species and 21 exotic species are being prepared for publication. The results obtained for four species will be used here to illustrate the findings.

The variation in growth within and between the four species is shown in FIGURE 35. Eight combinations of day and night temperatures were used, with an 8-hour photoperiod, and local seasonal temperatures were represented by the averages for the 900 m. elevation. Temperature differences due to altitudinal and exposure differences would be less than the seasonal differences and are encompassed within the temperatures used, except that the winters at high altitudes were not represented.

Chamise, *Adenostoma fasciculatum* H. & A., is the most prevalent native shrub in the southern California chaparral. This plant grew well under the cool and moderate temperature conditions that exist in the local mountains when soil moisture is available. Cold and hot days and warm nights retarded its growth.

Prostrate coyote-brush, *Baccharis pilularis* ssp. *typica* (DC.) C. B. Wolf, is from the coastal region of central California. Plants of this species grew relatively well over a wide range of temperatures, including those of summer. They exceeded the growth rate of chamise over the entire range of temperatures studied. Coyote-brush grew best under slightly warmer days or nights than occur in the average local winter. Optimum temperatures do occur, however, during the period in which soil moisture is available for plant growth. This plant, because of its prostrate form and its good temperature-growth relation, holds great promise for introduction as an erosion control plant in the San Gabriel mountains.

Coral gem, *Lotus bertholetii* Maf., is a prostrate legume from the Cape Verde Islands and the Canary Islands. Plants of this species, like those of the prostrate coyote-brush, grew best under slightly warmer days and nights than the local average winter conditions, but the plant's growth rate

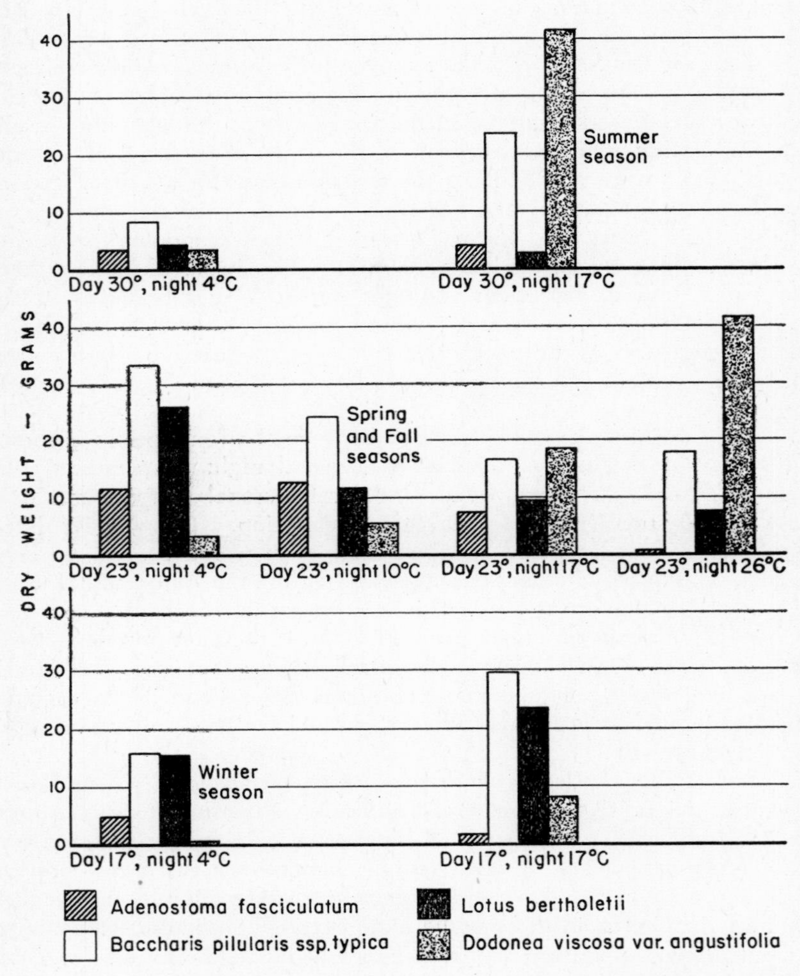

FIGURE 35.— Top growth of 4 plant species grown for 6 months under 8 different combinations of day and night temperatures. Experiments of HELLMERS and ASHBY.

was markedly depressed by high day temperatures. At high day temperatures the plants grew spindly and soon lost their leaves. Although not adapted to as wide a temperature range as coyote-brush, coral gem possibly could be used to advantage on the cooler North-facing slopes of the San Gabriel mountains.

Hopbush, *Dodonea viscosa* var. *angustifolia* L., is native to Arizona. This plant was included in the test because of its ability to grow rapidly on very steep dry sites in a region of lower rainfall than that of the San Gabriel mountains. In this test the plant required high temperatures to grow, which accounts for its rapid growth in Arizona where much of the annual rainfall occurs in the summer months. Hopbush has to be ruled out for introduction into the San Gabriel mountains because it did not grow well under the temperatures that exist locally when soil moisture is available.

In addition to prostrate coyote-brush and coral gem, two other exotic species grew relatively well under local temperature and soil moisture conditions. They are *Calycotome villosa* (Link.) from the eastern Mediterranean region, and Spanish broom, *Spartium junceum* (L.), from Spain. These four most promising exotic species were outplanted in 1954 to test their ability to withstand the long summer drought and to grow on rapidly eroding sites. Previous field plantings of Spanish broom in the San Gabriel mountains have provided evidence that this species can grow on disturbed soils, as on road fills, in the absence of competition from native shrubs.

Seeds of approximately 30 exotic species are on hand and will be tested in the laboratory as soon as possible. Seeds of additional species are being received through the continued coöperation of botanists and ecologists in other parts of the world.

Conclusions:— Sufficient information has been obtained to allow an evaluation of the usefulness of the Earhart Plant Research Laboratory in solving certain field problems. The laboratory results have two advantages over any results that would have been obtained by direct field testing. First, the laboratory results show not only that certain species cannot grow in the San Gabriel mountains, but also why they cannot grow there. Second, the laboratory results have greatly reduced the time and cost of selecting the best plants to use either for quick soil protection after a fire or to replace or supplement the native vegetation on rapidly eroding slopes. The time required to test the growth response of a species to the wide range of temperatures that occurs in the field was reduced from a period of 5 to 10 years or longer, depending on the weather fluctuations, to less than 1 year. The number of species to be field tested for drought resistance was reduced by more than 80 per cent.

PART III

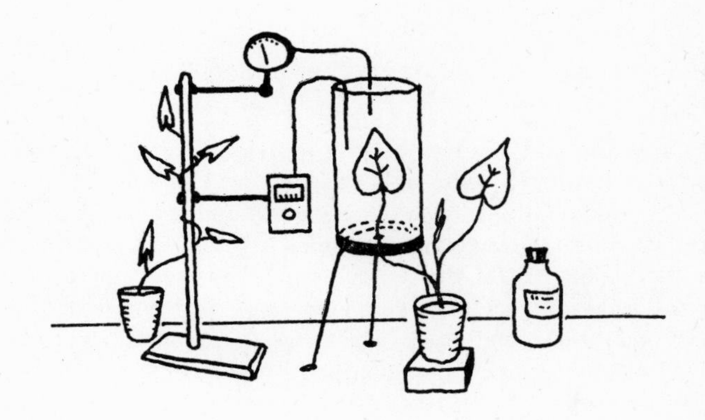

GENERAL DISCUSSION

Introduction:— Whereas in the previous section the specialized responses of individual species and varieties were described, in the following chapters the general information obtained in the Clark greenhouses and the Earhart Plant Research Laboratory will be discussed. The previous section could be called the autecology of some important experimental plants; the following section deals with general physiological problems, and with ecology and climatology as far as plants are concerned. Again it should be stressed, that the multiplicity of subjects precludes an adequate literature coverage. Since this book is a record of experimental work in these new air-conditioned greenhouses, it seems justifiable to mention only those facts and conclusions which were forced upon the investigators in these greenhouses in the course of their own work; their evaluation in connection with our vast body of accumulated knowledge will have to be left to a more monographic treatment.

Chapter 15

GENOTYPIC AND PHENOTYPIC VARIABILITY

Variability of Experimental Material:— Among the most important subjects studied in the Earhart Plant Research Laboratory is biological variability. Remarkably few investigations in the field of Botany have been directed towards an analysis of the basic reasons for variability. In almost every biological investigation the spectre of excessive variability rears its ugly head, and this often limits the extent to which conclusions can be drawn. To cope with variability three approaches are possible: (*1*) elaborate statistical treatment of the results to analyze the limits within which they can be considered reliable, (2) arrangement of the experimental lay-out in such a manner that systematic errors can be avoided or accounted for, or (3) reduction of the variability.

In the following paragraphs the statistical or post-facto approach will not be discussed: this is adequately treated in many books. It does not give us a better insight into the functioning of a plant nor into the reasons for variability. Therefore, this chapter will be mainly an analysis of the problem of biological variability itself, as a basis for reducing it in experimental work with plants. In view of the practical and fundamental importance of biological variability it is surprising how little work has been done to find the basis for it, and how the overwhelming majority of investigators acquiesce in an often shaky statistical security or near-security. Men like GALTON and JOHANNSEN performed a signal service to biology in analyzing variability and establishing the degree to which it is a function of heredity and environment. The genetical background of variability is now either well understood or is under investigation (MATHER 1949), but its dependence upon environment has either been neglected or has been made a political issue by the LYSENKO controversy. That this controversy could develop at all is at least partly due to a lack of experimentally sound evidence as to the effects of environment on organisms, and this in turn was due to the technical difficulties involved in experimentation on the effects of environmental factors on the growing plant. Since it is now possible in the Earhart Laboratory to control the environment to a degree not heretofore achieved, the effects of environment on variability and the level below which variability can not be decreased can now be discussed. This subject has been treated in somewhat greater detail elsewhere (WENT 1955*c*).

In any biological material we find a certain amount of variability. The significance of experimental results based on differences between parallel groups depends on the *variability* within a group in relation to the observed difference between groups. In addition we have another factor, *reproducibility,* which cannot be deduced from the variability within one experiment, and which is of paramount importance in the evaluation of results. Both variability and reproducibility are improved in the Earhart Laboratory.

If all factors which influence a process were under experimental control, complete reproducibility could be expected. But we cannot be sure that all variables are under control. When light intensity plays a role, differences in response may be expected from summer to winter when natural daylight is used. Or, when atmospheric pollution influences plants, results may differ from day to day. By controlling in the Earhart Laboratory temperature, humidity, light duration, light quality and light intensity (in the artificial light rooms), rate of air movement, previous growing conditions, nutrition, water supply, root medium and atmospheric pollutants (through smog filters), reproducibility has reached its highest attainable degree. Yet, we do not know whether or not other variables exist which we have not controlled as yet. Therefore, even though everything conceivable has been done in the Earhart Laboratory to achieve absolute reproducibility, it still is advisable to repeat experiments occasionally. In most cases, quantitatively the same results were obtained. TABLE 12 clearly shows the degree to which reproducibility of experiments is improved when plants have been grown in the Earhart Laboratory.

Variability of experimental material depends upon (*1*) genetic differences between plants, (2) uniformity of growing conditions, (3) proximity to the optimum conditions, and (*4*) innate variability, of which the source lies in the discontinuity of matter, such as is considered in quantum mechanics.

Genotypic Variability:— In most investigations in the Earhart Laboratory, the genetic variability is controlled by using the best selected varieties available. There is considerable difference in the genetic purity of seeds of different plants. Because of its usual self-fertilization, pea seed derived from single-seed selections within a uniform well-established variety is genetically among the most uniform material available. This genetic uniformity is accentuated in the Earhart Laboratory, where insect pollination is eliminated. Yet, more than genetic uniformity is required to get reproducible seed material. The experiments of Dr. H. HIGHKIN have shown that the growing conditions of the previous generation will affect the development of genetically identical pea plants. Therefore, to obtain the highest degree of reproducibility and uniformity we must not only control the growing conditions of the plants under investigation, but also the growing conditions of the parent generation.

Whenever available, genetically uniform seed material was used in our experiments. It is gratifying to note how genetically uniform most commercially available strains of tomato, tobacco and other plants are, especially for growth and yield characters (*see, e.g.,* PLATE XX). Sugar beets, on the other hand, are very variable and have to be used in fairly large numbers to obtain statistically significant results. The same thing is true of corn unless inbred strains are used. In the greenhouse these inbreds are preferable to hybrid corn, not only because of their greater genetic uniformity, but also because of their more manageable size. Clones — plants vegetatively reproduced from a single individual — are perhaps most desirable for experiments, but are not available in the case of many annual plants. In the Earhart Laboratory strawberries, potatoes, *Cymbidium lowianum, Cattleya trianae, Saintpaulia,* carnations, grasses and many other

TABLE 12: *Height of warts in mm. in the Wehnelt bean test for traumatin activity. Individual tests carried out on different days with 11-12 beans, each time using a standard solution (5mg./cc) and half strength (2.5mg./cc). All values are given with their standard error, and for each value the coefficient of variability (standard deviation as per cent of average) is calculated. In addition the coefficient of proportionality (standard error of proportion in wart height between the two test solutions as percentage of the average proportion) and the coefficient of reproducibility (coefficient of variability when comparing individual tests) are shown in the last two columns.* Data of D. VIGLIERCHIO:—

	Standard solution		*½ Strength solution*				
NO. OF TEST	AVERAGE HEIGHT OF WART	COEFF. OF VARIABILITY	AVERAGE HEIGHT OF WART	COEFF. OF VARIABILITY	PROPORTION BETWEEN FULL AND ½ STRENGTH SOLUTION	COEFF. OF PROPORTIONALITY	COEFF. OF REPRODUCIBILITY
1*	0.71 ± 0.039	18	0.61 ± 0.022	12	86		
2	0.46 ± 0.026	19	0.39 ± 0.041	35	85		
3	0.65 ± 0.046	23	0.54 ± 0.046	25	83		
4	0.71 ± 0.023	11	0.60 ± 0.032	18	84		
5	0.77 ± 0.048	22	0.52 ± 0.040	23	68		
6	0.73 ± 0.035	16	0.63 ± 0.029	15	86		
7	0.81 ± 0.035	14	0.67 ± 0.027	13	83		
8	0.78 ± 0.041	17	0.52 ± 0.031	19	67		
9	0.74 ± 0.036	15	0.51 ± 0.024	15	69		
10	0.78 ± 0.030	13	0.58 ± 0.037	21	74		
Average	0.714	16.8	0.557	19.6	78.5	9.8	13.3
11**	0.95 ± 0.027	9	0.77 ± 0.021	9	81		
12	0.95 ± 0.022	8	0.78 ± 0.025	10	82		
13	0.97 ± 0.017	6	0.78 ± 0.018	7	81		
14	0.95 ± 0.021	7	0.76 ± 0.019	8	80		
Average	0.955	7.5	0.772	8.8	81.0	0.9	0.9
15***	0.86 ± 0.026	10	0.68 ± 0.022	10	79		
16	0.87 ± 0.031	9	0.67 ± 0.019	8	77		
17	0.86 ± 0.022	8	0.67 ± 0.022	10	78		
Average	0.863	9.0	0.673	9.3	78.0	1.1	0.7

* Tests 1-10: Commercial variety, grown out-of-doors.
** Tests 11-14: Oregon Giant, grown in Earhart Laboratory 20° day, 14° night.
*** Tests 15-17: Morse's 191, grown in Earhart Laboratory 20° day, 14° night.

plants are propagated vegetatively and are available in the form of clones for experiments.

Phenotypic Variability:— After reducing the genotypic variability to a minimum by means such as mentioned in the previous paragraph, the phenotypic variability is usually accepted as inevitable. Yet, observations in the Earhart Laboratory (WENT 1953*b*) have shown that most of the phenotypic variability under ordinary growing conditions can be eliminated by more rigorous control over the growing conditions, or in other words, genotypic uniformity can be translated into phenotypic uniformity by subjecting all plants to exactly the same conditions of temperature, light, air movement, watering and nutrition, as closely as possible to their optimal growing conditions. In this way, the coefficient of variability is reduced so much that significant results can be obtained with far fewer plants, or that much smaller differences can be detected. In TABLE 12 the coefficient of variability of different batches of beans as far as their response to traumatin is concerned is shown, together with the reproducibility from test to test. These data were collected by VIGLIERCHIO (1955) in the course of an investigation of the components of traumatin (*see* BONNER and ENGLISH 1938). For this test almost ripe pods of string beans are used. A drop of each solution to be tested is placed in a seed chamber of the longitudinally split pods, using one seed chamber of each pod for one solution. After two days a wart is produced in the seed chamber where the drop touched the cells, and the height of the wart is a measure of the activity of the solution and the reactivity of the cells. In TABLE 12 only data are given for the response to a standard solution and the same solution diluted to one-half. The coefficient of variability refers to the differences between pods in individual tests, of which each was carried out on a different day with a different batch of beans. The coefficient of reproducibility refers to the variability between tests carried out on different days. The coefficient of proportionality refers to the variability in relative activity of the two dilutions of the standard source of traumatin.

As far as the variability is concerned, it can be seen in TABLE 12 that for the beans grown in the Earhart Laboratory this is less than half when compared with beans grown out-of-doors. The same decrease in variability to about one-half was found for tomato plants grown in air-conditioned greenhouses, in comparison with plants of the same variety grown in an ordinary greenhouse (WENT 1953*b*), and also for the variability of the plasmolytic concentration of the cell sap in individual cells of the epidermis of *Rhoeo discolor*. This was half as great for plants grown in the Earhart greenhouses as for plants in an ordinary greenhouse (WENT 1955*c*). Therefore, the uniformity of cells, organs and whole plants is about twice as great when plants are grown at controlled temperatures.

Reproducibility has been increased much more, about ten-fold according to TABLE 12, when the experimental material was grown under controlled conditions. The same conclusion was drawn earlier with respect to tomato stem elongation rates (WENT 1944*a*) and with respect to the Avena and pea tests, when the test plants were grown in the Earhart Laboratory at the exclusion of smog (WENT 1955*c*). The same was experienced with almost all other plants investigated in the Earhart Plant Research Laboratory. Therefore it can be stated quite generally, that reproducibility of test plants and of experimental results is increased several-fold, and variability is reduced to less than half in plants grown with ordinary air-conditioning in greenhouses. From the fact that reproducibility is improved relatively more than variability we can draw the conclusion that a greater proportion of phenotypic variability is due to uncontrolled temperatures and variable smog conditions than to any other external variables.

The greatly increased consistency, not only in individual tests, but also in the proportionality in response to various concentrations of a standard test solution, leaves no doubt that air-conditioning of all rooms used for biological testing is not only desirable, but economically advantageous because of the greatly increased statistical significance of results.

Considering the actual variability found in groups of plants grown under standard conditions in the Earhart Plant Research Laboratory, it becomes possible to calculate the number of plants required to obtain statistically significant results. Uniformity is acquired by *1*) using genetically uniform plants, and 2) pre-selecting plants of uniform size and development for each experimental group. To this end, usually three to four times as many seeds are germinated as needed in the experiment, and 50 per cent more are planted, so that upon the beginning of an experiment the smallest and tallest and abnormal plants can be discarded, leaving a really uniform set of experimental plants.

The differences in growth and development in response to the temperature and light treatments in the Earhart Laboratory are usually so large that the number of experimental plants per group can be reduced to a minimum of about four. The growth of these four plants is so uniform that the size of any one of the four is outside the size range of four plants from any other treatment. This can be seen in PLATES X*a* and X*b*, where the four tomato plants of each group have been photographed together on their truck. It also can be deduced from the homogeneity of the three-dimensional graphs of FIGURES 18 and 19, where each point is the average weight of four plants only.

If, occasionally, one plant lags behind in growth, it can be excluded from the average, since in most cases it is due to injury. In this way determinations of the growth response, instead of being complex statistical problems, resolve themselves into determinations in triplicate or quadruplicate, and thus resemble chemical determinations, where usually the sampling and analytical errors are much smaller than the differences sought.

This decrease in the variability has not only the advantage of increasing precision, but at the same time it simplifies experiments. Fewer plants are needed, and thus the investigator can carry out more experiments and needs less space. Although the costs of providing for and maintaining the space in air-conditioned greenhouses and artificial light rooms are considerably more than those for ordinary greenhouses, the increased efficiency of the research worker and the decrease in needed working space more than offset these higher costs. In addition, the improved reproducibility reduces the number of times an experiment has to be repeated. Therefore, the time of the investigator is used more efficiently, and the results are more significant.

When the genotypic variability of the experimental material is great, statistical analysis will have to show the size of each experiment to obtain the required significance. In such cases it is advisable to use each plant as its own control, and study the change in growth rate or other process by subjecting the same plant to a series of different conditions.

Selection and Variability:— Another device to decrease the experimental error is pre-selection. Instead of selecting the groups of experimental plants at random, the containers with plants for one experiment are lined up in order of their estimated weight. Except when all plants are *very* even in size and appearance, such as shown in PLATE XX, a strong correlation between estimated and actual weight exists. It is then possible to make groups of experimental plants of which the average weight differs much less from the average than random selection would allow. This allows in fairly uniform material elimination of 50-70 per cent of the variability between groups. If 10 experimental groups of 10 containers each have to be selected, numbers 1, 11, 21, etc. of the lined-up containers are used for the first group; numbers 2, 12, 22, etc. for the second, and so on.

Furthermore, it is advisable to start many more plants than will be used in a single experiment. The smallest and tallest plants can then be eliminated before the beginning of the actual experimental treatments. In this way, plants with differing growth potentials, as far as these are already expressed in the early stages of development, will not cause inequalities in the results. When the experimental plants are not genetically uniform, great care should be taken not only to use enough plants to get significant results, but also to keep the plants under uniform conditions during the whole growing period preceding the actual experiment. Otherwise, selection of different genetic types could occur. Even in genetically uniform material different degrees of induction may take place, making the material physiologically inhomogeneous.

As an example of the effects of pre-treatment on later development the following experiment is described. Sugar beet seeds of a variable strain, US 22/3, were sown in 5 different temperatures (7°, 10°, 17°, 23° and 30°C) in a 16-hour photoperiod. At the lowest temperature the seeds were sown three weeks, and at 10° and 17°C two and one week earlier than those at 23° and 30°C. In this way, the plants were all about the same size when the experiment was started. The largest plants were selected from the seedling flats (about 5 times more seedlings had developed than were necessary) and were transplanted into cups with vermiculite. The question was, whether the plants thus selected would behave differentially under different growing conditions.

On April 15, 1954, these beet plants were divided into 3 groups and placed in the Red, Yellow and Purple greenhouses (30°-23°C, 23°-17°C and 17°-12°C respectively). It was then found that the plants in the warmest greenhouse had formed more leaves when they had been germinated at 17°C, in the medium greenhouse when they came from 10°C, and in the coolest greenhouse they had more leaves when they came from a 7°C germination temperature. The beet weights were quite variable as usual in this variety (expressed as the coefficient of variability in the following data), but the beets which germinated at 7°C were least variable in the coolest (17°-12°C) greenhouse (20 against 30 and 40 per cent variability), those coming from 10° and 17°C were least variable in the 23°-17°C greenhouse (25 and 20 per cent against 30, 40, 45 and 50 per cent), and those germinated at 23° and 30°C were least variable in the warmest (30°-23°C) greenhouse (35 and 40 per cent against 55, 55, 65 and 70 per cent). This can be seen from PLATE XXI, where on the left-hand side the beets which grew in the moderate greenhouse, and on the right-hand side those in the cool greenhouse are shown (12 plants per group). Those germinated at 7°C did better than the others and were more consistently well developed in the cool greenhouse; in the moderate greenhouse the heaviest and most uniform beets came from the 17°C germination temperature. Since in each group the heaviest beets had about the same weight regardless of germination temperature, the pre-treatments, as such, apparently had no influence on later development, but different populations had been selected from the seedling flats. In the cool greenhouse the plants selected from the coldest germination conditions did best; in the moderate greenhouse the plants which germinated at intermediate temperatures did best, whereas those coming from the warmest germination conditions developed most uniformly in the warm greenhouse. Beet plants not specially selected in the seedling stage are very variable, as the data of ULRICH (1952) show, in which an overall coefficient of variability of sugar beet root weight of 48.1 per cent was found for the same variety (US 22/3) in experiments in the Earhart Laboratory which had 20-25 per cent variability under pre-selection conditions. This shows that by using pre-selection this coefficient of variability was cut to less than half.

Not only the variability between sister plants decreases as the environment is better controlled, but also the variability within a single individual decreases. This was found in determining the percentage of plasmolyzed cells in strips of the lower epidermis of leaves of *Rhoeo discolor*. By placing these strips in a series of sugar solutions at 0.01 molar intervals, it was found that the coefficient of variability was only 4.6, 3.9 and 3.6 for the leaf cells under the midrib of plants grown in the Earhart greenhouses, whereas the coefficient of variability was 10.0 for similar cells from leaves grown in a greenhouse without precise temperature control, but with smog eliminators.

Chapter 16

ANALYSIS OF GROWTH

This term usually refers to a mathematical analysis of the variation in size, weight, or dry matter of organisms as a function of time and growing conditions. In this chapter it will not only be used in this sense, but also for a physiological analysis of the factors which control and limit growth in a plant. It is quite obvious that the accurate determination of the growth characteristics of so many plants must have produced a vast amount of data which can be used to check existing theories and formulate the growth process in an exact manner.

Mathematical Analysis of Growth:— The simplest case of growth is provided by unicellular organisms, where the experimental conditions can be arranged so that the individual cells do not exert any direct influences on each other (in greater dilution), or, using a chemostat, the mutual influence can be kept constant. For such unicellular organisms, as bacteria and yeasts, we can distinguish between an initial lag-phase, after which the growth rate becomes exponential, which is usually called the phase of logarithmic growth. During that period the population is doubled per generation time.

The length of this logarithmic phase depends on the volume of culture medium, the concentration of nutrients and many other extraneous factors. When through growth the nutrient concentration decreases, or when inhibitory metabolic products start to accumulate in the medium the population will not increase exponentially any more until ultimately the culture becomes stationary. For such a bacterial or yeast culture the complete growth from beginning to end can be expressed as a sigmoid curve. In any formula for the intrinsic growth rate of these organisms only the lag and exponential or logarithmic phases should be considered; the final size of the culture only depends on experimental limitations imposed by size of culture vessel and nutrient concentration.

When we follow the growth of any multicellular organism, then we see that it follows the same general pattern as a population of unicellular organisms. In the great majority of cases the sigmoid curve is not smooth, but shows more or less marked slow-downs, such as caused by periods of dormancy, flower initiation, opening of flowers, interruption of growth at seed stage, etc. In exceptional cases a more or less smooth sigmoid curve for growth occurs (such as published by ROBERTSON 1923). These exceptional cases have been compared with the curves obtained for a monomolecular autocatalytic reaction, for which the following formula holds:

$$\frac{dx}{dt} = k \cdot x\,(a - x)$$

in which *a* is the final size to be attained and *x* the size at time *t*. In most discussions about the applicability of this formula only those growth curves were reproduced which fitted the formula best. Yet, in not a single case is the fit between growth curve and the curve for the above formula really close, particularly at the early and late stages of growth, where deviations of over 50 per cent may occur. This is to be expected for many reasons:

1) In previous work it had been found that growth is not a simple phenomenon controlled by a single factor. In early growth of plant embryos the embryo factor limits development (VAN OVERBEEK *et al.* 1942), then auxins start to control seedling growth and still later, when the plant reaches maturity, it is not auxin but carbohydrate translocation which regulates development (*see* later in this chapter).

2) Whereas in the youngest embryo, cell division may be in three directions, which results in exponential growth, it soon becomes surface growth and still later intercalary growth when cell divisions and cell elongation in stems and roots occur in a single direction. Then the growth rate becomes constant. This succession of very different types of growth leads to a growth curve which from exponential gradually becomes a straight line, like the first half of the sigmoid curve for a monomolecular autocatalytic reaction, but unlike the latter, this shape is not due to the progression of a single reaction, but to a transition from one to another controlling process.

3) The slowing down of the reaction rate towards the end of the monomolecular autocatalytic reaction is determined by the conditions imposed upon it at the outset of the experiment, namely, the total amount of reactant. There is really no place where the curve is straight. In the growth of the plant its rate may remain virtually unchanged for weeks or months, as long as the experimental conditions are not such as to terminate the growth. In many of the growth curves reproduced here (FIGURES 22, 23, 26) this straight portion is very pronounced, which it could not be if the curve conformed to formula (1). The termination of growth may occasionally be due to inherent morphogenetic characters, such as determinate growth, but usually it is due to conditions influencing development and flowering during their course. Thus, this termination is not a result of conditions within the plant system or existing at the beginning of growth, and, therefore, the final size of such plants could not possibly enter into its general formula, which is already determined at the start of growth. Or, in other words, the final size of the plant is the result of causes, acting on it during its growth, and the growth of the plant is not controlled by the final size it reaches. If we want to continue research on plant growth, we have to assume that causality, and not finality, reigns during development, in spite of DRIESCH's considerations.

4) The growth of a whole plant is the summation of the growth of its component parts. The top growth of a wheat plant, *e.g.*, is due to a series of growth cycles of the individual leaves, terminated by the growth of the ear. This is shown clearly for the elongation of the pea stem in FIGURE 26, where total growth is the summation of the growth of individual internodes. Thus at least two different sets of growth controls enter into the top growth, one conditioning stem, the other leaf growth, and a completely different set of factors controls root growth. When viewed in this way, the sigmoid shape of the over-all growth curve of a plant is purely fortuitous; this is also evident from the fact that most growth curves are *not* sigmoid.

All these different lines of approach show that the only proper way to study plant growth is to measure and investigate each individual growth stage and growth process separately, instead of looking for a simple "master" reaction or process which limits development at all times.

Stages of Growth:— Since we have come to the conclusion that at different stages of development different processes control growth, the response of plants to external conditions has to be differentiated according to growth stages. This is, of course, known for the photoperiodic response. Flower initiation, flower development, fruit growth, each may proceed optimally under different photoperiods. At 20°C for instance, initiation of the inflorescence of strawberries is a short-day response, whereas the outgrowth of these primordia to flower stands occurs fastest in long days. The best example of differential response of plants in their various growth stages is found in the work of BLAAUW (*see* WENT 1948*a*). In the hyacinth, *e.g.*, root growth has an optimum temperature of 28°C, leaf and flower initiation of 35°C, preparation for elongation of 13°C, and actual stem elongation of 20°C. This means that continued growth is impossible at a single constant temperature, and that for optimal development the plants have to be shifted from one condition to another.

In the plants investigated in the Clark and Earhart greenhouses a shift in optimal conditions was commonly observed. This can, *e.g.*, be seen from the graphs in FIGURES 19, 21, 22 and 47. They show that in the early development of the tomato and of peas the optimal night temperature is very high and decreases gradually as the plants grow up and mature. In other plants the shift in optimal temperature is less regular, as in *Eschscholtzia californica* which germinates best at about 20°C, then needs a cooler temperature for several months, to end up with a fairly high optimal temperature. In addition to these gradual shifts in optimal temperature (*see* FIGURE 47), there are induction effects, where temperature or photoperiod cause responses long after they were applied, as is the case in vernalization and photoperiodism.

The responses of plants to environment are very complex as indicated in the previous paragraphs. A full growth analysis, therefore, requires a complicated experimental set-up in which plants in different developmental stages are subjected to a wide range of experimental conditions. Only in exceptional cases will one be able to follow a complete and normal life cycle of a plant under a single set of environmental conditions.

For convenience in experimentation the life cycle of a plant can be divided into several of the following stages:

1) Germination.
2) Seedling growth above ground until transplanting time.
3) First week after transplanting, usually required for recovery from shock.
4) Recovery from transplanting to flower initiation.
5) Flower initiation treatment.
6) Flower initiation until opening of flowers.
7) Opening of flowers.
8) Open flowers to ripe fruit.

For a complete growth analysis each stage should be subjected to different conditions. In the Earhart Laboratory most work on tomatoes was carried out on stages 4, 6 and 8: during stages 1, 2 and 3 they were all kept under the same conditions (constant 26°C and darkness for stage 1 and 26°C day and 20°C night temperature for stage 2). Sturdiest plants were obtained by having them grow at 23° day and 17°C night temperature during stages 2, 3 and 4. When working with *Cymbidiums,* stage 5 seemed to require intermediate day and night temperature, preceded by long days in stage 4. In stage 6 the temperatures can be kept high again (26° day, 14°C night): such conditions produce fastest inflorescence growth and satisfactory vegetative development. In coffee, stage 5 requires short days: 6 proceeds best at high temperatures, and 7 occurs only when the temperature has suddenly been lowered or when the plants have been subjected to artificial rain.

Experimental Procedures in a Growth Analysis:— To study the succession of optimal conditions in a particular plant, the ideal method would be to germinate and grow enough plants so that each combination of conditions can be tested in a factorial experiment. This would lead to $n \cdot C^x$ plants to be grown in which n stands for the number of replicate plants, C for the number of conditions tested simultaneously, and x the number of growth stages to be recognized. With only 5 conditions, 4 plants per treatment and 4 growth stages tested this would involve 2,500 plants. Since we usually have to compare a much larger number of different conditions simultaneously, the 2,500 plants would constitute only a small experiment. Yet, if it were a tomato experiment, in which each plant takes about 30 × 30 cm. growing surface, it would take up the whole plant growing area of the Earhart Laboratory. Therefore, the possibility of a complete factorial experiment is usually excluded for the specific reason that too many conditions are available simultaneously in the Earhart Laboratory. This leaves several other possibilities.

In the first place, one can study the requirements of the experimental plants one stage at a time. After the optimal germination conditions have been found, these are applied in a new experiment and stage 2 is then investigated. In the next experiment comes stage 3, etc. This method was used by Blaauw and co-workers in their studies of the temperature requirements of bulbous plants.

In the second place, one can keep a series of sets of plants continuously in the same series of conditions. This was done in the early experiments with tomatoes and then it was found that in any one condition the plants go through a whole series of responses. Starting with stage 2 or 4, plants grown at high night temperature grow very fast during the first days or weeks. Their growth rate then gradually declines. In peas this decline in growth rate is very sudden. In Figure 21 it can be seen that at 23°C growth gradually rises and then slowly declines. But at 26°C the decrease in stem elongation is very sudden after February 14. At a night temperature of 26°C growth of tomatoes continues for several months at approximately the same rate. At lower temperatures stem elongation will become severely restricted when there is a heavy fruit set. At still lower temperatures, 4°-10°C, growth is very slow at the start, and gradually increases in rate. From this it can be concluded that in the course of the development of a tomato plant, there is a shift in optimal temperature requirements, from high to low. But this conclusion is based upon the assumption that there are no aftereffects of previous temperature treatments. Such effects (as the "delayed" optimum of BLAAUW) can only be found in complete factorial experiments. However, tomatoes, chili peppers, peas and many other plants exhibit this lowering of the optimal temperature during the

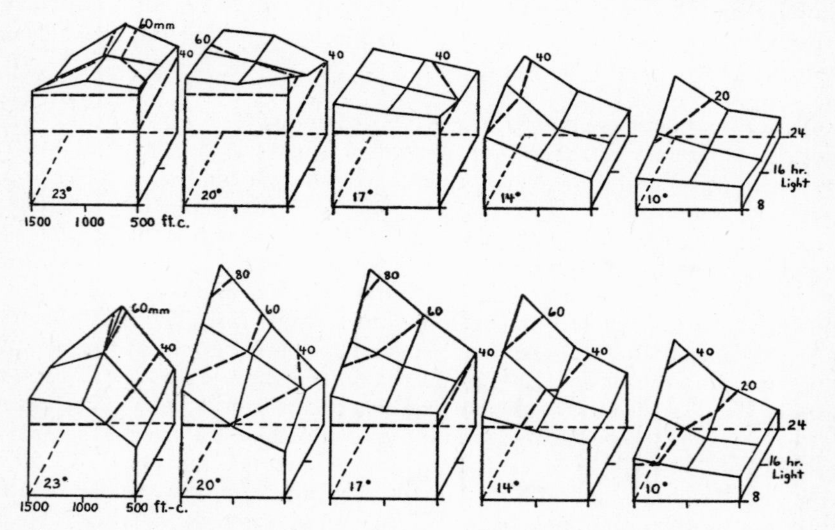

FIGURE 36.— Stem elongation in mm./week (*ordinate*), for Unica peas (averages of 8 plants). *Upper row:* 11-18 days; *second row:* 18-25 days after sowing. From left to right diagrams show growth at decreasing temperatures. In each diagram *abscissa* gives light intensity, *third axis* length of daily photoperiod.

course of development, as found in experiments of restricted size and scope, and as confirmed in more complicated experiments, and, therefore, this method seems to be satisfactory in many cases.

In the third place, it is possible to study the effect of several variables by varying one while the others are kept at a constant level. Thus it is possible, to study the effects of day temperature at the optimal night temperature and optimal photoperiod, whereas the night temperature effects are measured in plants kept at a constant, optimal, day temperature. PLATE XVII shows an experiment with *Coleus* carried out in this manner. By adding a few other combinations, it becomes possible to judge whether interactions between these factors exist, and in a follow-up experiment the area of possible interaction can be analyzed in more detail. Photoperiod is then studied only at a few temperature combinations, both optimal and extreme. If the plants to be used are not very big, such as young tomatoes, *Saintpaulias* or lettuce, they can be placed at different distances from light, using only a single truck with narrow shelves at different levels (*see* PLATE V). An example of a multifactorial experiment is represented in FIGURES 36, 37, 38 and 39 for peas, in which the effects of age, temperature, photoperiod and light intensity were determined on stem elongation and leaf production of two pea varieties.

Whereas in the previous paragraphs the difficulties of the factorial experiment have been considered, it should be pointed out that in plant growth only the factorial experiment can produce results which have

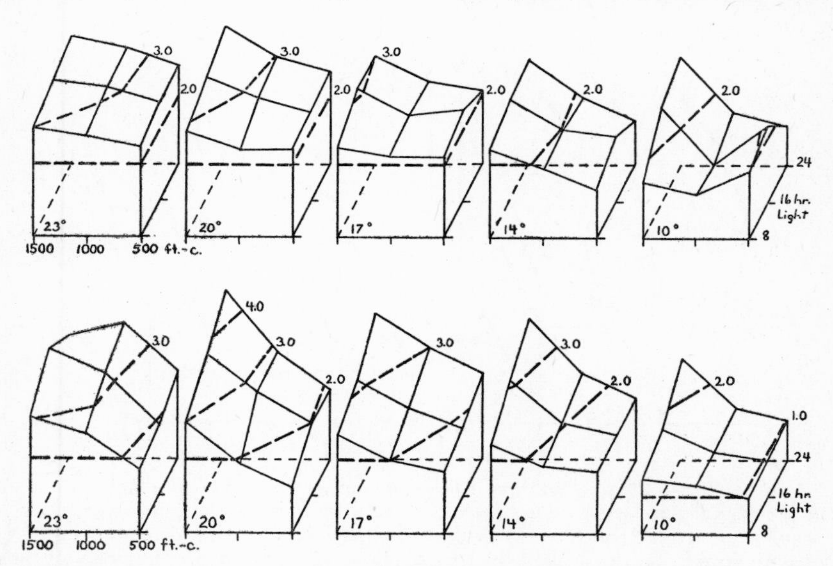

FIGURE 37.— Morphological development (*ordinate:* increase in node number per week) for the same Unica peas shown in FIGURE 36 which see for further explanation.

direct practical value. This is generally recognized in plant nutrition experiments, where the effect of changing one nutrient element changes the responses of the plant to the others to such an extent that, *e.g.*, potassium application may cause magnesium deficiency, or lowering of the iron supply may result in manganese toxicity.

In the previous chapters many examples have been given where the photoperiodic response changed under different temperatures, or where the optimal temperature varied with the light intensity. In such cases, the analysis of a single variable leads to results of only very limited applicability, namely, when in practice none of the other factors vary. But in temperate regions the progress of the seasons is attended by simultaneous changes in phototemperature, nyctotemperature, photoperiod and light intensity. Although it is possible that in certain cases no interactions between these factors occur, in general these factors are interdependent and, therefore, can be studied only in more complex experiments, where all of the significant factors can be varied independently and simultaneously.

After exploring the possibilities of analyzing the growth response of plants by fitting the growth curve of the individual plant as a function of time, or of a variety as a function of temperature, to some mathematical expression, it must be admitted that these formulae are either inaccurate in their fit or that they are too complex to be useful as a basis for explanations (*see* also "Climatology").

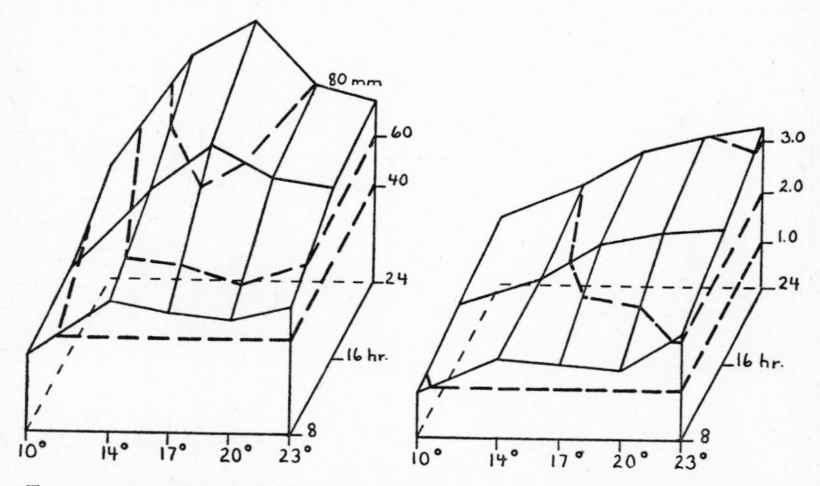

FIGURE 38.— Stem elongation (*ordinate:* mm. per week, left diagram), and morphological development (*ordinate:* increase in node number, right diagram), of Vinco peas, for the period of 18-25 days after sowing. In each diagram temperature in degree Celsius is plotted along *abscissa,* and photoperiod in hours along *third axis.*

Physiological Analysis of Growth:— The tomato plant has been most thoroughly studied as far as the physiology of its growth response is concerned (WENT 1944*b*). Not only has the change of growth rate as a function of time and of external factors been analyzed, but a number of processes which together make the plant function have been studied individually. In FIGURE 40 the rate of a number of these processes in the tomato plant has been plotted as a function of temperature. To begin with, the growth rate of the whole plant is shown. This curve shows a typical optimum at about 18°C in the rate of stem elongation. This particular curve has been chosen since it also coincides with the curve of dry matter production. If we plot the growth rate of individual parts of the plant, an entirely different curve is obtained. P. R. WHITE (1937) has studied the dependence of the growth of isolated tomato root tips on temperature and found that the optimum temperature lay beyond 30°C. By measuring the growth of tomato stems, of which the region of elongation only was enclosed and kept at controlled temperature, it was found that at 26°C stem elongation was faster than at 18°C, and that, therefore, the elongation of stem cells also has an optimum above 26°C. Similarly, a number of investigators, among whom DE CAPITE (1955) is the latest, have shown that the optimal temperature for tissue cultures is about 30°C in light, which is much higher than for intact plants. The optimum growth rate of the tomato plant when exposed in its entirety to different temperatures lies at 18°C, and therefore we must conclude that the discrepancy between optimal growing temperatures for the intact plant and its individual parts lies in the integration of the parts into an organism.

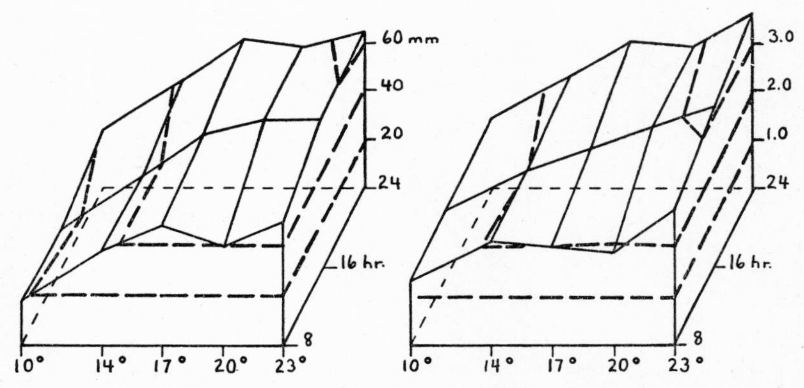

FIGURE 39.— Similar to FIGURE 38, except that all data refer to Unica peas (as in FIGURES 36 and 37).

This integration depends on: (*1*) the food relations between the different parts, and (2) their hormone relationships.

Rather extensive tests of the auxin production and auxin content of tomato plants, under different conditions, were carried out (WENT 1944*b*). It can be said in general that the auxin content was very variable and that there was no correlation between high growth rate and high auxin content. On the contrary, young plants before they have reached their maximum growth rate invariably have a higher auxin content than older, faster growing plants (KRAMER and WENT 1948). This would make one believe that auxin is not the factor which limits the growth of tomato plants as a whole. This conclusion is strengthened by the observation that decapitated tomato stems continue to grow at their original rate for 24 hours after removal of the tip. It is only on the second day after decapitation that their growth rate drops; at that time the auxin supply has become limiting as shown by continued growth at the original rate when auxin has been applied (WENT and D. BONNER 1943). Furthermore, no cases have been described in which auxin applications have increased growth of intact tomato plants. The experiments in Chapter 25 form the only exception to the rule that growth of intact plants is not increased by auxin applications. Therefore, we have to envisage the function of auxin in the growth of the tomato stem mainly in relation to geotropic and phototropic responses, and not as an absolute limiting factor.

Sugar Translocation:— The translocation of sugar in a tomato plant has been studied in considerable detail employing a series of techniques. The first indication of a temperature coefficient of less than one for sugar translocation was obtained in the examination of sugar content in tomato leaves at different times of the day and at different temperatures (Went

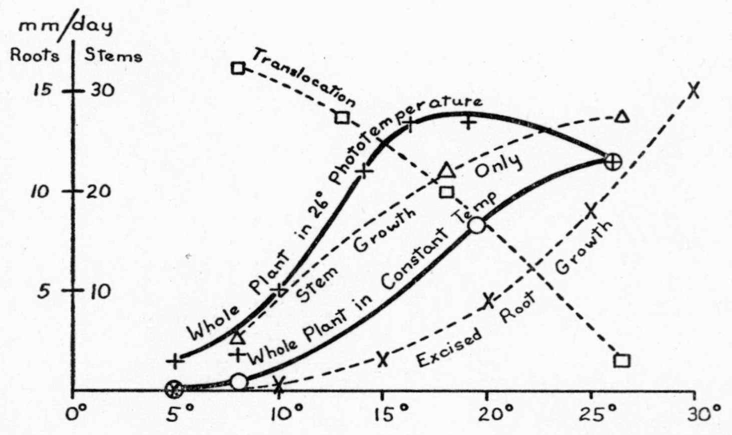

Figure 40.— Growth rate and physiological processes in the tomato plant as a function of temperature (*abscissa:* in degree Celsius). *Heavy lines:* stem elongation of intact plants. *Circles:* plants kept at a constant temperature. *Plus signs:* growth as a function of the nyctotemperature only. *Crosses:* excised root growth. *Triangles:* stem elongation when only growing zone of plant is enclosed in jacket at indicated temperature. *Squares:* translocation of sugars in the tomato stem as a function of temperature. Redrawn from Went (1944*b*).

1944*b*). Only the non-reducing sugar values showed a clear-cut periodicity from day to night. During day, the sucrose content of tomato leaves increases in a sigmoid way as shown in Figure 60. During night, most of the sucrose disappears again both by respiration and translocation out of the leaf. As shown in the chapter on photosynthesis, respiration of the whole plant uses less than 20 per cent of the carbohydrates formed during the previous day. Only part of this respiration occurs in the leaves and, therefore, we should expect that in these leaves less than 10 per cent of the formed sucrose would be respired during night. Therefore, we can expect that the sucrose content of the leaves at the end of the night mainly reflects the amount translocated during night. In numerous sugar analyses

(Went 1944*b*), it was invariably found that after a warm night (26°-30°C), in spite of the greater rate of respiration, the sucrose content of leaves was considerably higher than after cooler nights (17°-20°C). Therefore, less sugar was translocated at high temperatures than at low temperatures.

Another generally accepted method for measuring translocation was used to check this conclusion. Tomato stems were ringed with a jet of steam killing all living cells, including the phloem, in the ring. This caused an accumulation of sucrose above the ring and the sugar concentration above the ring was a measure for the amount of sugar translocated. It was found that at 18°C night temperature there was more sugar accumulation above the ring than at 26°C, again indicating a greater rate of sugar translocation at 18° than at 26°.

The most extensive series of experiments on sugar translocation in the tomato plant were carried out with a different technique (Went and Hull 1949). When tomato plants were decapitated near the ground, their stumps bled, and the rate of bleeding was a function of the sugar content of the root system. Plants which had been fed sucrose prior to decapitation bled more than similar root systems not so treated. When the stems were ringed before the sugar application to the tops, no increase in bleeding took place. Therefore, the rate of bleeding was a function of translocation in the phloem of sugar or a derivative of it. By recording the rate of bleeding with an automatic recorder it was possible to measure the difference in bleeding between several sets of plants, of which one was not given sucrose and the other two groups were fed sucrose to one or two leaves. The stems of the two latter groups were kept at different temperatures by a water-cooled airjacket around them. It was then found that 8 to 15 hours after sugar application, the rate of bleeding of the plants fed with sugar was increased beyond that of the controls. The lower the temperature of the stem was kept the sooner the rate of bleeding would increase and the greater the rate of bleeding was. This indicated that the rate and the capacity of sugar translocation increased upon lowering of the temperature.

A fourth method of measuring sugar translocation was used by Hull (1952), who applied radioactive sugar to leaves and afterward measured radioactivity of other parts of the plant. This method also indicated that at low stem temperatures at least as much sugar, if not more, was translocated. These results are at variance with the results of other investigators who claim that sugar translocation is slower at low temperatures. However, they usually measured the effect of cooling or heating of the petiole (for instance Hewitt and Curtis 1948) and their results agreed with ours inasmuch as translocation was reduced at temperatures above 20°C.

Other physiological processes in the tomato plant were measured as well, as far as their response to temperature was concerned. The effects of temperature on the photosynthetic rate were relatively slight, but it increased with increasing temperature. Transpiration or the opening width of stomata did not show responses with an optimum at 18°C. Therefore we can conclude that there is not a single individual physiological process in the tomato plant which shows an optimum at 18°C.

Growth Limitation by Alternative Processes:— The explanation of a low optimum temperature for the growth of an intact plant must therefore lie in the balance between different physiological processes, one with a Q_{10} of more than one and the other with a Q_{10} of less than one. By assuming that below 18°C the growth process in the individual cells is limiting and that above 18°C the rate of sugar translocation towards the growing region has become limiting, the shape of the growth curve of the tomato plant as a whole in relation to temperature can be explained (FIGURE 40). There are a number of phenomena which find a simple explanation with this assumption:

1) When tomato and other plants are young, the distance between food producing and energy consuming areas is small and consequently translocation could be assumed to be less critical. Actually, FIGURES 19, 21, and 47 show that the optimum temperature for growth and fruiting is high in young plants and gradually shifts to lower temperatures as the plants grow older. That this is not a function of age but of size, is indicated by experiments with *Capsicum annuum* (DORLAND and WENT 1947). Two series of plants, one kept at a phototemperature of 26°C and the other at 18°C, were subjected to a range of different nyctotemperatures. In both these series there was a general shift towards lower optimal nyctotemperature as plants grew older. But this shift proceeded faster at the high than at the low phototemperature. When the optimum nyctotemperatures were plotted, not as a function of age, but as a function of the size of a plant, then the optimal nyctotemperatures for the two series were practically superimposed. This strongly indicates that the lowering of the optimal nyctotemperature depends on the distance between the regions supplying and utilizing food materials and consequently that translocation is involved.

2) At high nyctotemperatures tomato fruit set is very poor, and is strongly inhibited by vegetative growth. When tomato plants (San Jose Canner) grown at 26°C during night (and consequently not setting fruit) were decapitated, immediately a few fruit did set at the highest inflorescence. This shows that at high temperatures there is a strong competition between vegetative and fruit growth which can easily be explained on the basis of competition for sugar.

3) At low temperatures fruiting is also poor, but cannot be increased by decapitation. At 10° and 14°C nyctotemperature, auxin sprays strongly stimulated fruit set, whereas at 26°C nyctotemperature auxin applications were ineffective (OSBORNE and WENT 1953). This also indicates that at low, but not at high, temperatures chemical growth processes are limiting.

4) Not only fruit, but also flower development is strongly reduced at high nyctotemperatures, and excessive abscission occurs. Sugar sprayed on the plants at 26°C nyctotemperature prevented flower abscission and made the flowers develop to normal size. This shows that the poor flower development at high temperature was due to insufficient sugar supply to the growing region.

5) If the previously mentioned theory is correct, we would expect that at low temperatures an excess of carbohydrates will accumulate in the growing regions because it is not being all used in the growth process. At high temperatures on the other hand, the sugar supply is insufficient, and whatever reaches the growing point is immediately used in growth. This explains why tomato plants, previously grown at high night temperatures, showed very much reduced growth after transfer to cool

night conditions; on the other hand, plants first grown in cool nights increased their growth rate to more than 50 per cent above the steady growth rate, when transferred suddenly to high night temperatures (*see* Figure 1 *in* WENT 1945). This is perhaps better proof than anything else that at high night temperatures potential growth is very much greater than the actually observed growth, if through previous treatment the supply of carbohydrates is high.

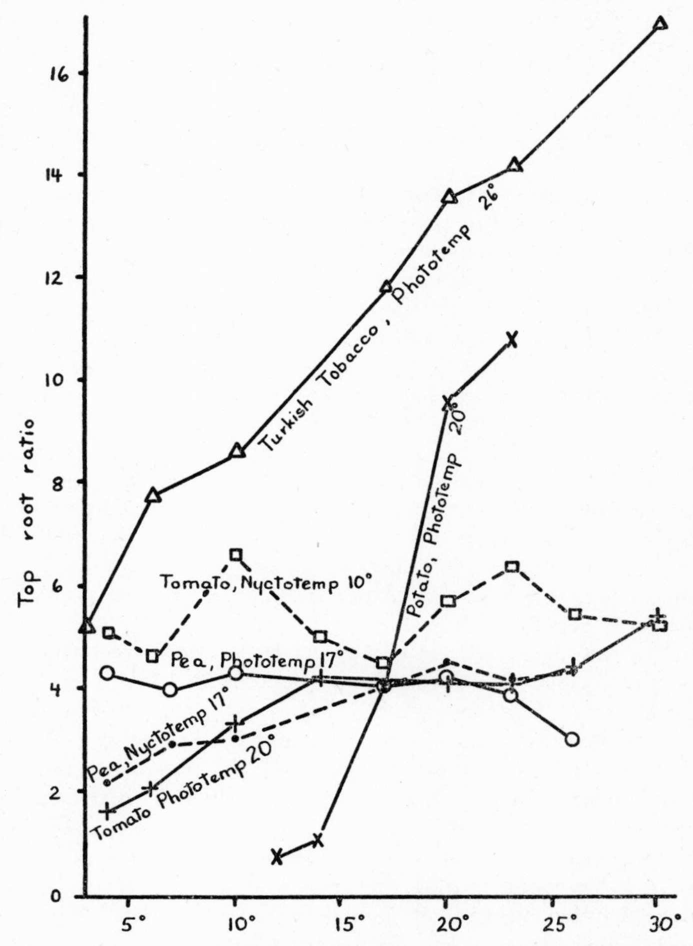

FIGURE 41.— Top-root ratio (*ordinate*) as a function of nyctotemperature (*solid curves*) or phototemperature (*broken curves*). In the potato, both root and tuber weights were combined.

6) The effects of night temperature could be expected to be greatest on the root system, which is farthest removed from the photosynthesizing cells. When the top-root ratio of plants is plotted as a function of the nyctotemperature, a straight line relationship is found with a minimum at low temperatures. Therefore, at the lowest night temperature a greater proportion of photosynthates is used in the growth of roots.

The same thing holds for potato tuber formation, for which the proportion also increases as the nyctotemperature increases (FIGURE 41).

7) The sweetness of tomato fruits is higher at low nyctotemperature. Also, individual fruit size is greater at the lower temperature (this is true for strawberries as well; *see* FIGURE 31). Both these facts are an indication of the better sugar supply at low temperatures, since it has already been shown that respiration removes only a small fraction of the sugars formed during day.

8) As shown in FIGURE 33, the percentage of sugar in sugar beets is highest at the lowest nyctotemperatures.

9) The lasting quality of many flowers depends on their sugar content, and can be increased by sugar application. A more effective way to increase their lasting qualities is to keep plants at cooler temperatures just prior to picking of the flowers. This was found to be the case in *Cattleya* and *Phalaenopsis* in the Earhart Plant Research Laboratory.

Practically all previous considerations of the relationships between growth and temperature in the tomato plant were based on the nyctotemperature. There are two reasons why this could be expected to be more important than the phototemperature in the development of the tomato plant. Practically all its growth occurs in darkness (WENT 1944*a*), and consequently, the nyctotemperature should have a direct effect on its growth. Light intensities above 500 ft.-c. have this effect on the repression of growth. A second reason for the importance of nyctotemperature in the development of the tomato plant is that, apparently, most of the sugar translocation occurs during night. This conclusion is based largely on the work of TSCHESNOKOV and BAZYRINA (1930). They found that in the potato and in *Petasites* translocation of photosynthates occurs during night, whereas in peas translocation coincides with the light hours. Since the tomato and potato are closely related and since they behave physiologically very much alike, it is likely that in the tomato sugar translocation occurs predominantly during night. If we take the top-root ratio as the most sensitive indication of the rate of sugar translocation, then we would expect that this ratio in the tomato would depend far more upon night than day temperature. This was actually found to be the case, as FIGURE 41 shows. At a constant nyctotemperature of 30°C, there is a change from 5.1 to 5.2 in the top-root ratio from 4° to 30°C phototemperature. At a constant phototemperature of 20°C the top-root ratio increases from 1.6 to 5.4 over the range from 4° to 30°C nyctotemperature. The same increase of top-root ratio from low to high nyctotemperature is found in different tobacco varieties and the potato (both shown in FIGURE 41), and in many other plants. It is highly suggestive that in peas the dependence of the top-root ratio changes markedly with the phototemperature, whereas it changes much less with nyctotemperature as shown in FIGURE 41. These effects seem to indicate that in plants in which translocation occurs in light (peas) it is the phototemperature which controls the top-root ratio, whereas in plants in which translocation occurs during night (tomato, tobacco and potato) it is the nyctotemperature which controls this ratio.

From the previous discussion it must have become clear that it is possible to explain the decrease in growth rate of plants above the optimal temperature through limitation by translocation. By analyzing the growth curves in another way a similar conclusion can be reached. In most figures, where the growth rate is plotted as a function of temperature, we find first a range where the rate increases exponentially with the temperature. It is obvious that at these lower temperatures a chemical process controls growth. This chemical process can be speeded up by increasing the temperature, or by increasing the concentration of the reactants involved. Since we know that auxin and vitamins are involved in a number of these growth processes, it follows that auxin or vitamin applications should be effective at lower temperatures. This is actually the case. When auxin is applied to improve fruit set in tomatoes, it is only effective below 15°C (at 10° and 14°C; OSBORNE and WENT 1953). Application of thiamin to the root medium increases growth of *Cosmos* only at 17° and not at 26°C (BONNER 1943). And in this book in Chapter 25 by GALSTON, he describes how auxin application to corn was only effective at low temperature. Therefore, at higher temperatures either other components of the growth process are limiting (but thus far none have been found which would speed up growth processes at higher temperatures), or the process controlling the growth is not a chemical process any more.

Growth Control by a Diffusion Process:— By looking at the curves in FIGURES 24 and 36, and PLATES XI and XIII*b*, we see that especially in younger plants there is a fairly wide temperature range (for instance from 17° to 26°C), where the growth rate is practically constant. Only above 26°C do deleterious effects of high temperature come into play, such as in the growth of peas (FIGURE 24). Therefore, below 17°C a chemical process limits pea growth. Above 26°C an injurious process limits their growth, whereas between 17° and 26°C some other process with a temperature coefficient near one is in control. Such a process with practically no temperature coefficient can be assumed to be of the nature of a diffusion process. The hypothesis of growth control by a diffusion process under optimal growing conditions of a plant is in agreement with a number of facts which are hard to explain in another way:

1) Diffusion is a process which cannot be speeded up by increasing the concentration of reactants and only very slightly by temperature. There are actually no good ways in which we can change diffusion experimentally. If growth control under optimal growing conditions were by a chemical process we could expect to find methods or substances which would speed it up and we would not expect to reach a maximum growth rate. The fact that such a ceiling for growth is being reached (*see* FIGURE 42) indicates that the control of growth under those conditions is by some process which cannot be influenced experimentally, such as the diffusion process. Therefore, in this respect, our hypothesis agrees with the experimental facts. It is possible to draw curves like FIGURE 42 for many other plants and many other plant processes. The sugar content of sugar beets by improved growing conditions, nutrition and breeding, has been increased during the last 150 years from well below 10 per cent to about 20 per cent, and in spite of very intensive work, it has been impossible to surpass this percentage. The same thing is true for sugar cane. With wheat, maize and potato production, a similar asymptotic approach to a maximal yield is found. This limitation is at least partly due to the reaching of maximal growth rate.

2) The variability of plants grown under optimal temperature conditions is very much reduced (Went 1953*b*). This also shows that a ceiling is reached beyond which growth cannot be pushed, but up to which it can be increased. Therefore, the low coefficient of variability at intermediate temperatures can be explained by limitation of growth by a process which is independent of environmental fluctuations, and again a diffusion rather than a chemical process fits the experimental data.

3) Whereas at lower temperatures the application of chemicals was found to improve growth, under optimal growing conditions no chemicals, organic or inorganic, have been found to increase this growth rate, again indicating that under optimal growing conditions it is not a chemical process which limits further growth.

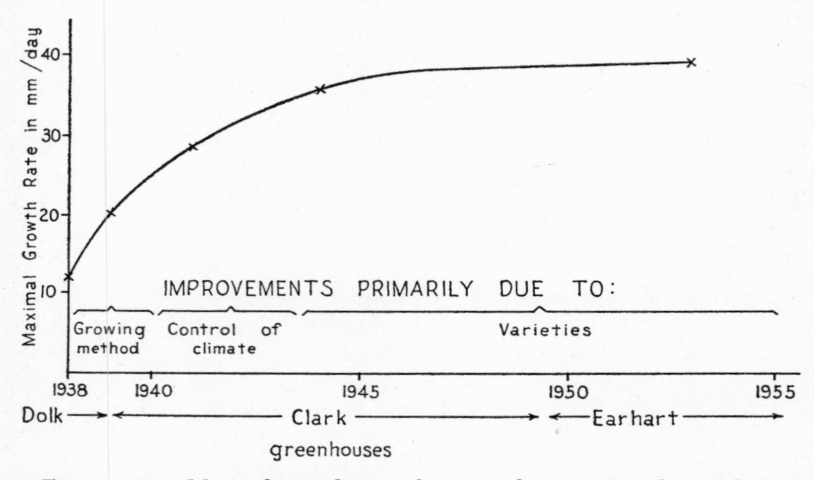

Figure 42.— Maximal growth rate of tomato plants in mm./day reached in different greenhouses as a function of time in years, increased experience, improved growing conditions and faster growing varieties. This maximal rate reaches 40 mm./day asymptotically.

4) When the growth rate of peas is followed from day to day, we find that under the optimal temperature conditions a sort of compensation mechanism occurs which regulates the growth rate within a narrow range (Went 1953*b*). Plants, which have been growing for a few days at a rate faster than the average, will slow down in the succeeding period, whereas those growing slower are speeded up in the following period. In this way, an average growth rate is obtained which is highly uniform for a whole population. This compensating mechanism of growth control would not be expected if a chemical process were limiting, because then the faster growth of a pea would indicate a greater supply of the limiting growth factor which presumably would be formed at a greater rate in the larger plants. Actually, at low temperatures where a chemical process is limiting growth, no such compensation mechanism is found and variability is very much greater.

When we summarize the evidence presented on the processes limiting growth, we find that in tomatoes, peas and other plants the chemical reactions leading towards growth (although presumably the same over the whole range of growing conditions) are in control only at lower temperatures, but above 15°-20°C other processes become limiting. These are either translocation or diffusion, both physical processes, and both have a temperature coefficient of about one or lower. Therefore, experimental limits and theoretical considerations lead to the same picture of growth control under optimal growing conditions. If control is exerted by a diffusion process, the chances that this can be influenced by experimental treatments are very slight, and therefore, we might reach the conclusion that no further increase in growth can be expected beyond what has been achieved by breeders and growers. On the other hand, these considerations only hold for monopodial growth in length. Increased total growth of a plant could be achieved by having lateral buds start to develop. Although this would not increase the absolute height of a plant, it would make it possible to increase the total rate of cell and dry matter production, and therefore, although the outlook for increasing the rate of morphological development in plants is gloomy, no limits can be seen to an increased rate in physiological development up to the highest possible utilization of available energy. This latter point is discussed in Chapter 20 (Photosynthesis).

Growth Responses in Different Plants:— The work thus far performed in the Earhart and Clark greenhouses does not give a complete picture of the climatic responses of plants, since only so few plants were investigated in detail, and since the number of plants on which less complete information is available is relatively small. In addition to the cases in which a plant responds predominantly to nyctotemperature (tomato), phototemperature (pea), seasonal thermoperiod (*Veratrum*), or photoperiod (*Xanthium*), there are different or more complex inter-relationships. For instance, in the Marshall strawberry *both* temperature and photoperiod are very important in their behavior, with little influence of seasonal variations in temperature. In *Saintpaulia* we find a lower optimal photo- than nyctotemperature; in alpine annuals like *Saxifraga bryophora* or *Linanthus ciliatus* very low optimal temperatures occur, whereas, on the other hand, there is a lack of temperature sensitivity of *Begonia semperflorens,* or a large temperature differential between day and night for optimal growth in some succulents.

Within the orchid family, optimal temperatures vary over a wide range, which is understandable on the basis of the wide latitudinal and altitudinal range of distribution of this family. *Phalaenopsis* has the highest optimal nyctotemperature (20°C), *Cattleya* comes next with 17°C, and *Cymbidium* and *Cypripedium* thrive at 14°C (or lower).

With the information available, it is possible to make a few generalizations. In most plants, one particular climatic factor, such as nyctotemperature or photoperiod, overshadows all others in importance, since it generally seems the factor controlling the developmental process which is limiting. If we ask now which of these is the most commonly controlling climatic factor, then this seems to be temperature, particularly the nyctotemperature. Photoperiod comes in the second or third place, and affects flowering in a number of annuals, and vegetative growth in trees and shrubs. The great importance attributed to photoperiod in the development of plants finds its origin in several directions: (*1*) Length of day is easily controllable in experiments; therefore, such a large number of plants which respond to photoperiod have been investigated, (2) from a practical standpoint light is a more easily controllable factor than temperature, and (3) intensity of the supplemental light can be low. This emphasis on experiments with photoperiod has probably caused a somewhat wharped idea of its importance in controlling plant growth in general. The recent emphasis on construction of phytotrons very likely will result in a more balanced concept of the factors controlling plant growth and distribution.

Speaking from an evolutionary standpoint, perennial plants are the more primitive. These plants can be divided into those with periodic and those with continuous growth. Many tropical plants belong to the latter group (*Cestrum, Saintpaulia,* coffee); these have no photoperiodicity in their vegetative development but may be dependent upon daylength for flower intiation. The temperature range over which they will grow is not very wide, and usually lies intermediate or high. Tropical plants with a yearly cycle in their vegetative development (like *Hevea*) do not seem to respond to photoperiod, but may be synchronized with the seasons through response to rainfall.

Perennial plants from temperate regions are mostly periodic in their growth. Among the evergreens, control of their vegetative cycles may be photoperiodic (like in *Camellia*), but in deciduous plants (Chamaephytes and Cryptophytes) no leaves are present to perceive the length of day, and therefore, the breaking of their dormancy is usually due to a temperature response (peach, *Veratrum*). Their flowering is also controlled by temperature (*Camellia,* peach). Reaching of the dormant state, however, is due to photoperiod (peach).

Annuals have to be considered as types derived from perennials: many are photoperiodically insensitive, but respond to temperature (*Amaranthus,* tomato, *Pectis* and many other summer and tropical annuals). Others are predominantly photoperiodic and grow at almost any temperature (*Xanthium*). Winter and spring annuals require low temperature for germination and growth, and are long-day plants (*Baeria, Phacelia*). Autumn-flowering annuals are short-day plants, with rather high temperature requirements (*Chrysanthemum, Zinnia, Callistephus*). Finally, there is a group of annuals which require low winter temperature (or vernalization of their seeds, like winter rye and winter wheat); these plants are usually also long-day plants. Dr. N. Barber has investigated requirements in pea hybrids, and found that photoperiodism and vernalization were either dependent upon the same gene, or alternatively, were so closely linked that no segregation occurred in his cultures.

As far as photoperiodic behavior is concerned, several cases were encountered in which flowering was speeded up by a daylength of 12 hours (the day-neutral type of GARNER and ALLARD), especially in plants coming from the tropics (*Emelia*, a Bolivian strawberry, and *Cestrum*). A fifth type, flowering only in long *and* short days, but not in a 12-hour photoperiod, was discovered in the form of *Madia elegans* (LEWIS and WENT 1945). This type might be called the ambiperiodic group. This leaves us with long-day, short-day, day-neutral, ambiperiodic and indeterminate plants.

CHOUARD (1951) has distinguished a seasonal and a daily thermoperiodicity in the temperature response of plants. Seasonal thermoperiodicity is exhibited by many perennial, deciduous plants from temperate or cold climates with pronounced seasonal changes in temperature. Unless peaches are subjected to cycles of cold and warm temperatures of several months' duration, they will not initiate flowers nor open their buds. For tulips, hyacinths and other bulbs this seasonal thermoperiodicity was well known through the work of BLAAUW (1930, 1941). He and his collaborators had shown that each morphological or physiological stage in the development of these plants had a different temperature requirement, and that for normal development these bulbs had to pass through a succession of higher and lower temperatures with a length of cycle of approximately one year. The sequence of temperatures could not be speeded up more than twice; in nature, the developmental cycle is synchronized with the climatic cycle through the yearly succession of low and high temperatures. These bulbous plants cannot grow in the tropics, even at high altitudes, since they are not subjected to a sequence of different temperatures there.

In other liliaceous plants, such as the lily-of-the-valley (*Convallaria majalis*), HARTSEMA and LUYTEN (1933) showed that a chilling period of a definite length of time (3 weeks near freezing) was necessary for breaking of dormancy of the corms and their subsequent development. This same behavior was found in *Veratrum viride*, except that in this case much longer chilling periods, with an optimum of 5-6 months, were required. Also, plants with winterbuds like *Dicentra formosa* have such dormancy which can be broken by prolonged treatment with temperatures near freezing.

A somewhat different response to cold temperature was found in *Saxifraga bryophora*. The bulbils of this plant would only grow at a temperature of 10°C, unless they had been pre-treated for several months with 4°C, when they developed also at 17°C. This cannot be called strict dormancy, but it also tends to synchronize their development with the seasons at the high altitudes where they occur.

Daily thermoperiodicity is a very general response of plants. The majority of species tested in the Clark and Earhart greenhouses grow considerably better when subjected to a daily change in temperature, the optimal phototemperature being higher than the optimal nyctotemperature. This does not mean that plants cannot grow in a constant temperature, just as photoperiodism does not imply that plants cannot be grown or cannot flower in continuous light. From many plates, figures and descriptions in this book it can be seen how plants respond favorably to a temperature fluctuation from day to night. Just to mention a few cases, we observe that *Coleus* (PLATE XVII) develops optimally in a 16-hour photoperiod when the phototemperature is 23°, and the nyctotemperature 17°C. In FIGURE 18 the optimum phototemperature for tomato plants growing in artificial light of 1,500 ft.-c. is 20°C, and the optimal nyctotemperature 10°C. In daylight these figures are 23°-26° during day and 17°-18°C during night (FIGURE 40). In FIGURE 44 all plants marked (*Bellis,* B; *Papaver nudicaule,* Pa; *Mathiola incana,* M; *Ageratum,* A; *Callistephus,* C; *Zinnia,* Z), except *Saintpaulia* (S), have their optimal growing conditions at lower nyctotemperatures than phototemperatures, the differential being 4°-6°C. This is the basis upon which the decision was made to have the temperatures in the Earhart greenhouses fluctuate from day to night, with a temperature differential of 5°-7°C. In this way it is unnecessary to move most plants each morning and afternoon to keep them under optimal growing conditions.

As discussed earlier, the difference in optimal temperature in light and in darkness must be attributed to different optimal temperatures for the processes which occur in light (photosynthesis) and in darkness (growth and translocation of sugars). Therefore, the diurnal thermoperiodicity is not due to one basic process which is periodic, like the autonomous 24-hour rhythm of the Bünning cycle. And, consequently, it should not be surprising that there is a plant which has a thermoperiodicity in reverse, namely *Saintpaulia.* As PLATE XVI shows, optimal development of the African Violet occurs at a phototemperature of 14°-17°C and a nyctotemperature of 23°-26°C. This climatic cycle does not occur anywhere in the world, and, therefore, the *Saintpaulia* response cannot be attributed to adaptation. In other tropical plants the optima may lie close together; in the coffee plant, *e.g.,* the optimal daily thermoperiodic range is not more than 3°C.

In plants from dry climates, like cacti and *Mesembryanthemums,* the optimal daily fluctuation of temperature exceeds 10°C; therefore, a considerable degree of adaptation of the daily thermoperiodic response of plants to the naturally occurring daily temperature fluctuations has occurred.

Generalization of Growth Response:— Viewing all these results together, it is obvious that almost as many different reaction types of plants to climate exist as plants have been investigated. Each species and variety has its own optimal requirements which differ qualitatively or quantitatively from other plants. This infinite variety is based on the very complex nature of the interactions between environment and growth and development. These responses can vary either in degree or range or type. Furthermore, each process, such as leaf or flower initiation, root growth, fruit set or breaking of bud dormancy, has a different temperature or light dependence.

In this sense no generalizations are possible. When we group plants taxonomically or ecologically, however, some general rules emerge:

1) Closely related plants usually are most strongly affected by the same climatic variables, whereas plants from different families may respond to other climatic factors. Thus, the development of the *Solanaceae* investigated was primarily controlled by the nyctotemperature, whereas in the annual *Papilionaceae* the phototemperature was more important. The responses of *Liliaceae* are in many respects similar. The plants of this family which have been investigated in detail (tulip, hyacinth, *Convallaria,* and *Veratrum*) all require a seasonal fluctuation in temperature, with a period of several months' duration during which they must be exposed to low temperatures (0°-10°C), alternating with a period (or periods) at higher temperatures. A similar seasonal thermoperiodicity is exhibited by many deciduous trees, particularly in the *Rosaceae* (peach, pear). As far as germination requirements are concerned, *Amaranthaceae, Nyctaginaceae* and some tribes of the *Gramineae* (*Chlorideae, Andropogoneae*) germinate at high temperatures, whereas the *Aveneae* and *Festuceae* of the *Gramineae,* the *Polygonaceae* and *Polemoniaceae* germinate at low temperatures. Therefore, it seems that as a first generalization we can say that families and tribes generally differ qualitatively in their response to environment.

2) Differences between varieties of the same species or between different species of the same genus or between genera of the same family are usually of a quantitative rather than qualitative nature. Even races, varieties or ecotypes of a single species may differ in their response. The ecotypes of *Achillea* differ so much in nyctotemperature requirement that their range of distribution in California covers localities along the coast to mountain altitudes of 3,000 m. (CLAUSEN, KECK and HIESEY 1948). Yet, it is mainly response to nyctotemperature in which these ecotypes differ. The cultivated varieties of tomato also differ in their nyctotemperature requirements; for them the range in optimal temperature is rather narrow, however, and the optima for fruit set do not seem to differ more than 4° (14°-18°C) for the most extreme varieties (greenhouse tomatoes like Ailsa Craig and Michigan State requiring the lowest, and California varieties like Beefsteak and San Jose Canner requiring the highest nyctotemperature). Other varieties, like Earliana, although not differing in optimal temperature, have a wider range over which they still will set fruit. This explains why a variety like Bounty, which is grown in the most continental areas of the United States, with short hot summers, bracketed by very cool weather in the early and late parts of the tomato growing season, was used in breeding tropical tomato varieties (like the Pearl Harbor). Among cultivated plants, the tobacco has a very wide range of distribution, with some varieties growing optimally in the lowlands of the tropics, whereas others are grown as far North as 52° N. Lat. This is reflected in the big differences between varieties in temperature response. Although two cases (*Achillea* and tobacco) have been quoted to indicate wide differences between varieties of one species in their nyctotemperature response, the general rule is that such varietal responses are usually covering only a rather narrow range of temperatures. Thus, peas are cool temperature plants and so is cabbage, whereas corn and tomatoes are only grown commercially in warm climates, and no degree of breeding has produced varieties of either group which can successfully be grown next to those of the other group. Therefore, the potential range of climatic response within a species is limited, and in most cases it is *very* limited in spite of extensive breeding work. In potatoes, it is primarily nyctotemperature which controls tuber formation, but the optimum for the variety tested lay at 12°C, well outside the range of the tomato varieties. In the chili pepper, an even lower optimum was found in the older plants, but still, nyctotemperature was the controlling factor. Therefore, within the family *Solanaceae* quantitative differences between varieties and species exist which result in some of them being tropical and others temperate region plants, but qualitatively their climatic responses are similar.

3) When considering the climate of origin of different plants, then we find that

in general their optimal growing conditions very closely parallel the climate existing in their natural habitat. This means that a considerable degree of adaptation has occurred or that plants have migrated towards areas in which the climate agrees more closely with their requirements. This is of course essential for cultivated plants. It was also found that a plant becomes a weed, or, in other words, can hold its own between other plants, when its optimal growing conditions coincide with the existing climate. In these considerations, largely the evolutionary significance of thermoperiodicity and the temperature response of plants in general has been stressed, with little mention of photoperiodism. It seems that the photoperiodic response is more easily changed in the course of evolution than the temperature response. There are more examples of plants having a wide latitudinal range of distribution than a wide altitudinal range. The work of OLMSTED with *Bouteloua* is a good example of ecotypes which differ quantitatively in their photoperiodism and whose distribution is closely tied up with their flowering response to length of day. Within one genus we may encounter opposite photoperiodic behavior, such as in *Nicotiana,* in which long-day, indeterminate and short-day plants occur. It does not seem possible to designate long-day or short-day response as a family characteristic.

Therefore, in spite of the fact that almost each plant investigated had different optimal growing requirements as far as temperature, light and other climatic factors are concerned, the above three generalizations can guide us in estimating the climatic requirements of a plant not previously investigated. By inquiring into the region of origin of the plant and by comparing it with the closest relatives of which the climatic response is known, we have a fair chance of coming fairly close in judging their environmental response. This is of particular importance for greenhouse growers, who have to decide under what conditions they should try a newly introduced plant, and for agriculturists who have to judge which new crop plants should be tried in a particular locality, or who have to choose the localities where a particular new crop plant should be tested.

Chapter 17

PLANT CLIMATOLOGY

In the previous discussions, we have considered the plant's response to separate climatological factors; the Earhart Laboratory was actually designed to get this differentiated information, and to dissect the climatic response rather than integrate it. However, in nature, we are not dealing with the individual factors, but with their integration, which is weather, or, when time is added as a parameter, climate. It is questionable whether the term "integration" can be used in this sense, since a number of variables of very different nature have to be considered. Rain, humidity and dew all refer to H_2O; they can be expressed as weight per surface or weight per volume. But temperature and light have completely different dimensions, and are generally expressed as energy. Other factors such as time (photoperiod), air pressure and wind velocity have different dimensions again. The result is that it is impossible for us to make a simple system of weather or climate. Thus, in most cases, a simplification is strived for considering only the most important climatic factors, and dividing the whole spectrum of them into broad bands.

Climatic Systems:— A graphic representation of the geographic distribution of climates all over the world was given by KÖPPEN and improved by THORNTHWAITE. This is the most useful from a biological point of view. In it, first a general division is made on the basis of temperature, from high to low, with large or small yearly fluctuations. Then the temperature regions are divided according to rainfall, total and seasonal distribution being taken into consideration and evapotranspiration, bringing water requirements in relation with temperature and humidity. Other botanically important parameters are: length of frost-free period, snow cover, intensity of rainfall, frequency of high winds, etc. For each of these weather factors special maps have been prepared, giving for instance the frost-free period in the various regions of the United States, indicating whether the growing season is long enough to grow crops of frost-sensitive plants. Other maps indicate the frequency of hail storms or of hurricanes, all of which factors have to be taken into consideration if a new crop is to be developed in a region where it was not grown before.

An outgrowth of this method of climatic representation was the homoclimatic map, such as made by MEIGS for the arid countries of the world, which tried to stress similarities in different regions of the world, but, like most other climatological studies, was predicated upon the requirements of man.

All such attempts to classify climates and map their geographical distribution are based on a yearly cycle in climate, using the declination of the sun for synchronization. Such presentations are of importance when growth of perennial plants has to be considered, but they have no justification in connection with the growth of annual plants. When we compare in California the climates of the Imperial and the Salinas Valleys, they seem totally different. The Imperial Valley has a hot desert climate, whereas the Salinas Valley has an almost oceanic climate with very cool summers. Precipitation is also very different in these two locations. The same annual crop plants which are grown in the Imperial Valley during winter (lettuce, carrots) are grown in the Salinas Valley during spring, summer and autumn. As far as these crop plants are concerned, the climates of these two localities are comparable — but only during part of the yearly cycle, and not at the same time of the year. Therefore, it will not be immediately apparent from climatological or homoclimatic maps which areas are suitable for specific annual crops, unless we could introduce a more flexible time-axis.

In spite of the fact that in previous centuries climatological information was very scanty, a number of attempts were made to correlate occurrence of plants with climate. The best known early work in this connection was that of Alexander von Humboldt. As a result of his South American travels he pointed out that the regression of vegetation from equator to arctic and from lowland to alpine heights was very comparable, and that from a vegetational standpoint the alpine and arctic climates were analogous. The physical basis for comparison was largely temperature.

The Heatsum Concept:— Comparisons of other climates in relation to plant growth in those days were also largely based on temperature. Réaumur seems to have been the first to make a comparison of the quantity of heat received by a plant and its stage of development (Thornthwaite 1952). Adanson, 200 years ago, proposed that the time of development of plants in spring was determined by the total amount of heat they had received during winter.

Boussingault, Quételet, and Alphonse de Candolle (1855) stressed the importance of temperature in the development of crop plants. They showed that, when the daily average temperatures for the whole growing season of a plant were summated, a so-called heat sum was obtained which expressed the total amount of heat to which the plant was subjected during its whole growing season and which was required for its maturing. It was found that for individual crop plants the heatsum for a growing season was fairly constant, and that, *e.g.*, for wheat this amounted to 2120-2260 degree-days, irrespective of latitude or altitude of the growing locality. Whereas in first approximation a quantitative relationship seemed to exist, these early investigators noticed that the heatsum was not very constant for a number of plants. Therefore, they suggested modifications to improve the correlation between observed temperatures and plant growth. In general it was found that low temperatures apparently were proportionately less effective than higher temperatures and that growth was not proportional to the temperature expressed in degrees centigrade. QUÉTELET believed that growth was proportional to the square of the temperature, and consequently his heatsum was the sum of the squares of the daily temperatures. DE CANDOLLE subtracted a certain minimum temperature from his daily averages, presumably the number of degrees below which no growth occurred. This value differed for different plants: for barley it was 5°C, but for *Zea mays* 13°C had to be subtracted.

More recently, heatsums have been used extensively by, *e.g.*, NUTTONSON (1948) who applied a correction factor for the photoperiod in the case of peas.

In all these cases it was considered that the major effect of climate on plants could be expressed in terms of a single variable: average temperature, and that there existed a direct proportionality between this temperature or a derivative of it and growth. In DE CANDOLLE's case the relationship was:

$$\Sigma(t - x) = k \qquad (1)$$

in QUÉTELET's calculations it was: $\Sigma t^2 = k$ (2)

and in NUTTONSON's peas he assumed: $\Sigma[(t - x) \times ph] = k$ (3)

In these formulas t stands for the average daily temperature, x is a factor depending on the plant and the temperature scale, ph is an expression of the photoperiod during the growing season, and k equals the heatsum which varies from plant to plant.

It is amazing that these heatsums come out as constant as they do, for in most plants, growth is not a straight-line function of temperature such as:

$$g = ct + d \qquad (4)$$

but varies more like: $g = at^3 + bt^2 + ct + d$ (5)

In this formula a is always negative and of the order of magnitude of −0.2, b is greater than 1, the value of c is near that of the optimal temperature, and d depends on the lowest temperature at which growth is still possible. FIGURE 43 gives a graphical representation of formulas (4) and (5).

A square equation cannot express both the exponential increase in growth rate with temperature in the lower range and the dropping off in the higher range. A cubic equation evidently gives a fair mathematical approximation of the relationship between temperature and growth (*see* FIGURE 43 as compared with FIGURE 40). But we cannot use this to express the behavior of plants in the field. In the first place, the formula is too complicated; in the second place, the parameters are not constant throughout the growing period of a plant; and, in the third place, the formula has no theoretical significance whatsoever. In this connection it should be pointed out that heat is considered in all these formulae as a quantity, which it is not. Heat energy cannot be used by any plant for growth; the energy used is all chemical energy present in the stored food. Heat can only control the *rate* at which this chemical energy can be made available and the efficiency with which it is used, or it can influence the *rate* of photosynthesis. Therefore, since heat is not a form of available energy for plants, and only modifies other processes, it is logically impermissible to talk about — or even calculate — heatsums.

The only satisfactory use of temperature data in relation to field growth of plants of which I am aware is that of J. MEDCALF, published in 1952 in the Hawaiian Pineapple Planters' Record. He has measured the

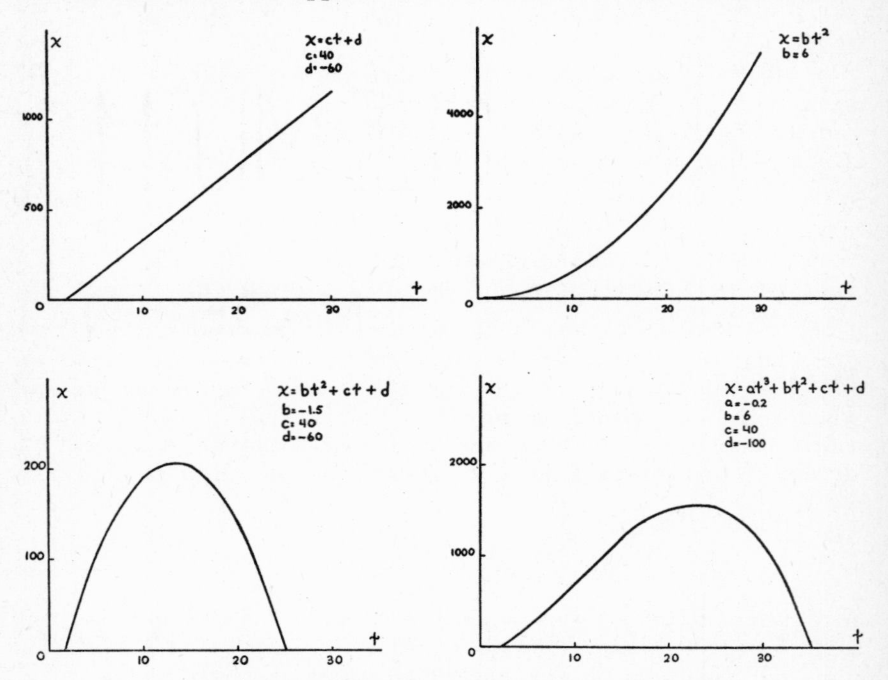

FIGURE 43.— Growth rates (X) as a function of temperature (*abscissa:* T) when different equations hold: direct proportionality (as commonly used in phenology), exponential (like QUÉTELET assumed), a square, or a cubic equation.

amount of growth of pineapple plants at different temperatures as the basis for his calculations. He recorded the temperature with a thermograph and counted the number of hours that a certain temperature range had occurred. He then multiplied this number of hours with the growth rate at that particular temperature. By adding all these temperature-corrected growth rates, he arrived at a total amount of elongation which very closely agreed with the actually observed growth. From this, one can conclude that no other effects of high or low temperatures occurred on the growth rate of these pineapples and that they immediately adjusted themselves to the new growth rate corresponding to the different temperature.

Plant Distribution as a Function of Temperature:— In nature, we seldom find that the temperature level stays constant throughout the year. This is only the case in the tropics. We can find there daily temperature ranges at any level by selecting the proper altitude. The difference in average temperature between the warmest and coldest months of the year is less than 1°C at localities less than 10° from the equator. Therefore, we can find in the tropics localities which are a complete counterpart, as far as temperature is concerned, of the greenhouses of the Earhart Laboratory in which the same daily temperature range (approximately 6°C) is maintained throughout the year. In Colombia, use of these conditions is being made by the Rockefeller Foundation Agricultural Program. Many different crops in all the available varieties are being grown at different altitudes. The altitudinal range in their established stations is 50, 1000, 1500, 2200, 2600 and 3100 m. Different varieties of wheat, corn, bean,

TABLE 13: *Altitudinal range of distribution of some common weeds near the equator in Colombia and Panama, as observed in Panama City, El Salvador, Palmyra, Medellin, LaCaja, Chinchina, Bogota and Usme:—*

		Found outside tropics as:	
WEED GENUS	ALTITUDE	SUMMER WEED	WINTER & SPRING WEED
Phyllanthus, Pilea	ca. 0-500 m.	−	−
Amaranthus, Cynodon, Cyperus, Portulaca	ca. 0-1500 m.	+	−
Borreria, Commelina, Emelia, Ipomoea	ca. 0-2500 m.	−	−
Eclipta, Sida	ca. 500-1500 m.	−	−
Ageratum, Erigeron, Raphanus	ca. 500-2500 m.	±	±
Chenopodium, Poa annua, Sonchus, Stellaria	ca. 1500-2500 m.	−	+
Holcus, Rumex, Taraxacum, Trifolium	ca. 2500-3500 m.	−	+
Spergula	ca. 3000-3500 m.	−	+

potato and other crop plants behave very differently at these six altitudinal stations. Each variety has only one or two adjacent altitudes at which it grows optimally, whereas at the other stations it is outproduced by other varieties, or other crop plants.

By observing the weed vegetation in these fields at different altitudes, a very nice sequence of weeds can be prepared which each have a different range of occurrence. This is presumably based on a different range of temperatures, with each weed displaying another temperature requirement, because the other meteorological factors such as illumination, daylength, precipitation, etc., either are closely similar, or are made uniform by irrigation. This behavior is shown in TABLE 13, which was prepared after a rather cursory study of cultivated fields at different elevations in Colombia. It is based on few observations, and, thus, we can expect that an intensive investigation will produce many changes in the altitudinal distribution of these weeds as presented in TABLE 13. Necessary additions to this study should consider distribution of these weeds in connection with soil type, crop plant, etc. In spite of the incompleteness of the data, several conclusions seem to be warranted. A number of weeds occur only in the lowlands (*Phyllanthus, Pilea*). They are not found as weeds outside the tropics and, therefore, are restricted in their climatic tolerance to the warmest climates. The second group has a wider altitudinal distribution,

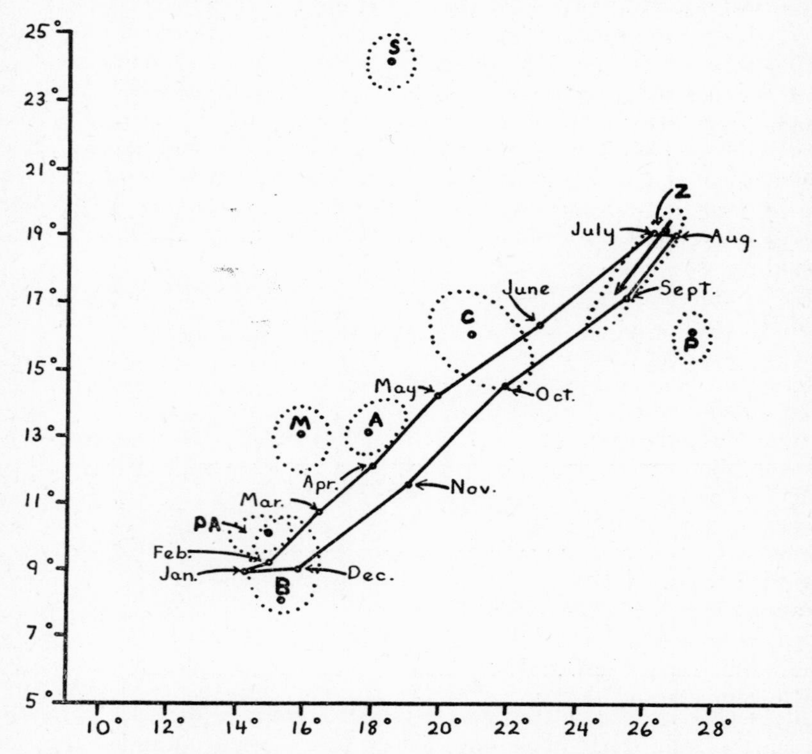

FIGURE 44.— Within a system of coordinates (nyctotemperature: *ordinate* and phototemperature: *abscissa*) the optimal growing conditions for a number of plants have been placed: B, *Bellis perennis* (English daisy); PA, *Papaver nudicaule* (Iceland poppy); M, *Matthiola incana* (stock); A, *Ageratum conyzoides;* C, *Callistephus chinensis* (China aster); Z, *Zinnia elegans;* P, *Petunia;* S, *Saintpaulia ioantha* (African violet). Within the same grid of coordinates the climate of Pasadena (California, U.S.A.) is entered by connecting the monthly averages for both photo- and nyctotemperatures, resulting in an elongated ellipse, which transects the optimal growing conditions for different plants at different times of the year.

from 0-1500 m., and these plants are all found as weeds outside the tropics as well, but exclusively as summer weeds (*Amaranthus, Cynodon, Cyperus, Portulaca*), or at least in fields which were ploughed in late spring or summer. Apparently, they find the same climatic conditions for germination and growth in the tropics as during summer in temperate regions.

The third group is just as interesting: they have an even wider altitudinal range in the tropics, but usually do *not* occur outside the tropics. This means that a climatic factor other than temperature (perhaps an even 12-hour photoperiod as in *Emelia*) controls their distribution.

The next 4 groups are similar in that they occur only at altitudes higher than 1000 m., and that they are common weeds outside the tropics, particularly among crops planted in winter or early spring. These 4 groups differ only in the height at which they occur in Colombia.

If a more thorough investigation had been carried out in Colombia, it might have been possible to distinguish another group of weeds which occurs in temperate regions but not in the tropics. This group might include such plants as *Agrostemma* and *Galinsoga,* which perhaps temporarily need lower temperatures for germination or growth and could not develop in climates with even temperatures. Thus we can see how weeds could be developed into very sensitive climatic indicators, in the same way as different crop species and varieties are useful in describing or indicating climate. Being of such wide distribution, they are particularly useful, and seem better suited as "plant-indicators" in the sense of CLEMENTS than wild plants, of which many different morphologically indistinguishable ecotypes may occur.

Outside the tropics, we find a more or less pronounced seasonal fluctuation in temperature, and under such conditions an analysis of the relationship between the temperature and growth becomes more complicated. The heatsum tries to take this into account, but, as pointed out before, the heatsum is not a good measure for the response of the plant. The simplest case for the growth analysis in a fluctuating climate exists when we are dealing with short-lived annual plants. It is then possible to consider their development over a relatively narrow range of temperatures. To show the yearly fluctuations in temperature, the average day and average night temperatures throughout the period of a year are plotted on a two-dimensional grid as shown in FIGURE 44. We find then that a rather elongated ellipse appears, which is most elongated in the most extreme continental climates. This presentation of climate can now be used in connection with the optimal growing conditions of plants as they have been determined in the laboratory. It has been found that, whenever the climatic ellipse passes through the optimal growing conditions of a plant, that is the time when it grows best in that particular climate. Therefore, we have reached here an expression of climate which is immediately applicable to the growing conditions of plants.

We should, however, also consider a seasonal or periodical shift in the optimal growing conditions of a plant. In most plants, the optimal temperature gradually decreases as the plant grows older. Therefore, we should not express the optimal growing conditions of the plant as a point or a circular area in the day and night temperature grid just discussed, but we should express this in a grid which also has a time-axis. This is shown in FIGURE 47, in which the optimal nyctotemperatures for growth of a tomato plant are plotted against the age of the plant in months. This time scale is somewhat elastic, because, if at any time the plants were growing under sub-optimal conditions, the time scale is lengthened. We can compare this figure with FIGURE 46 in which the progress of nycto-temperatures in 5 arbitrary climates is shown. It is obvious that by starting tomatoes at different times of the year we can make different portions of

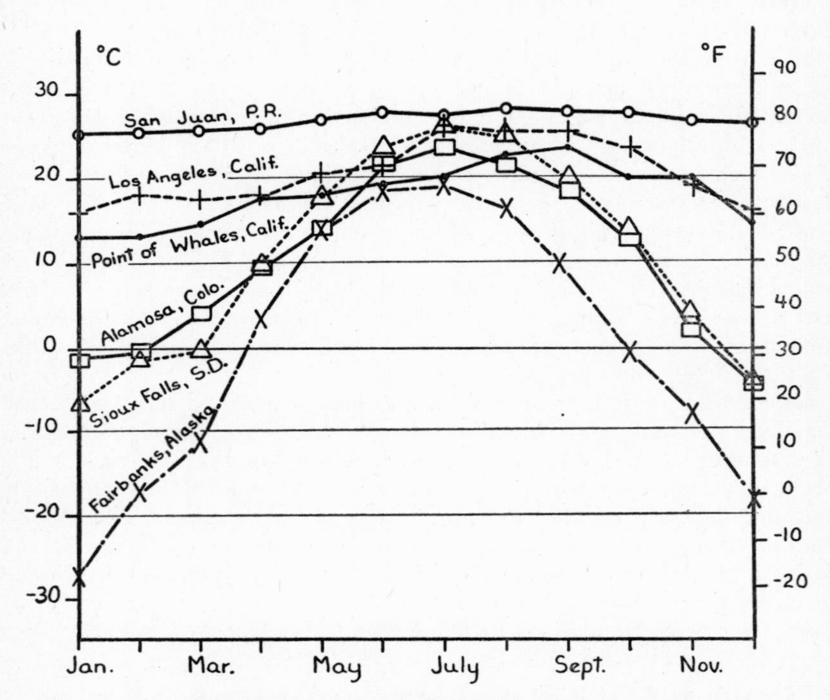

FIGURE 45.— Monthly averages of the phototemperature of 6 different localities, illustrating: a tropical climate (San Juan, Puerto Rico), an oceanic climate (Los Angeles and Point of Whales, 300 Km. further NW along the California coast), a continental climate (Alamosa in the high plains of Colorado and Sioux Falls in South Dakota), and a continental arctic climate (Fairbanks in the center of Alaska).

their optimal temperature curve coincide with these climates. It is, for instance, possible to have the flowering and fruiting stage coincide with the summer of climate C or D, provided the seedling stage can be passed at a higher temperature than is available in those climates. This usually is done by starting tomato plants in greenhouses, or by germinating them in southern areas and shipping them North at the correct time. On the other hand, best growth of tomatoes can be achieved in climate E by germinating them in late summer, and letting them flower and fruit during the winter when the night temperatures are lowest. In other plants, we

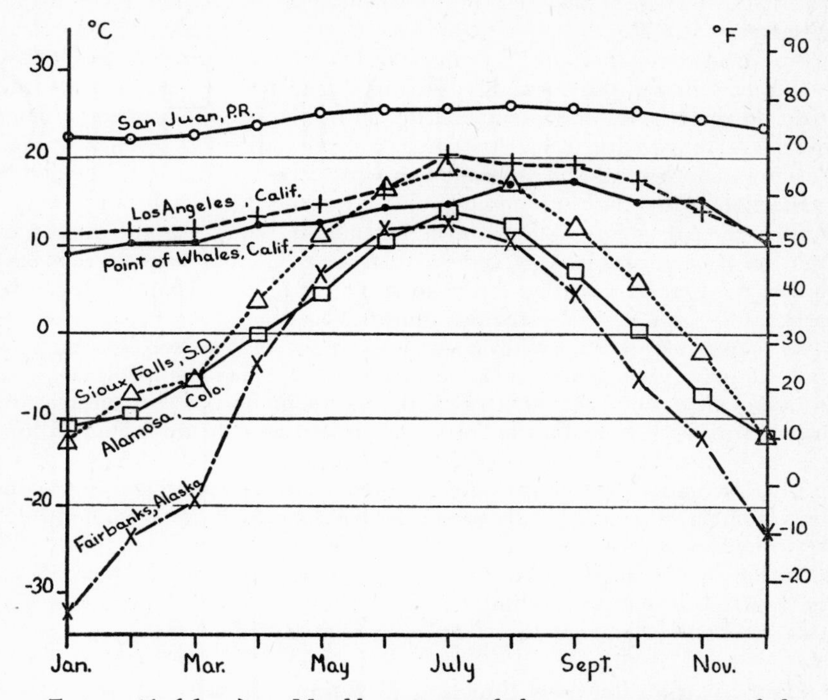

FIGURE 46 (*above*).— Monthly averages of the nyctotemperatures of the same localities as illustrated in FIGURE 45.

FIGURE 47 (*below*).— Shift in optimal nyctotemperature (*ordinate*) with age (*abscissa*) for tomato (an out-door variety, like Pearson), chili pepper (a bellpepper variety) and *Eschscholtzia californica.* Coordinates the same as in FIGURE 46; if transferred on tracing paper, FIGURE 47 can be slid over FIGURE 46 along the abscissa, showing where and when the plants concerned may be successfully grown.

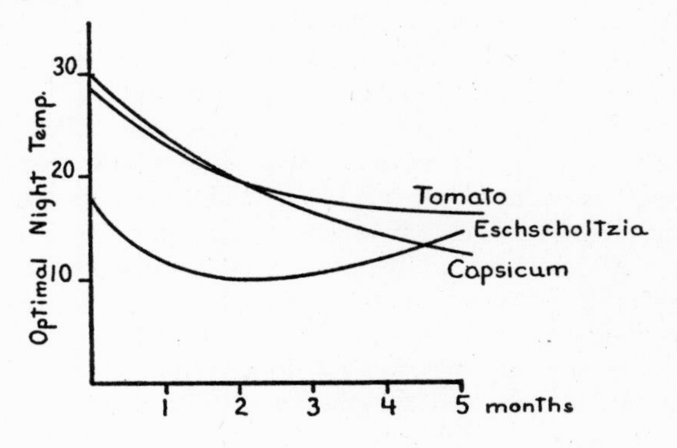

have very different seasonal requirements, such as in *Eschscholtzia.* Here a period of relatively low temperatures has to intervene between the higher germination and flowering temperatures. Thus, *Eschscholtzia* development can be made to coincide with climate D by being germinated in autumn.

Whereas in FIGURE 44 and PLATE XXII one type of correlation (with stress on nycto-, and photo-temperature, and photoperiod) between climate and plant growth has been attempted, a combination of FIGURES 46 and 47 allows another type of correlation in which the time factor is stressed in connection with the nyctotemperature. By transferring FIGURE 47 on transparent paper and sliding it over FIGURE 46, which has the same time scale on its abscissa, making certain that the 0°C lines overlap, it is easy to find the time of year that a tomato, a pepper or an *Eschscholtzia* can be successfully grown in a particular climate.

As mentioned in the section on ecology, many plants need low temperatures at some time during their development to break their dormancy, or to induce flowering. In such cases, the representation of climatic requirements of a plant, as in FIGURE 44, is insufficient and should include a time axis, as in FIGURE 47.

The fluctuations of temperature in a temperate climate make it possible for a number of the weeds shown in TABLE 13, which are separated there in altitude, to grow in one locality but at different times. Thus, the weeds occurring at the highest altitudes in the tropics are found as winter or spring weeds in temperate climates, whereas some of the low altitude weeds, such as *Amaranthus,* are found growing with summer crops.

Plant Distribution as a Function of Rain:— In the case of irrigated crop plants, precipitation plays only a minor part as a climatological factor. This makes growing practically independent of rainfall. To the natural vegetation, however, rainfall determines whether or not the plant will grow. Thus, areas with summer rains and those with winter rains are entirely different as far as plant-climate is concerned, even though the temperature sequence in both cases will be the same. In the coastal areas of southern California the rainy season occurs in winter. Since rainfall is very deficient during summer, the vegetation becomes very dry giving rise to many bare areas. When the first rains come in late autumn or winter, germination (especially of annuals) is abundant, but these are all winter annuals. For this reason, neither corn nor tomatoes germinate spontaneously, and do not become established as weeds, since by the time that the temperatures have become high enough for their germination, a complete plant cover has been established, which prevents further germination. In New Mexico on the other hand, winter rains are rare; therefore, these summer rains fall on partially bare soil and allow summer annuals to become established. Among these summer annuals belong corn and tomatoes. There they are actually found growing as weeds along roads. On this basis, we should look for the country of origin of corn in areas with summer rains or tropical areas with a pronounced dry season. This dry period should produce bare areas where germination of annuals after a good rain could occur. We can summarize this by saying that the effective climate for corn and tomato is one at which the first rains after a drought period occur at high temperatures. In practice, we can control the time at which these two factors (temperature and bare soil) coincide by removing all pre-existing vegetation by ploughing or harrowing, thereby giving the plants the bare ground they need to germinate without competition.

Multidimensional Representation of Climate:— For all photoperiodically sensitive plants, the length of photoperiod should be included in the presentation of climate. We can take the two-dimensional grid of FIGURE 44 for instance in which the optimal growing conditions for various plants are plotted against day and night temperature, and expand this by plotting photoperiod on a third axis. This has been done in PLATE XXII, where the optimal growing conditions for a number of garden plants are plotted against 3 independent variables: day temperature, night temperature, and photoperiod. In this same three-dimensional graph several climates have been included, one semi-tropical (Pasadena) with mild winters, and another continental (Denver) with cold winters. The summer conditions, however, are much alike, although the period of higher temperatures is passed more rapidly in Denver than in Pasadena. From PLATE XXII the best time for growing these garden plants can be deduced with more precision than from FIGURE 44 in which the photoperiod was neglected. Further variables, such as rainfall, time, morphological development, flowering, etc., should be included in this correlation between plant development and climatic factors, but this would require 4, 5 or 6-dimensional representation. This poses grave difficulties for our perception. We usually think, read, or talk in one dimension (linear) and the three-dimensional graphs of FIGURES 18, 19, 20, 21, 27, 28, 29, 31, 34, 36, 37, 38, 39 and 48, and PLATE XXII require a certain amount of effort to become intelligible. How much greater would be the difficulties, if we wanted to comprehend more complicated inter-relationships, such as encountered daily by any farmer or agriculturist. Yet, it is possible to get at least an inkling of such highly complex relationships between plants and climate by forcing ourselves to envisage them. FIGURES 36, 37, 38 and 39 are an attempt to show this. In each three-dimensional model either stem elongation or morphological development of two pea varieties is plotted as the variable, as a function of both photoperiod and light intensity. This produces two sets of three-dimensional models. By lining them up as a function of temperature, a fifth dimension is introduced, and time is indicated by two sets of models for the first and second weekly growth periods. Thus these figures represent, incompletely, the inter-relationships between 7 variables: variety, either growth or morphological development, time, temperature, photoperiod, and light intensity.

Any agriculturist, or botanist, or scientist, should train his perception so that he can envisage more complex inter-relationships than simple one-dimensional correlations; this desirability becomes a necessity when we start to consider the plant in relation to climate. The plant is already a four-dimensional concept, in which the time-axis is all too often neglected, but once we consider this four-dimensional object in its relationship to the individual and independent climatic variables, highly complex multi-dimensional correlations develop, which *have* to be understood to explain the response of the plant to its environment.

Although we admit that more dimensions should be added to the graph of PLATE XXII to include other climatic variables, even then the graph of FIGURE 44 is an over-simplification of the actual relationship between plant growth and climate. FIGURE 48 shows that the optimal growing conditions for a tomato in relation to photoperiod and temperature cannot be expressed as an orbicular area. The climatic requirements of the tomato present a much more extensive relationship, in which only the nyctotemperature extends over a narrow range, which, however, is influenced by the phototemperature in the sense that the optimal nyctotemperature is slightly higher as the phototemperature rises. This can be concluded from FIGURE 18. If a time-axis could be included, the pillow-like range of the optimal conditions would be seen to descend along the nyctotemperature axis, without being much affected by phototemperature and photoperiod.

In FIGURE 44 an attempt has been made to include the time-axis for *Zinnia* in the graph. As a young plant this requires a higher photo- and nyctotemperature than when flowering, and this is shown as an elliptical area, an arrow indicating the shift with time. Since for optimal development of *Zinnia,* we also must take photoperiod into consideration (to obtain large vigorous plants they should be started under long-day conditions, and then transferred to shorter days to induce flowering), the presentation of its optimal climate in PLATE XXII should have the form of a slightly bent sausage, with its long axis substituting for the time-axis.

The future will have to tell whether this three-dimensional presentation of climate has practical significance in a better understanding of the relationships between plants and climate. At least, it emphasizes the complexity of climate as a concept, and it points out the importance of a study of the interactions of the climatic variables on plants. Therefore, the study of climatic tolerance and optimal climatic conditions for a plant should, if possible, encompass all variables, and these variables should not only be tested singly, but also in combination, to detect interactions between variables which are very likely to occur. This is possible to a considerable degree in the Earhart Plant Research Laboratory, in which each climatic factor can be studied in relation to most others.

One of the greatest difficulties encountered in correlating climate and plant development is that when we talk about climate we talk in terms of averages. It is quite obvious that the average temperature per 24-hour period, which is most easily obtainable from meteorological summaries, is of no value whatsoever when it has to be used in relation to plant growth.

In most plants, growth occurs largely during night and, consequently, in most plants, we find a close parallel between nyctotemperature and plant growth rate. But not only does the nyctotemperature differ from the average daily temperature, the actual temperatures can also differ considerably from the weekly or monthly average. In southern Texas, *e.g.*, during winter, either a cold air mass from the North or a warm air mass from the Caribbean Sea covers the country so that the temperatures in January in

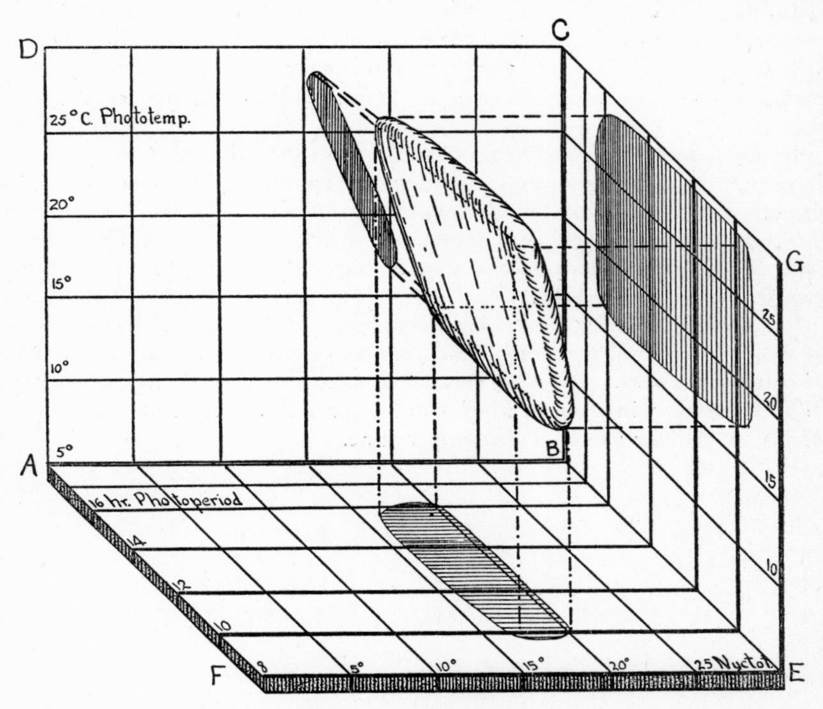

FIGURE 48.— Interrelationship between optimal phototemperature (*ordinate*), optimal nyctotemperature (*abscissa*), and optimal photoperiod in fruit set of the tomato. From WENT (1950).

the Rio Grande Valley are *either* tropical *or* near freezing, whereas the average temperature for the month indicates a very temperate and pleasant climate.

The only climatic variable which theoretically does not vary from year to year is daylength. But as far as the plant is concerned this is only true in theory. In the morning of a clear day the light intensity gradually increases, until it surpasses the critical intensity above which the plant perceives it as light, and in the evening an equally gradual decrease occurs, with also a point where the metabolism of the plant changes over from light to dark operation. On cloudy days, this critical light intensity is reached later in the morning and earlier in the evening, and, therefore, it is obvious that the effective daylength of photosynthesis or photoperiodism varies not only with the season, but also from day to day according to the degree of cloudiness. Since for each plant the critical light intensity and photoperiod are different, it becomes virtually impossible to express the effective photoperiod under natural conditions in exact figures. A shaded plant, and the lower leaves of tall plants are subjected to shorter effective photoperiods than the upper leaves of plants in full sunlight, and variable cloudiness further complicates the problem. Furthermore, the number of successive cloudy days will affect different plants in different ways. Whereas in *Xanthium* one single short day may induce flowering, in other plants 4-20 successive short days are required before flower induction occurs.

In the preceding considerations only the macroclimate was taken into account. Local differences in shade, sun exposure, drafts or wind, rain run-off, snow drifts and air-drainage materially modify the local climate. By consulting the book of Geiger (1950), corrections can be made for each locality in relation to the meteorological variables, using the official weather records as a basis.

For many centuries, gardeners have been making use of the protection of walls, to cut out the cold North winds, or to produce afternoon shade, or to reduce drafts. A good example of microclimatic effects can be found in the use of windrows. They can either reduce the intensity of local winds, or provide shade at the proper time.

Chapter 18

ECOLOGY

The Earhart Plant Research Laboratory is ideally suited to study the autecology of plants, or in other words, the relationships of the individual species, variety or ecotype to its surroundings. This relationship has been described for a limited number of plants in Chapters 6-14. In the following chapter we will consider to what extent this new autecological information helps us to explain the occurrence and distribution of plants in nature.

The general outlines of the relationships between plants and climate are well-known, since the gross effects are obvious. The desert vegetation is of course conditioned by drought; the tundra or alpine treeless areas are the result of a cold and short growing season, and deciduous tree and shrub growth are related to periodicity in the climate with regard to either rainfall or temperature.

In succession we will discuss the various climatic factors as they influence the occurrence and distribution of plants. We will start off with temperature.

Temperature:— As has been shown, temperature plays a controlling part in most plant growth. Yet, little precise knowledge about the response of mature plants to temperature was available. Among the exceptions belongs the work of BLAAUW and co-workers at the Agricultural College in Wageningen, on temperature responses of bulbous plants, especially during their storage life. Less precise information was obtained in ordinary greenhouses when during winter outside temperatures were low enough that more or less constant temperatures could be maintained by controlled heating. THOMPSON and co-workers at Cornell University, and ROBERTS and STRUCKMEYER at the University of Wisconsin were among those who contributed a great deal to our knowledge of optimal growing temperatures for many greenhouse crops. Information along these lines is available in such books as LAURIE and KIPLINGER: Commercial Flower Forcing, or THOMPSON: Vegetable Crops.

Another source of information on temperature requirements of plants is phenology, in which plant behavior in nature is recorded and correlated with meteorological information. The results are largely expressed as heatsums, required for crop ripening or breaking of dormancy. This has been discussed in Chapter 17 on Climatology.

Although the following considerations could have been based on the work mentioned in the previous paragraphs, it was not until after the experiments in the Clark and Earhart air-conditioned greenhouses were performed that a clearer picture of the climatic control of plant distribution started to emerge. Our earlier ideas were largely influenced by KERNER VON MARILAUN (1888) and the remarkable first edition of SCHIMPER'S Pflanzengeographie auf physiologischer Grundlage (1898). DAUBENMIRE (1947) and WALTER (1949 and 1951) have summarized our present knowledge more recently.

Nyctotemperature:— SACHS (1872) has shown that in many plants growth occurs predominantly during night. This would imply that the night temperature is then of paramount importance in growth. This was actually found to be true in the case of tomatoes, potatoes, chili peppers, corn and many other plants.

Let us first consider the yearly trend of night temperatures. This information is not available in any published meteorological records. Usually, they only give average 24-hour temperatures or daily or monthly maximum (t_{max}) and minimum (t_{min}) temperatures. From the latter we can approximate both average photo- (t_{pho}) and average nyctotemperatures (t_{nyc}) as follows: $t_{pho} = t_{max} - \frac{1}{4}(t_{max} - t_{min})$ and $t_{nyc} = t_{min} + \frac{1}{4}(t_{max} - t_{min})$. The average nyctotemperature changes from winter to summer, in all but tropical climates. In the tropics there is little yearly change, the less the closer to the equator. In Java at 7° S. Lat., there is only 0.9° difference in nyctotemperature between the warmest and the coolest month. In San Juan, Porto Rico at 18° N. Lat., this difference is already 3.9°, and at Point of Whales (California, along coast, at 36° N. Lat.) it is 8.2°C. Whereas near the coast of oceans the large body of water also tends to equalize nyctotemperature throughout the year, as we move inland the yearly range increases. For instance, at about 38° N. Lat. a series of localities show the following range in nyctotemperatures between warmest and coldest months: Palo Alto, 24 Km. from coast, 10.0°; Lake Eleanor, 220 Km. from coast, 21.0°; Ellery Lake, 270 Km. from coast, 22.0°; Alamosa, Colorado, 1400 Km. from coast, 28.3°. The latter locality has a typical continental climate. In Fairbanks, in the interior of Alaska, the yearly range is greatest, 45.0°C.

Low humidity also increases the yearly range in nyctotemperature, and amounts to 31° for Death Valley, California, which compares with 9.2° for Los Angeles near the coast, and 21° for Lake Eleanor, at about equal distance from the coast as Death Valley, but in the moister area.

FIGURES 46 and 49 show a number of curves of the yearly progression of nyctotemperature for a number of localities. They are all typical sinusoids, with different amplitudes and absolute heights. It is, therefore, possible to characterize the nyctoclimate of any locality by giving the nyctotemperatures of the warmest and coldest month; the others could then be derived with a fair degree of accuracy.

In FIGURE 49 the yearly nyctotemperature progression is shown for three stations lying at different altitudes along an East-West transect through the center of California (recalculated from CLAUSEN, KECK and HIESEY 1940). The Palo Alto Climate is still strongly influenced by the nearness of the ocean; the two mountain stations at 1400 and 2800 m. altitude have almost congruent curves, the nyctotemperature of the higher station being 10° lower throughout the year. In this figure is also shown the length of growing season for the plants investigated by CLAUSEN *et al.* It can be seen that this growing season coincides with the period during which the nyctotemperature remains above 1.5°C. Since these curves represent the average nyctotemperature over the whole night and over a monthly period, it means that when the average nyctotemperature is 1.5°, during approximately half the nights the actual temperature drops below freezing.

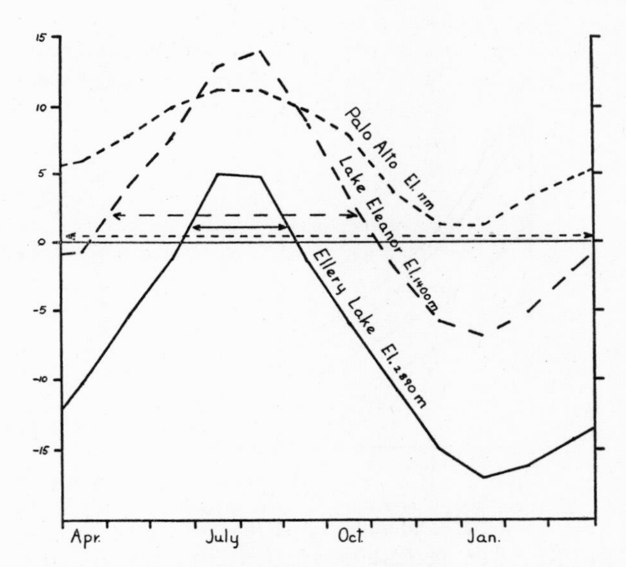

FIGURE 49.— Nyctotemperatures (*ordinate:* in degrees Celsius) throughout the year at 3 localities, at different altitudes, along the 38°N. parallel in California. The length of the growing season is shown between arrows, while drawn or broken lines correspond with the 3 climates. Recalculated from CLAUSEN, KECK and HIESEY (1940).

Therefore, plants, which can stand moderate frost, will start to grow when during the majority of the nights and during a sufficiently long time each night the temperature stays above freezing. There are some plants which are able to grow at 0°C, such as *Galanthus nivalis, Soldanella* and *Erythronium* species and others which will penetrate a snow cover, but the majority of plants grow at an appreciable rate only when the nyctotemperature is above freezing.

Other data concerning the three climates of FIGURE 49 could be presented, such as the average daily temperature, the average phototemperature, the average maximum or average minimum temperature, but none of these shows such a good correlation between a particular temperature and the length of the growing season as the ones reproduced.

Climatic Basis for Sharp Boundaries in the Distribution of Plants:— By drawing a whole family of parallel curves displaced 5 degrees from each other, like those of Lake Eleanor and Ellery Lake of FIGURE 49, the climates on a mountain slope at intervals of 750 m. altitude would be represented, and from them the length of growing season can be derived. Such a calculation is shown in FIGURE 50, in which the length of time that the average nyctotemperature is higher than 0°, 1.5°, 5° or 10°C is plotted against altitude, for a transect through the Sierra Nevada at 38° N. Lat. This family of curves nicely explains the reason for the sharp altitudinal delimitation of the occurrence of plants. If, for instance, a particular plant

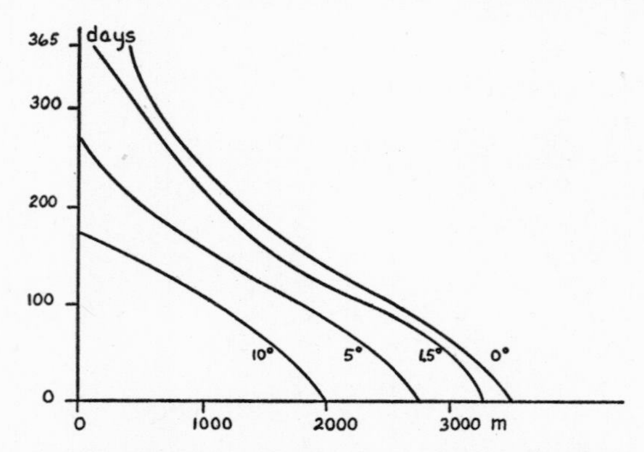

FIGURE 50.— Number of days per year (*ordinate*) that, at different altitudes, along the 38°N. parallel in California the nyctotemperature exceeds 0°, 1.5°, 5° or 10°C.

needs at least 60 days per year of nyctotemperatures above 0°, then this plant cannot grow above 3100 m. in the Sierra Nevada.

At both ends of the curve representing the length of growing season as a function of altitude, the rate of change is greatest. Thus, between 400 and 900 m. altitude the length of time that nyctotemperatures above 0° occur decreases 3 weeks per 100 m. rise, and between 3000 and 3500 m. the decrease per 100 m. is 2 weeks. But around 2500 m. the decrease is only 1 week per 100 m. increase in altitude. For this reason the critical component of a climate changes twice or three times as fast for a plant near its upper or lower limits of distribution. If in addition we take into consideration that we are dealing here with threshold values, in which, *e.g.*, a decrease of 2 weeks in the length of growing season cannot be tolerated, we can understand on a purely physical basis why usually the boundaries of the area of distribution of a plant are so sharp. It is probably for this reason too that a few hundred meters altitude near the coast in southern California means the difference between winter cropping (in the Imperial Valley below 100 m.) and a winter dormant season at a few 100 meters above sea level. This altitudinal difference is still more pronounced at timberline in the southern Sierra Nevada of California. There timberline lies at 3300 m., where the growing season is reduced to one month. Below this altitude the growth of both trees and herbs is rather luxuriant; only a few 100 meters higher, growth is severely reduced and the number of plants which occurs above 3600 m. drops very rapidly. The same sudden change in vegetation just above timberline is found in Lapland and in Alaska. Therefore, both the sharpness of the timberline and the sudden change in vegetation and growth a few hundred meters higher can be explained by the control of growth by night temperature. It also explains why timberline is equally high on South and North slopes. During daytime, big temperature differences may occur at the same altitude according to the insolation. During windless nights, however, a stratification of the air occurs, which evens out differences between North and South exposures.

Not only growth and, consequently, plant distribution is strongly influenced by nyctotemperature, but many other plant processes are, too; in tomatoes, *e.g.*, the optimal nyctotemperature for fruit set is 14°-18°C. The plants must receive this temperature during the period just after pollination, to insure fruit set. After this time, the temperature may drop below the critical point, for the fruits are already set, and will continue their development. This was found by an analysis of phenological data (Went and Cosper 1945) which confirmed laboratory experiments.

Although the following point has not been properly investigated, it is obvious that somewhere at a light intensity below full daylight the tomato plant switches over from day to night operation. The critical intensity for the switch-over to growth and elongation lies somewhere near 1000 ft.-c., but seems somewhat lower in the case of fruit set. But whatever this intensity is, it is clear that it is reached earlier in the late afternoon when plants are shaded against the West. Therefore, during spring, or any other time of the year when the nyctotemperatures are on the average too low for good growth and for fruit set, tomato plants growing on the East side of shade trees or walls will do better than those on the West side of a shading structure. In general, when plants are grown in too cool a climate, Eastern exposures should improve growth (if this is largely controlled by nyctotemperature), or in other words, afternoon shade is beneficial. This is a paraphrase of the well-known gardener's dictum that the morning sun is best for plants (*see* Went 1946).

Many plants not only will not grow when the night temperature is too high, but they die when exposed to it night after night. Lewis and Went (1945) have given several examples of such behavior (*Phacelia parryi*, *Baeria chrysostoma*). One such case has been investigated further by Loo (1946) who found that *Baeria chrysostoma* would die when grown at 26°C nyctotemperature, even though it could well support this temperature during the photoperiod. The plants also die under sterile culture conditions at the high night temperature, showing that death was not due to parasites or extraneous organisms, but was caused by temperature-induced metabolic disturbances in the dark processes. More extreme nyctotemperature sensitivity can be found in other wild plants (species of *Clarkia:* LEWIS, unpublished, and *Lupinus:* DUNN, unpublished). Therefore, we can accept this behavior as normal in many wild plants from temperate regions.

This intolerance of high night temperatures throws a new light on the distribution of many plants over the world. Originally it was believed that the disappearance of temperate region plants as one progressed towards the tropics was due to effects of survival of typical tropical plants in a struggle for existence with the temperate region plants. It is now an experimentally established fact that many of the temperate region plants would not survive in the tropics, regardless of competition with tropical plants.

Apparently the ability to grow at high or at low temperatures is not a character easily changed by the evolutionary process, for so many families are restricted to the temperate regions and the higher altitudes in the tropics (*Ericaceae, Gentianaceae, Ranunculaceae, Saxifragaceae*) or to the lowlands of the tropics (*Burseraceae, Icacinaceae, Dipterocarpaceae, Burmanniaceae, Rafflesiaceae*). In other families, some subfamilies are differentiated not only according to morphological characters, but also according to temperature response. In the *Rosaceae, e.g.*, the *Pomoideae, Rosoideae* and *Spiraeoideae* are temperate, but the *Chrysobalanoideae* occur in the tropics. Among the grasses, the *Festuceae, Aveneae* and *Hordeae* are temperate, and the *Bambuseae, Maydeae, Oryzeae* and *Chlorideae* tropical.

SCHIMPER (1898) already made this distinction between plants. He distinguished between "megathermic," "mesothermic" and "microthermic" plants; only the former are to be found in the lowlands of the tropics, the mesothermic plants occur in tropical mountains and in temperate regions, and microthermic plants are polar and alpine. He indicated how the members of individual families usually belonged predominantly or wholly to one or another group. As examples from his classification the *Polycarpicae* can be mentioned: *Ranunculaceae, Berberidaceae* and *Magnoliaceae* are meso- or even microthermic, whereas *Anonaceae, Myristicaceae* and *Monimiaceae* are megathermic.

Phototemperatures may be as critical as nyctotemperatures for other plants. FIGURE 24 shows the maximal rate of stem elongation of Alaska peas in response to temperature. Whereas at a 20° phototemperature a range of night temperatures from 7°-20°C made no difference in their growth in length, the effect of the phototemperature was very pronounced, with an optimum at 23°C. For other varieties this same behavior can be seen in PLATES XIII*a* and *b*.

Some of the best examples of temperature control in relation to the distribution of plants is found in the work of HIESEY (1953) and CLAUSEN *et al.* (1948). They studied the temperature response of a number of climatic races of *Achillea* from different altitudes and latitudes, and also of different species and hybrids of bluegrasses (*see* Chapter 11). Clones of a race of *Achillea* native to a uniformly cool but mild climate along the immediate coast of California grew successfully and flowered abundantly when grown at day temperatures of 20° or 30°C, and cold nights of 6°C, but failed to flower with warm nights of 17°C. Another race of the same species from the warm San Joaquin Valley, on the other hand, grew most successfully with the warm nights. Races of *Achillea* from higher altitudes, where the diurnal range in temperature during the growing season is large, were favored by a combination of high day and low night temperatures. In the bluegrass genus *Poa* the development of flowering stems in the northern temperate species, *P. ampla* and *P. compressa,* was found to be strongly favored by cold night temperatures of 6°C, and inhibited by warm nights of 17°C. The tolerance of different species and races of *Poa* to different temperature ranges as expressed in their growth was found to

TABLE 14: *Tomato production in two localities in California, in Kg. per plant. Data of* WENT *and* COSPER (1945):—

	AVERAGE NYCTOTEMP.	BEEFSTEAK IN KG./PLANT	EARLIANA IN KG./PLANT	NUMBER OF YEARS REQUIRED TO HAVE 100 × AS MANY PLANTS OF ONE VARIETY AS OF THE OTHER
La Jolla (along coast)	17.5°C	8 Kg.	5 Kg.	10 years
Temecula (inland)	15°C	2 Kg.	6 Kg.	4 years

vary with the climates of their origin, and interspecific hybrids combined in varying degree the tolerance of their parents.

Beefsteak and Earliana tomatoes provide an example how the differential temperature responses of closely related varieties may affect their distribution. In laboratory experiments it had been found that the optimal temperature for fruit production in the Beefsteak tomato was about 3°C higher than that for the Earliana (WENT 1945, VERKERK 1955). Both varieties were planted in the field in two localities: La Jolla where the nyctotemperature remains above 15° for many months during summer, and Temecula where the minimal nyctotemperature seldom reaches 15°C. The average nyctotemperature was 2½°C higher at La Jolla, although the maximum temperatures remained much lower there. TABLE 14 shows the fruit weight produced per plant at the two localities. These differences are exactly what we would expect from the behavior of these two varieties in the laboratory. If we now assume that seed production is proportional to fruit weight and that seeds of both varieties have the same chances for germination and survival, we can calculate how these two varieties would behave in competition with each other. If in the first year an equal number of plants of both varieties grew mixed in both localities, the next year the Earliana would out-number the Beefsteak 6:2 in Temecula, whereas in La Jolla the proportion would be 8:5 in favor of Beefsteak. The next year the proportions would be 9:1 and 2.5:1; thus, in four years the Beefsteak would have disappeared in Temecula (less than 1 in 100), but it would take ten years in La Jolla for the Earliana to disappear (less than 1 in 100). Thus, a complete separation of races is possible in a short period of 4-10 years, when they have a difference in optimal temperature of 3°C, and the localities where they grow have a 3°C difference in nyctotemperature. With 1°C difference this might be a matter of about 1,000 years, a very short time in terms of evolutionary history. Therefore, very slight differences in climatic response of annuals have a great potential value under conditions of competition, where the number of plants of different varieties growing is determined by the proportion of the number of their seeds. In reality the time factor would be greater, because in some years the average temperature would be higher or lower and counteract the selection in previous years.

Soil Temperature:— Many ecologists have ascribed an important role in the growth of a plant to the soil temperature. The experiments carried out in the Clark and Earhart greenhouses have not borne out the importance of soil temperature for the growth of tomatoes and potatoes. Newly potted tomato plants will wilt to some extent when they are taken from a 2° or 4°C dark room into full sunlight at 20°-26°C because of the low root temperature. But soon they become adapted and after the first week of cold nights is over, no more wilting occurs. This is probably correlated with the extensive root development at low nyctotemperatures (*see* FIGURE 41). For although water uptake is very slow at temperatures below 5°C, once a sufficient root surface has developed the root system is not limiting any more.

Just as the root system may limit water uptake, if it is not sufficiently developed, it may also limit growth of the above-ground parts of the plant. When a porous root medium and a complete nutrient solution is used in growing plants, the root system will not be the limiting factor in the development of the above-ground parts (except possibly at very high air temperatures), and therefore, even at fairly low root temperatures, growth is not retarded. This probably explains why in the Clark and Earhart greenhouses we have not found a considerable effect of root temperature on the general development of the plant, as it was claimed in earlier experiments. Under ordinary greenhouse conditions, using soil as a root medium, the root system is less extensive than when plants are grown in vermiculite and watered with nutrient solution. Since in most earlier experiments, in which the root temperature was controlled, aeration of the roots was also impaired, it is very likely that under those conditions the activity of the root system limited top growth. Therefore, we can expect that the soil temperature controls plant growth when the root system is small, restricted, or poorly aerated. This can be true in bogs or in soils with a hardpan near the surface, or in regions with perma-frost, but it is unlikely that in good soils the root system, and consequently soil temperature, restricts water uptake or top growth.

Seasonal Thermoperiodicity:— Not only the daily sequence, but also the long-range temperature sequences are important in the development of plants. The role of seasonal changes in temperature was first recognized by SACHS (1860), when he pointed out that different developmental stages of a plant required different temperatures. COVILLE in 1920 was the first to point out the significance of a long cold-period for the breaking of dormancy of buds in deciduous trees. Before that, numerous chemical and physical methods of making dormant buds resume growth had been described, but COVILLE was the first to tie in the breaking of dormancy with an actual climatic factor. BLAAUW and co-workers showed the necessity for long-range or seasonal temperature changes in the development of many bulbous plants and interpreted their results, not in terms of breaking of dormancy, but, like SACHS, by showing that each developmental stage has its own optimal temperature and range of effective temperatures.

In temperate or cold climates we find that a surprisingly large number of perennial plants, shrubs, and trees not only can withstand the cold winters, but even require them for continued development. If transplanted in the tropics, even at high altitudes where the average yearly temperature equals that of their native habitat, such plants die because they never are subjected to a sufficient period of cold to satisfy their "chilling requirement." The experimental plant physiologist is usually not sufficiently aware of the common occurrence of chilling requirements among plants, for several reasons. Most experimental work is carried out with annual plants which do not need a cold period during their development, except plants which germinate in autumn, and flower in the spring or summer after a cold winter. Winter wheat, *Arabidopsis, Draba, Turritis* are typical examples of such behavior. Another reason is that many plants requiring chilling during winter are too big to be grown in greenhouses, and thus, are experimented on outside (apples, cherries, and many other fruit trees, oaks, beeches, and other deciduous trees). The plants most commonly used as experimental objects, which need chilling, are beets (STOUT 1946), pears (BENNETT 1949), peaches (LAMMERTS 1943) and *Hyoscyamus* (MELCHERS and LANG 1948).

In the Earhart Laboratory many plants have been or are under investigation in which a chilling period is essential for development. The most outstanding example is *Veratrum viride* which needs a temperature of a few degrees above freezing for as long as 6 months during dormancy before it will start to grow. In nature it apparently receives this close-to-freezing treatment because the rhizomes are covered with snow during winter. This is obvious in *Veratrum californicum* which grows predominantly where snow remains on the ground until June, at altitudes ranging from 2000-3300 m. in the Sierra Nevada. In addition, it must have a continuous supply of water during summer. At those high altitudes the plants are subjected to low average temperatures during their growing season (June-September). Another species, *Veratrum fimbriatum,* which is found near the coast in northern California, has a much shorter chilling requirement (2 months) at an optimal temperature of 7°C, which is higher than in *V. viride.* Thus, this species is perfectly adjusted to a habitat where winters are short and not cold.

The peaches growing in the Earhart Laboratory can be kept continuously in vegetative growth by subjecting them to either high temperatures or long days or both, but these plants will not flower. They need a period of cold weather before pre-formed flowerbuds can open, and also no flower primordia are laid down under conditions of continued high temperatures. It was found that flower initiation occurs some months after the plants have been subjected to one month or more of less than 10°C. Under warm growing conditions these primordia develop into buds which require another cold treatment before they open. Thus, in nature the stimulus for initiation of flowers is given a year and a half before opening of the flowers, and the differentiation of the flowerbuds occurs in the summer following the first cold winter. The flowers then develop to the full-grown flowerbud stage, and remain dormant in that condition until a second cold stimulus (a second winter) breaks their dormancy.

A dormant bud of *Dicentra* came into the building among the rhizomes of *Veratrum viride* and, after a cold treatment, started to develop. It produced leaves and flowers, and died after producing a large number of basal dormant buds. When these buds had been kept another period of about 6 months at 4°C they started to develop rapidly at 17°C during the day and 12°C during the night. The dormant buds produced by these plants were stored at 4°, 7° and 10°C. Those kept at 4° for 4 months developed during the next growing period at cool temperatures.

The Joshua tree (*Yucca brevifolia*) has a very typical distribution in our western American Desert. It occurs only above 800-900 m. altitude and grows poorly or dies at lower altitudes, where other *Yucca* species thrive (*Y. whipplei, Y. shedigera*). It germinates over a wide range of temperatures, and growth of seedlings continues at a fairly rapid rate at 30° day and 23°C night, and 17° day and 12°C night temperatures. During their first three years the young plants continue to grow under the same temperature conditions. This agrees with seedling behavior of the Joshua tree in general, since they will grow at sea level. But after these three years, growth slows down, unless the plants are kept for a few months at 4°C. After their chilling period they would grow rapidly for over a half a year in the warmest greenhouse. This indicates that *Yucca brevifolia* requires a chilling treatment after the seedling stage, which it receives in the desert only above 800 m. altitude.

Other plants, such as the sugar beet, are known to need a cold treatment before they will flower. Some sugar beet plants were grown for years at the same daily thermoperiod (23° during day and 17°C during night). They continued vegetative growth and produced thickened stems of 1 m. length or longer with a leaf rosette on top. The monstrously big beets weighed up to 10 Kg. a piece. They never produced flowers and seeds, and ultimately rotted at the base, probably because the old parenchymatic cells in the base of the stem had reached their age limit. Therefore, such biennials requiring a chilling treatment for flowering would not reproduce in a climate with insufficient yearly fluctuation in temperature.

There is quite some evidence for the inability of many plants from temperate climates to survive at higher altitudes in the tropics, where the average temperature is just right but where no seasonal temperature fluctuations occur. On the other hand, a number of deciduous trees from temperate regions may survive, like a *Fagus silvatica* on the 3000 m. high top of the Pangerango in Java, even though it remains a puny shrub. A Himalayan cherry grew well at 1400 m. altitude in Tjibodas, Java. Here its periodicity remained pronounced on an 8-month cycle of flowering—leaf development—leaf drop. Several *Magnolia* species there continued to grow in a straggly fashion, with flowering—leafing out—leaf drop completely desynchronized over the whole shrub, each branch maintaining a different period.

In the previous pages the role of thermoperiodism in the response of plants has been discussed, as a basis for the understanding of their distribution in nature. Plants like *Veratrum viride* and *Dicentra formosa* can occur only in areas where the winters are long, and where a sufficient snow cover for 4-6 months insures soil temperatures of near freezing. The same control of further development by removal of an inhibition by low temperatures is found in *Convallaria majalis,* but in this case the cold treatment does not have to last more than a few weeks, and, therefore, this plant can be found in more oceanic climates. Many other plants require a seasonal drop in temperature for continued development for any one of two reasons: either they pass through a cycle of developmental processes (leaf and flower initiation, stem elongation and flowering) with very different optimal temperatures so that never at any one temperature all processes can proceed, or because a vernalization-like process is required for flowering. The first of these cases is exemplified by most of the bulbous plants studied by Blaauw and collaborators (tulip, hyacinth, *Iris, Narcissus,* etc.), the second by sugar beet, *Hyoscyamus* and peach. The latter plant, before flowering, has to pass through two low-temperature requiring processes, separated by a high-temperature process for (*1*) vernalization, (2) flowerbud initiation, and (3) breaking of the flowerbud dormancy. In this way it is the best example of adaptation to a seasonal climate. Plants without a seasonal sequence of different optimal temperatures can grow in the tropics, and at different altitudes according to their optimal temperature requirement. The coffee is an example of such behavior; orchids are too, but no other tropical plants have been investigated in sufficient detail in the Earhart Laboratory to give further examples.

Germination Controlling Plant Distribution:— Germination is another stage of development of plants which is strongly influenced by temperature, and this can account in part for the peculiarities in the distribution of plants. This effect of temperature is, of course, well known in the germination of agricultural and garden plants. SACHS (1860) had already shown the range of temperature over which corn, wheat and a number of other plants germinate. Amazingly enough the minimum temperature at which germination occurs is rather high for these agricultural plants. But this is the reason why most corn varieties should be sown only after spring is already fairly well along. (There are now a few corn varieties which germinate at a much lower temperature: $V_3 \times 38$). Tomatoes should be sown in the field not before the soil temperature has become fairly high, otherwise weeds will precede them in germination, and once these weeds are growing the tomatoes will not germinate. Besides, a period of cold inhibits their germination afterwards, which might be termed negative stratification.

These facts might be used to advantage in weed control, for just as the agricultural plants have definite ranges of temperature within which they germinate most readily, so are weeds restricted in their germination. The development of one or another weed can be accelerated or suppressed by ploughing or harrowing at certain times. This problem is discussed in some further detail in WENT, JUHRÈN and JUHRÈN (1952).

In wild plants the problem of germination is entirely different from that in cultivated plants and weeds. In our crop and garden plants a partly unconscious selection for ease of germination has occurred, for usually the most rapidly germinating seeds get an advantage over those germinating with more difficulty. Also, seeds are usually sown at the proper time for them to get the best chance for growth and flowering. This is entirely different with wild plants. Usually their seeds hit the ground at a time improper for germination. Seeds are the means by which annuals survive unfavorable weather conditions (winter cold, drought, summer heat, etc.). Therefore, generally speaking, their seeds should remain dormant until the proper conditions for the completion of a whole life cycle occur, which is usually half a year or more after ripening. In perennials, flowering usually occurs so that ripe seeds are produced towards the end of the growing season, and these seeds should also germinate at the beginning of the next growing season.

Therefore, immediate germination after ripening of the seeds would generally lead to failure of the seedlings of wild plants. Consequently, it is not surprising that we usually find that wild seeds are unable to germinate immediately after ripening. This may be due to dormancy which either gradually disappears with time or is broken by stratification (cold treatment). If germination were controlled only by temperature without an additional cold-requiring dormant period, plants would die out in temperate climates, because germination might occur either at the beginning or end of the season, when in spring or autumn temperatures are the same.

In desert plants the situation is different. The germination of plants of the Mojave and Colorado deserts in California in relation to climatic factors has been studied in considerable detail both in nature and in the laboratory (WENT 1948*b*, 1949; WENT and WESTERGAARD 1949; JUHRÈN, WENT and PHILLIPS 1956). There are essentially two yearly rainy periods in those deserts. The main period of rain is the winter, during which time even in the most extreme deserts (Death Valley and the area just East of the Salton Sea) a certain amount of precipitation can be expected each year. The rainfall ranges from about 35 mm. at sea level, 100 mm. at 600 m., to 200 mm. at 1400 m. Most of these rains are light, lasting many hours. During July and August occasional local thunderstorms occur at higher altitudes, which are usually accompanied by heavy showers of short duration; these occur only once every 5-20 years in any one spot. A very distinct flora of summer annuals develops after these summer storms (*Bouteloua barbata, B. aristidoides, Pectis papposa, Boerhaavia annulata, Euphorbia micromera, E. setiloba, Amaranthus fimbriatus, Mollugo cerviana, Portulaca oleracea*), and most of the shrubs and perennials also germinate only after summer rains.

The winter rains cause germination of *Gilia* species, such as *G. matthewsii, G. aurea, G. scopulorum* and many others, *Eriophyllum wallacei, Chaenactis carphoclinia, Chorizanthe rigida, Ch. brevicornu, Calyptridium monandrum, Nemacladus* spp., *Nama demissum, Baeria chrysostoma,* small *Oenothera* spp. such as *O. palmeri, Mimulus bigelovii, Malvastrum rotundifolium* and about 100 other annuals.

November rains near sea level and October rains at altitudes up to 1000 m. and summer rains at 1400 m. cause the development of a third group of annuals, most of them large with showy flowers. To these belong *Geraea canescens, Abronia villosa, Dithyrea californica, Oenothera deltoides, Oe. clavaeformis, Oe. cordifolia, Lupinus sparsiflorus, Phacelia campanularia, Mohavea confertiflora, Salvia columbariae, S. carduacea* and others.

It turns out that in the laboratory the same groups can be recognized. When desert soil, properly moistened, is placed at the highest temperatures (26°-30°C), the summer annuals germinate, with perhaps a few from the other groups. The same soil placed at low temperatures (10°C) gives seedlings exclusively from the winter annual group. At intermediate temperatures some from each group may germinate, but the emphasis is on the intermediate group. In nature, the separation between groups is more extreme, and there is less overlapping than in the laboratory. We can safely conclude that the seasonal differences in annual vegetation in the desert are mainly due to temperature differences after rains. This is also indicated by the fact that plants from the intermediate group may germinate at 1300 m. altitude after summer rains (*e.g., Abronia, Oenothera deltoides*); the same germination may occur at low altitudes after winter rains. Therefore, the germination is not connected with season or photoperiod, but whenever the typical germination temperatures for a species occur, and the rain conditions are right, too, the seeds germinate. Thus, a shift in rainy season without a change in total seasonal precipitation and in temperature could completely change the flora in a region. Therefore, we should be careful in attributing the disappearance of particular plants in the course of evolution to a shift in temperature, or a change in total rainfall. Although these effects will be less pronounced in perennials and trees, the same rules must hold as in annuals. For, ultimately, the presence of perennials is also dependent upon germination.

It is interesting to note that most desert shrubs germinate after the rare summer rains. Whereas an annual can get by on only a single rain which causes germination, and it will flower and set seed without any further precipitation so that the length of the following drought period is immaterial, a perennial can survive as a small plant, before it has a sufficiently large root system, only if it does not have to weather a long drought period. Since summer rains are infrequent, whereas winter rains occur yearly, germination after a winter rain means almost certain death for the perennial during the following summer. But after a summer rain the seedling can count on another series of rains ahead of it before it has to survive a longer summer drought period. Therefore, summer germination particularly insures a growing period of 9 months, including warm growing weather, instead of 5 months at rather low temperatures.

A number of seeds germinate at almost any temperature, whether low or high. Seedlings of these plants may be found at any time of the year in the desert. Most typical are: *Palafoxia linearis* which may develop into quite a large plant with repeated rains, or may remain very small, *Datura discolor* and *Cucurbita palmata,* seedlings of which can be found growing next to mature plants. The latter two are not frost resistant and, therefore, usually do not survive and reproduce when they germinate after autumn rains. One seldom sees annual plants dying in the desert before they have produced seed, but *Datura* is an exception and frequently one sees young plants that have been killed after winter frosts.

In other plants germination is restricted to a particular time of the year because their seeds are produced at that time and have to germinate soon after ripening since they have a short storage life. This is the case with *Yucca brevifolia,* the Joshua tree, whose seeds ripen in early summer. As soon as they drop from their pods they must germinate, because otherwise they are eaten by rodents. Thus, germination of the Joshua tree is a rare phenomenon in the desert, for there are few good seed years, and seldom do summer rains come at the proper time for their germination. Usually, only the seeds buried between rocks or in dense shrubs get a chance to germinate and well over 99 per cent are eaten, either by the larvae of the *Pronuba* moth or by rodents.

Little is known as yet about the specific effects of rain on the vegetation apart from its role in supplying water. It is again with desert plants that we have learned something about the ecology of rain. Observations in nature showed that germination of the seeds of desert plants was not related to moisture as such, but to rain of sufficient amount and duration. When the rainfall was below 15 mm., no germination was observed in the desert, with the exception of roadsides, where germination occurs with somewhat less rain, or along washes where rain water may run without any local precipitation. Yet along streams in the desert, where there is an abundant soil water supply, we find no germination except after rains. All these observations seem contradictory since after light rains, soil moisture in the zone of germinable seeds reaches the same value as after a heavy rain. Yet, there is one general conclusion: wherever rainwater in excess of 15 mm. has penetrated the soil, germination occurs, regardless of whether previously the soil was moist or not.

In the laboratory similar observations were made. Soil, collected in the desert and kept moist in flats, showed only slight germination. When the same soil was given an artificial rain of 20 mm. or more, profuse germination occurred. Again, the soil was equally wet in both cases. Thus it seems that dry seeds can distinguish between different sources of water and the quantity of precipitation. To what extent this is true was further investigated by Engr. A. SORIANO. FIGURE 52 shows the dependence of certain seeds on the amount of rain for their germination. *Eriophyllum* does not germinate at all with 10 mm. rain or less. On the other hand some Palestinian plants, like *Anastatica,* germinated independently of the amount of artificial precipitation. When the duration of rain was too short, an otherwise sufficient amount did not cause germination. When 15 mm. was given in 1 hour, 27 seeds germinated, when given in 10 hours 40 germinated, and when the 15 mm. precipitation was spread over 54 hours 64 seeds germinated.

The mechanisms which control the germination as a function of intensity and duration of rain are only partly known, and even then not in any detail. A short enumeration will show, how evolution has resulted in a number of vastly different mechanisms to prevent germination except under very favorable conditions. A first case is found in those seeds which contain water soluble germination inhibitors. Examples are *Euphorbia* spp. and *Pectis papposa.* The latter germinates after proper leaching with water. When the leached seeds were placed in their own leachate, they did not germinate, indicating that an inhibitor can be removed from the seed coat by water. If unleached seeds were soaked for a few minutes in a 1 per cent solution of sodium hypochlorite, they germinated right away, apparently because the seedcoat inhibitor was destroyed. Rain of sufficient intensity and duration can cause complete leaching of these seed inhibitors and thus causes germination.

The second case is also common in seeds: inhibition of germination by salt concentrations lower than those tolerated by growing plants of the same species. Rainfall in deserts is so low that salts are not completely leached out of the upper layers of the soil. After a heavy enough rain the surface layers of the soil, containing the viable seeds, may be sufficiently free from salt for a few days, so that germination can occur. In *Baeria chrysostoma* an osmotic concentration as low as 1 atmosphere in the soil water is sufficient to prevent germination, and this is true of many other plants. Therefore, these do not germinate along desert streams, which usually have a considerable salinity by the end of their run, as is evidenced by white salt incrustations on the surrounding soil particles. The lack of germination in saline spots in the desert is very marked.

In a third group of seeds delayed germination occurs. This may be due to encasing structures, such as husks in grasses. Without the husks germination of *Avena* starts one or two days earlier and in coffee the seedcoat retards germination a week or more. When after a light rain the upper soil layers are dry again within a few days, the delay in germination will have prevented these seeds from developing after insufficient precipitation. Such plants may develop even without rain in soil moistened by capillary water. Along a body of permanent water we may find *Bouteloua* plants growing during a rainless summer, but elsewhere in the desert they grow only after a heavy rain. At the same time, no *Pectis* will be found near that water, since its seeds require leaching.

In the fourth group of seeds water and oxygen uptake is prevented by hard or impermeable seedcoats. The seeds of the palo verde, *Cercidium aculeatum, e.g.*, have such a hard seedcoat that the embryo cannot possibly penetrate it. The seeds themselves have no dormancy, but will germinate within a day when the seedcoat is removed. In the desert such seeds will only germinate when after a heavy rain water runs through the normally dry washes, carrying large quantities of sand and gravel with it. The sand and gravel then grind the seedcoat off, till the embryo can penetrate it. This means that *Cercidium* germinates only in washes, where the soil carries enough water, and only after heavy rains. Therefore, plants with heavy or impermeable seedcoats are restricted to washes: *Dalea spinosa* (the smoke tree) and *Olneya tesota,* the ironwood, belong to this group, in addition to *Cercidium.*

In a fifth group of seeds, such as those of *Physalis* and *Lycium,* pulpy fruit coats have to be removed before germination can occur because they contain inhibitors. This removal may be effected by mechanical means or by bacteria. In the latter case the seeds have to be subjected for some time to moist conditions, such as may occur after a heavy rain or after a series of rains.

There is another group of seeds which, when ripe, are in a deep dormancy. This dormancy gradually wears off, but it means that not more than a limited percentage of seeds can germinate after each individual rain, and, therefore, not all of them will germinate after a single light rain. A yearly periodicity in the breaking of this dormancy such as described by BÜNNING may help to restrict germination to that season which is most conducive towards successful establishment.

Since water is the most important factor controlling plant life in the desert, it is understandable that in the course of evolution so many different mechanisms developed in desert seeds, to adjust their germination to the sporadic rainfalls, particularly in relation to the quantity of precipitation. Rain has, however, many effects other than on germination. It affects the later development of the plant, in the sense that seeds subjected to rain may give bigger plants with more and larger flowers (*see* Chapter 13: *Baeria chrysostoma*).

Rain:— Rain may have an influence on plants in many other ways. The flowering of a number of tropical plants, for instance, is induced by rain. In coffee (*see* Chapter 12) and in several orchids (like *Dendrobium crumenatum*) flowerbuds of sufficient size will start to enlarge after a heavy rain, and open 7-9 days later. For this reason a special rain room was constructed in the Earhart Plant Research Laboratory to investigate effects of rain on plants. In a few preliminary experiments it was found that the growth of *Veratrum fimbriatum* seedlings was stimulated when they were given rain each day for four hours, whereas the growth of tomato plants was decreased. In both cases the plants were watered daily with nutrient solution, so that water supply through the roots was sufficient in both the rained-over plants and the controls. This may be of importance in a decision about the type of irrigation to be applied to a particular crop.

The recent experiments of DUVDEVANI on water uptake through leaves indicate that dew may play a far more important role in plant growth than is generally conceded. He found that liquid water may be transported from the leaf surface to all other parts of the plant, and an excess may be excreted through the roots and roothairs into the soil. There it is available later for the transpirational needs of the plants. The extent to which liquid water on the leaves can be taken up by plants can be seen after nights of heavy dew or fog. Then the old leaves of plants may be dripping, whereas the younger leaves are almost dry, because they have absorbed all the moisture condensed on them. DUVDEVANI was able to show that liquid water taken up during night through leaves was sufficient to cover transpirational losses during day in the case of tomatoes, corn and watermelon plants.

It is not necessary that liquid water condenses on the leaf surface. If the water vapor gradient is such that the vapor pressure is lower in the leaf than in the surrounding air, water vapor may diffuse directly into the leaf without visible external condensation, although the principle of water uptake through the leaves remains the same. Such a water vapor gradient away from the leaf can exist only during night when the temperature of the leaf may reach the dew point of the surrounding air or even drop below it by losing heat through radiation. It is conceivable that the stomatal mechanism acts as a valve, facilitating water vapor uptake and inhibiting water loss. In many regions with several successive rainless months, and a water table which is too low to be reached by roots, dew or water vapor condensation during night is the only imaginable source of water, especially in shallow rooted plants, like the annuals. In the desert we may find several *Gilia* species alive and flowering in June or July after a number of rainless months. Their root systems do not penetrate deeper than 10 cm.

so that we can say with certainty that no water is available to those plants through the soil. This same discrepancy between water needs of desert plants and the available water supply was commented on by Evenari and Koller (1955). Their only conceivable water source is the air at night. The possibility of the air as a source of water for plants has been discussed in more detail elsewhere (Went 1955*b*).

Not enough work has been done yet in the wind tunnel of the Earhart Laboratory to draw conclusions as to the ecological significance of wind. The growth of most plants seems to be inhibited by wind velocities of 10 Km./hour or more. On the other hand, a minimal amount of wind is necessary to keep the CO_2 gradient air-leaf sufficiently steep to prevent limitation of growth by the CO_2 supply.

Photoperiod:— Photoperiod experiments in the air-conditioned greenhouses have not produced enough results to affect our conceptions of the effect of daylength on plant growth in nature. The majority of spring annuals growing in the deserts and valleys of California have been found to be long-day plants with respect to flowering. It might be well to point out that the optimal growing conditions for such long-day plants are germination and early growth under short-day conditions so that the plants may reach a sufficiently large size before they are subjected to the flower-inducing long photoperiod, which usually terminates vegetative growth.

Whereas photoperiod is definitely a major factor in the distribution of plants, the difficulties involved in the application of laboratory data to explain field observations have not been sufficiently realized. In the first place, few plants are sufficiently sensitive to photoperiod that a difference of a few minutes will mean flowering or vegetative growth. Most photoperiodically sensitive plants have a range of several hours between a daylength which will induce flowering in 100 per cent of the plants, or in which all plants will be vegetative. This should result in a very wide range of flowering dates. In reality the flowering of a species in nature is fairly synchronous, which would indicate that in addition to photoperiod another factor must be involved, making all individuals flower at the same time.

Observations on coffee and on *Cestrum* emphasize another difficulty relative to photoperiod. Its actual length is usually considered to be from sunrise to sunset. But different plants have different critical light intensities below which light is not effective any more in the photoperiodic response. In strawberries it was found (*see* Chapter 9) that temperature influenced this critical light intensity: at 14° and 17°C flowering was inhibited by supplementary light at 800 ft.-c. and not at 400 ft.-c., but at 10°C plants would flower even with 1200 ft.-c. At higher temperatures less light was required to suppress flowering.

In other short-day plants the critical light intensity is lower: slightly over 10 ft.-c. in coffee and about 1 ft.-c. in *Xanthium*. The same divergence of critical light intensities is found in long-day plants: *Baeria* requires 200 ft.-c. supplementary light to flower, whereas aster will flower with as little as 1 ft.-c. supplied during night. Therefore, the effective daylengths for various plants are entirely different, and the daylength as given in the official tables should be lengthened with as much as ½-1½ hours according to the species of plant under consideration and the declination of the sun.

However, even this correction is insufficient. On sunny days the critical daylength is much longer than on cloudy days, and a series of cloudy days may well give the stimulus for flower induction for short-day plants, as Dr. SACHS (1955) has recently shown for *Cestrum*. When plants are grown in shade, the effective daylength is also shortened, and it will be different for different leaves on a single plant, since the upper ones usually shade the leaves farther down the stem. As pointed out in Chapter 12 on coffee, this typical short-day plant will flower in the tropics, but probably only when subjected to sufficient shade in early morning and late afternoon. It is quite possible that some plants grow better in moist than in dry climates or *vice versa,* because, on account of cloudiness, in the former they are subjected to shorter photoperiods on the average. Thus, their occurrence may have nothing to do with the rainfall but only with cloudiness.

Ecologically speaking the effects of daylength on vegetative development may be of much more importance than those on flowering. Although not many observations were made on this aspect of photoperiodism in the Earhart Laboratory, it was obvious that in many plants the length of day greatly influenced vegetative growth and other characters, such as anthocyanin formation in *Coleus*. PLATE XVII shows that in short photoperiods only the center cells of the leaves form anthocyanin, whereas at 20- and 24-hour photoperiods anthocyanin is produced to within a very short distance from the margin of the leaf. And although for flowering the tomato is indeterminate and initiates flowers in all daylengths provided the plants grow at all, vegetative development is strongly affected by length of day.

Photosynthesis:— Several remarks can be made concerning light intensity and plant growth. Plants are divided into shade and sun plants, according to the light intensities under which they usually grow. Thus, most orchids are considered shade plants, and are generally shaded in greenhouses. Tests in the Earhart Laboratory have shown that the optimal light intensity for *Cypripedium insigne* hybrids and *Phalaenopsis amabilis* is about 750 ft.-c. *Cattleyas* can, however, be grown in much higher light intensities, provided the surrounding air temperature is kept cool enough. Apparently, the thick leaves act as heat traps in strong light. With sufficient cooling these *Cattleyas* can be grown in full sunlight without damage to their leaves; growth is actually better at higher light intensities, and 4 or more new shoots may be formed per year per pseudobulb.

The leaves of most other plants tested were light saturated at about 1000 ft.-c. It seems amazing that there is not more variation among the different plants. It is also remarkable that light saturation of leaves is so much below full sunlight intensity, when most field plants seem to be saturated only at full natural light intensity so that any shading will decrease their growth (*e.g.*, G. E. Blackman and Wilson 1951). The light intensity is at its highest for only a few hours every day. In the morning and the evening intensities are of the order of magnitude of 1000 ft.-c. On cloudy days the light intensity may remain well below 1000 ft.-c. even at noon. Therefore, plants are usually subjected to light of much lower intensity than full sunlight. But, most important of all, in most sun-grown plants there are many layers of leaves shading each other. The upper leaves may get much more light than they can utilize; the lower leaves, however, will never be subjected to a saturating intensity. Therefore, no matter how high the outside light intensity is, the mature plant as a whole will never be saturated with light, and theoretically evaluable light saturation curves for photosynthesis can only be obtained when the plant is a seedling and has only one layer of leaves. We find in general that shade-plants have only a single layer of leaves. When the newly formed higher leaves of a plant decrease the light falling on the lower leaves to below the compensation point, the latter die. Tomato plants grown in the artificial light chambers of the Earhart Laboratory receive an intensity of 1500 ft.-c. at plant top level, whereas the light intensity near the lowest living leaves is about 100 ft.-c.; all leaves more than 40 cm. from the top die. In the full sunlight of the greenhouses tomato plants watered with the same nutrient solution and grown in the same temperatures retain their leaves over 100-120 cm. of stem. There is another factor to be considered in this respect. This is the position of the leaf in relation to the direction of the light. When a leaf is spread horizontally, it will receive very little light in early morning and late afternoon, whereas it is exposed to about 10,000 ft.-c. at noon. A vertically placed leaf will be subjected to an even light intensity from sunrise to sunset amounting to about 4000 ft.-c., at least if it faces West or East. If it faces South, it will follow the total radiation curve of the day in summer, whereas in winter it will receive a relatively much higher light intensity in the middle of the day.

It is likely that several of the phenomena found in the study of photosynthesis in tomato plants have ecological significance. When the gain in weight of plants in light intensities below 100 ft.-c. was compared with that in darkness, the plants in low light intensity had lost more weight than those in darkness and they had grown less. Apparently, this response to low light intensity is different from that of shade plants, several of which can grow in intensities well below 100 ft.-c. as *Synchonium* plants in the back of living rooms prove. In the tomato plant low light intensities seem to be deleterious, and it is perhaps for that reason that the lower leaves of tomatoes die and that they cannot grow in deep shade, even though their light utilization at higher intensities is similar to that of shade-plants. Whereas a tomato plant under optimal light and temperature conditions (1000 ft.-c. at 17°C) respired 5-10 per cent of the photosynthates produced during photoperiods of 12 hours, in perennial plants this percentage may be much higher. This is probably due to the much larger proportion of nonphotosynthesizing tissues (stems, rhizomes, bulbs and tubers). In old Marshall strawberry plants the compensation point where photosynthesis just balances respiration in the whole plant lay at 1500 ft.-c., and thus these old plants are barely able to maintain themselves even in full sunlight. This is probably the main reason why strawberry plants are left in the field for only two seasons, and then are replaced by young plants (current year runners). This also explains why old, leafless pseudobulbs of orchids should be removed to get best growth and flowering.

When tomato plants have been kept in darkness for more than one day, they are unable to make full use of the subsequent light. This is due to a lack of carbohydrates, for when such previously darkened plants are sprayed with sugar before being exposed to light, they have a normal rate of photosynthesis. That these tomato plants became depleted of sugars was not so much due to respiration, since this removed only 1/3 to 1/4 of the photosynthates during the days in darkness; the greater amount of photosynthates was used for growth. Good shade plants usually grow slowly and do not use up much sugar. The difference between shade and sun plants then may lie more in the properties just mentioned than in differences between their saturating light intensities.

In the virginal tropical forest it seems to be largely light intensity which limits growth. If the faster growing or taller growing plants were favored, soon the number of tree species would become decimated. Usually 100-200 tree species are found growing intermixed in a rainforest, and the differences in growth rate between them are enormous. Thus, if selection occurred on the basis of growth potential, only a few trees would be able to compete successfully. But if the light intensity is limiting, all plants have a more or less equal chance because of their similar photosynthetic system. Which of the smaller trees will take over after the shading tree has disappeared is entirely due to chance: the ones which are nearest the new clearing will fill in the gap, and not the ones which grow fastest.

Summary:— Reviewing to what extent the study of individual environmental factors can contribute to the understanding of Ecology and Evolution, we can say that it is mainly temperature, rain and light requirements of plants which determine their occurrence, and that the study of these factors has been rather neglected. The Earhart Plant Research Laboratory offers unique possibilities to study autecology and the results obtained to date show that the distribution of ecotypes over the various habitats can be explained on the basis of their response to temperature and light. The results also indicate how very much the germination behavior of plants contributes to an understanding of their occurrence. The survival of plants depends to a large degree upon whether sufficient restrictions are imposed upon their germination, which will cause them to germinate only when the subsequent growing conditions are adequate as far as space, temperature and moisture are concerned. In desert plants evolution was directed to a remarkable degree towards germination control, whereas within families or tribes the temperature requirements are very little affected. It is likely that in future work the importance of rain or other forms of precipitation will be found to be of much more importance than previously assumed, and that this will explain many puzzling problems in plant distribution in arid and semi-arid regions, where soil moisture alone cannot account for the occurrence or absence of plants.

As a general conclusion from the previous discussion we can state that in many instances the distribution of plants in nature can be explained on the basis of their response to a fairly large number of individual climatic factors or a combination of them, acting on germination or during the seedling or mature stages of development. When germination or seedling growth is possible only over a rather narrow range of climatic conditions, and, therefore, is limiting distribution of a species, and when vegetative and reproductive growth are good over a much wider range of conditions, we may find the largest mature specimens at the limits (upper or lower) of the distribution of the species. This is clearly shown in the mountain forests of Java, where the largest *Podocarpus imbricata* trees are found at the lower limit of its distribution range (1450 m.), whereas *Altingia excelsa* grows tallest at the upper limit (1450 m.) of its range. Similarly, very large trees of *Pinus cembra, Larix europaea* and *Pinus aristata* are found at timberline, where at present we do not find seedlings any more. In these cases the optimal growing conditions for seedlings and mature plants differ very much, like in tomato and chili pepper (FIGURE 47). Just the opposite condition, in which the ecological range of seedlings is wider than that of mature plants, was found in *Betula tortuosa*. Mature shrubs of this species occur at timberline in the mountains of Swedish Lapland at an altitude of 700 m. However, up to 1000 m., seedlings of this *Betula* were found in July, 1949, which obviously could not survive at that altitude. Therefore, in this case the growing conditions of the mature plant limited the distribution of this birch.

Chapter 19

GERMINATION

A plant passes through a number of growth stages during its development from zygote to zygote, which each have their special requirements as far as external conditions are concerned. Whereas most of these stages have rather similar requirements, germination is usually entirely different from the other developmental stages in its optimal conditions. In Chapter 18 on Ecology it has been pointed out how important this is for the control of distribution of plants, and how, particularly in desert plants, evolution of physiological characters has been directed more towards germination control than towards any other single character.

The seed stage of the plant is remarkable in many respects (for a general discussion of germination: *see* CROCKER and BARTON 1953). It means a cessation of activity, in which development comes to a complete standstill and metabolism is reduced to such a level that even after years the major portion of storage food and protoplasm remains unused and unchanged. It is the only developmental stage of the plant in which the protoplasm can stand dehydration (except in acorns, coffee beans and several other large seeds); soon after germination the protoplasm loses its resistance against dehydration. Whereas an older pea plant cannot support severe wilting at all, young seedlings can still dry out almost completely and revive when watered anew.

The extraordinary resistance of seeds against high and low temperatures is due to their low water content, and the drier they are the more resistant they become. Surface temperatures in the soil where viable seeds are found may become 70°C. in the desert; in the case of seeds which germinate specifically after a fire, germination is stimulated by subjecting dry seeds to temperatures of 80°C or higher (*see e.g.*, WENT, JUHRÈN and JUHRÈN 1952).

Investigations, especially with wheat and other cereals, have shown that the rate of respiration of the seeds is a function of their water content. Below 13 per cent water content the gas exchange of such seeds drops to practically zero, and dry grain will retain its germinability for many years. Apparently, in seeds the condition of anabiosis or suspended life can persist for long time intervals provided no respiration occurs. Respiration may be reduced or suspended in a number of seeds by keeping them moist (BARTON 1945), or by drying them. Theoretically we might expect that completely dry seeds would retain their viability forever. To test this, a seed longevity experiment was started in Pasadena (WENT and MUNZ 1949).

Longevity of Seeds:— In 1947, seeds of almost 100 kinds of California plants were sealed in vacuum in glass tubes, after having been dried sharply over P_2O_5. Each species was divided over 20 tubes, and one set of tubes is going to be opened and tested for germination every 10-20 years. Under normal storage conditions, it might be expected that on the average every five years the viability of the seeds would be halved, with big differences from species to species. The first results concerning the effects of drying and one year storage were published (WENT and MUNZ 1949) and since then, another set of tubes was opened after five years' storage.

The results show that a few species lose their germinability almost immediately after drying in vacuum. As an example can be mentioned *Chaenactis glabriuscula* var. *tenuifolia.* In all cases of reduction of viability the length of time required for germination had increased very markedly, too. In many seeds, like *Godetia* spp., *Nemophila maculata* and *Chaenactis orcuttiana* germination remained constant throughout the five-year storage period. If we exclude the seeds which lost their viability within one year and those which had a low germination percentage to begin with, we find that in 15 cases germination was the same after five years' storage, in 11 cases it was greater and in 11 cases lower. On the average there was no change.

After the opening of the tubes, stored for five years, the extra seeds not necessary for the first germination test were left in the open tubes in the laboratory under ordinary storage conditions. The species could be divided into three groups according to their subsequent behavior. Whereas for all groups together five years' storage in vacuum had caused no change in viability (61 per cent in 1947, 62 per cent in 1952), their germination changed upon three years' open storage. In *Sisyrinchium bellum, Carpenteria californica* and two other species germination rose from 50 to 74 and 84 per cent in one and two years of open storage. In another set of seeds (3 *Godetia* species) there was practically no change in two years, but a drop afterwards from 78 to 75 and 73 per cent, but in the majority of species (10, among which *Eschscholtzia* and 2 *Phacelia* species) germinability decreased to almost 0% in two years: in half of them germination dropped from 65 to 48 to 28 per cent in two successive years, in the other half from 48 to 16 to zero per cent. This is the normal behavior of seeds: in those needing afterripening germination increases upon ordinary storage; in most seeds however, it decreases more or less rapidly. In contrast with this normal behavior, there was no change in viability or germinability of seeds kept for five years in vacuum.

In other plants, viability is lost almost immediately upon sharp drying, as in the case of the coffee seed. When kept at room temperature, the viability decreased to less than half during half a year's storage. Viability disappeared completely within two days of bringing the seeds into vacuum. When stored in 30-50 per cent relative humidity they retained their viability for at least a year at temperatures of 14° and 26°C, but not at 4°C; at 60-80 per cent humidity there was complete loss of viability at all temperatures.

The loss of viability seems to be connected largely with a decrease in resistance against fungi and other saprophytic organisms. In a pea-storage experiment (WENT 1943c), it was found that with increasing age, the percentage of seeds which would germinate decreased exponentially, but the viable seeds germinated as well, and formed as vigorous plants, as recently-harvested seeds. A much larger percentage of seeds did not germinate at all any more, but rotted or molded right away. It seems likely, therefore, that aging in these peas is largely a matter of disappearance of antibiotics, which protect the seeds when they are exposed to the most completely contaminated medium in existence, *viz.*, soil. It is likely that the formation of antibiotics in the seed also affects the respiration and germination of the seed itself. On this basis, the experiments of BARTON (1945) with *Amaranthus* could be explained. She found that upon wet storage of these seeds they became almost completely dormant and at the same time reduced their rate of respiration. Distribution of a plant depends on its climatic tolerance not only in its vegetative growth but also in germination. Since germination often differs in its requirements from vegetative and reproductive growth, it is sometimes germination which limits the distribution of a plant.

It is a common observation in germination experiments that the viable seeds remain relatively free of epiphytic fungi and other microorganisms, whereas the seeds which have lost their viability are completely overgrown with fungi. But another observation is equally significant. After one or more weeks many bacteria have developed on the filterpaper in the germination dishes, forming an almost continuous cover, particularly noticeable when these are colored. In many species (*Godetia, Clarkia, Boisduvallia*) several mm. wide colorless areas occur around the viable seeds, indicating formation of antibiotics by them.

Another observation in germination experiments has not received the attention it should. Upon aging, the first observable change in seeds usually is a delay in germination. Fresh seeds of *Godetia* and *Clarkia* germinate, *e.g.*, within one or two days, whereas older seeds may take two to four days for germination. Once the seedlings emerge, their development is the same. Therefore, it seems as if there is an increase in the amount of inhibitors in these seeds upon aging. The actual act of germination does not seem to be connected with growth, but with the overcoming of an inhibition.

Delay of Germination:— Most seeds do not germinate immediately after ripening, but have special mechanisms to delay germination until a favorable season has arrived. For plants growing in temperate climates, a favorable season usually occurs once a year so that germination controls should only tide the seeds over a single winter. In desert plants favorable seasons occur only once every few years when enough rainfall has occurred to insure normal development of seedlings. In such cases the simple germination controls of the temperate regions would be ineffective and much more complicated systems have developed.

Most of our knowledge about germination is derived from work with seeds of cultivated plants. These have been and are being investigated in great detail in seed testing laboratories all over the world. In most of these plants germination tests are relatively simple because germination occurs without delay when favorable moisture and temperature conditions are present. Their ease of germination is in sharp contrast with the usual difficulties encountered in germinating seeds collected from wild plants. It is obvious that in the case of crop plants those seeds which germinate most readily will give the plant an advantage in selection. For the sowing of agricultural plants is carried out at the time that optimal development of the plants can be expected. Plants developing from seeds which are delayed in their germination will presumably produce smaller plants at time of harvest and produce less seed.

Upon introduction of a new plant, there usually occurs an unintentional selection for ease of germinability. If the seeds cannot be germinated to any extent such species will not be grown under cultivation. Whereas the original wild seeds often germinate with great difficulty, after some generations of cultivation they germinate usually to a much larger percentage. As mentioned earlier, in nature such ease of germination would be a disadvantage, and we should realize that the difficulty of germinating seeds collected in the wilds is a necessary corollary for survival of the species.

Temperature:— The germination of a large number of plants has been investigated in the Earhart Laboratory. These plants can be divided into several categories. In the first place, there is a group of seeds which germinate proportional to the temperature. This can be seen when the rate of germination expressed as the inverse of the number of days required for 50 per cent germination is plotted against temperature. A good example of such behavior is *Avena sativa,* as shown in FIGURE 51. At 20°C the rate of germination is twice as great as at 10°C, and through extrapolation it can be expected that these plants would have germinated even at temperatures just above freezing.

The second group of seeds also shows a gradual increase in germination rate at higher temperatures, but when this rate is extrapolated towards the abscissa it is found that below a certain temperature no germination could be expected at all. Examples of this behavior are found in FIGURE 51 for two tomato varieties. In the third group there are seeds which show a very marked optimum in germination at relatively low temperatures. The winter germinating desert annuals belong to this group and in FIGURE 51 it is represented by *Brassica arvensis*.

In FIGURE 51 other germination figures are plotted for special experiments carried out with the Extra-Early tomato. Seeds were laid out in Petri dishes at temperatures ranging from 0° to 14°C. After 3 days in these conditions the Petri dishes were transferred to 26°C and at the same time a set of non-pretreated seeds was laid out in another Petri dish. It was then found that the seeds which had been pre-treated with a temperature of 14°C germinated faster than the controls which had not been pre-treated. This indicates that, as expected, part of the germination process had actually been carried out at these low temperatures. But at

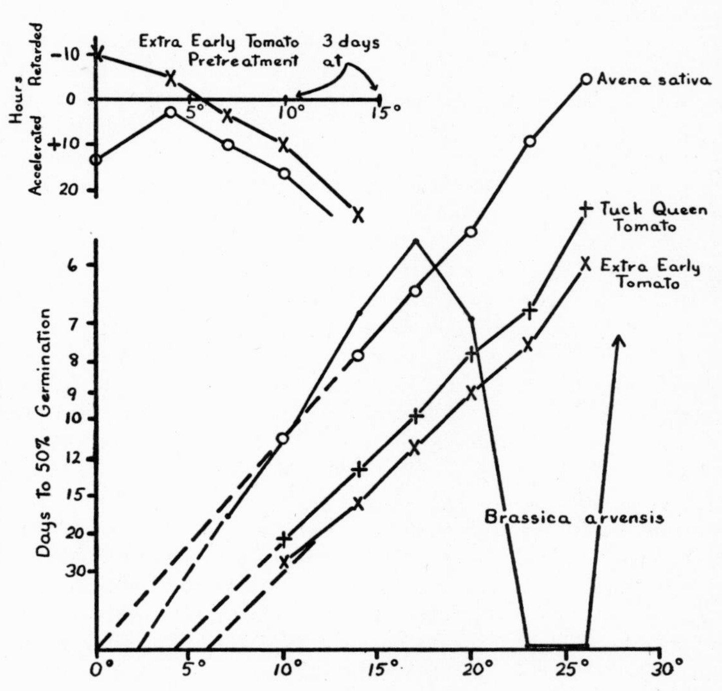

FIGURE 51.— Rate of germination (*ordinate:* number of days required for 50 per cent germination) at different temperatures (*abscissa:* degrees Celsius) for several plants: oats (*Avena sativa*), mustard (*Brassica arvensis*) and two tomato varieties (Tuckqueen and Extra Early). *Inset in upper left hand corner:* number of hours that germination of Extra Early tomato seeds was retarded or accelerated, when the seeds were pre-treated (wet, on filter paper in petri dishes) for 3 days with 0°, 4°, 7°, 10° and 14°. *Crosses:* seeds afterwards placed on filter paper alone; *circles:* seeds placed on filter paper overlying charcoal.

0° and 4°C pre-treatment germination was retarded compared with the controls. This means that at 0° and 4°C a sort of negative germination did occur. When these points of retardation or acceleration of subsequent germination are connected, then the line transects the zero line at 6°C which would indicate that at 6°C neither acceleration nor retardation of germination of Extra-Early tomato seeds occurs. It is probably no accident that the extrapolation of the curve for a rate of germination transects the abscissa for a germination rate of zero also at 6°C.

Is it possible to arrive at some conclusion about what happens in this condition of negative germination? It is tempting to assume that germination inhibitors are formed below 6°C and that the rate of formation increases with decreasing temperature down to 0°C. This hypothesis was tested by laying out Extra-Early tomato seeds for 3 days at different low temperatures and then germinating them on charcoal at 26°C. Any inhibitors present in the seed would be absorbed by the charcoal and thus germination independent of the presence of inhibitors could be tested. It was found that at any temperature, even after pre-treatment at 0°C, germination was speeded up by the presence of charcoal, and, therefore, it is obvious that retardation of germination after cold pre-treatment was largely a matter of germination inhibitors which were formed at the low temperatures.

From these experiments we arrive at the following picture of germination of seeds which will not develop below certain temperatures. At all temperatures there is the formation of an inhibitor which retards germination. At the higher temperatures the germination process exceeds in rate the formation of inhibitors and, therefore, germination can proceed although at a slower rate than if those inhibitors were not present. But at low temperatures the rate of germination is less than the rate of inhibitor formation and thus no germination can occur at all. It is very likely that these inhibitor mechanisms of germination control are much more developed among wild plants than in cultivated ones where most germination inhibitors have been bred out through selection.

Thus far, it has not been possible to work out a mechanism by which the germination at low temperatures can be explained, such as for *Brassica arvensis.* Experiments with charcoal showed only retardation of germination which indicates that substances essential for germination were removed by the charcoal. At low temperatures germination was very slow to start, but once started, almost 100 per cent of the seeds germinated in a few more days. At 26°C germination started much earlier, but only a very small percentage actually developed. At 30°C germination was very rapid and complete. It may seem as if at 26°C inhibitors are being formed which almost completely suppress germination. At 30°C germination may have been faster than the rate of inhibitor formation.

Some indication that this explanation is correct is found in further experiments, in which *Brassica* seeds were first placed at 4° or 7°C for various lengths of time, but in all cases too short to cause visible germination. When these seeds were transferred after 7-14 days to 26°C, almost 100 per cent germinated, showing that the inhibition at 26°C only occurs in the earliest stages of germination.

Rain:— With this new information on germination it now becomes possible to understand something more about the behavior of desert plants as discussed in the section on Ecology. It had been found that rain leached inhibitors diffusing from seeds away from them down into the soil. Consequently these desert seeds germinated after sufficient rain. This mechanism prevents premature germination when the rain has not been heavy enough to insure the complete development of seedlings. However, the presence of inhibitors in seeds is not sufficient to understand why a succession of light rains would not deplete the seeds of inhibitors the same way as happens after a single heavy rain and thus result in germination. It, therefore, seems that after light rains or after rain in the wrong season the supply of inhibitors in the seeds is replenished. Thus the seeds of *Pectis papposa,* which contain an effective germination inhibitor, will germinate at high temperatures immediately after a rain, before a sufficiently high concentration of inhibitors has been re-formed, whereas at low temperatures inhibitors are replenished faster than the seeds can germinate, as in the case of the tomato at low temperature.

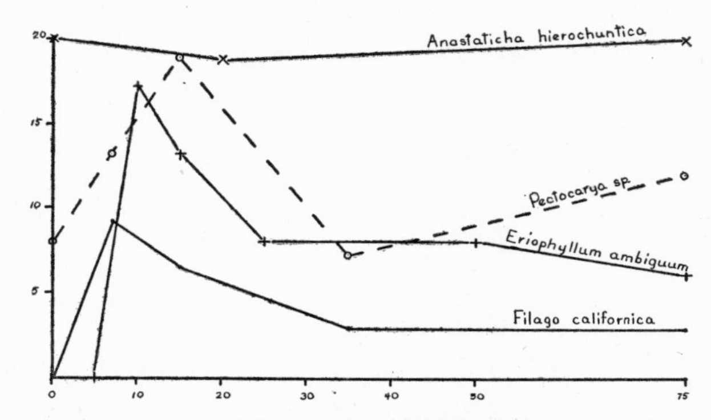

FIGURE 52.— Germination (*ordinate:* in number of seeds germinated) of a Saharian desert plant (*Anastatica hierochuntica*) and California desert plants (*Pectocarya, Eriophyllum* and *Filago*) as a function of amount of artificial rain in mm. (*abscissa*). Data from A. SORIANO (1953).

This makes a summer germinator out of *Pectis,* and it allows the recharging of the germination inhibition mechanism after every rain at low temperatures of sufficient magnitude to wash out the inhibitors. Only old seeds, unable to re-form the necessary inhibitors, may germinate after a rain of insufficient magnitude.

As an example of the effects of rain on germination FIGURE 52 is added which presents data obtained by SORIANO (1953*b*). Whereas *Anastatica hierochuntica* from the Israeli and Sahara deserts germinated fully regardless of the amount of rain (all seedling flats were completely wetted before starting experiments), the other California annuals (*Eriophyllum, Filago* and *Pectocarya*) germinated poorly or not at all without precipitation, had maximal germination with 9, 12 and 15 mm. of artificial rain, and with still more precipitation germinated at much lower rates.

SORIANO found, and this is also reported in Chapter 13 on *Baeria,* that the initial rain treatment had a pronounced effect on the subsequent development of the seedlings. When any of the seedlings developed without rain, the plants remained small and had few and small flowers. With increasing amounts of rain a gradually increased amount of growth was produced, and after a large amount of precipitation the plants were 2-4 times larger than without precipitation. This response is an aftereffect, and manifests itself one or more months after the initial stimulus. Thus, the phenomenon is comparable with other induction phenomena, like vernalization, which can be imposed upon seeds.

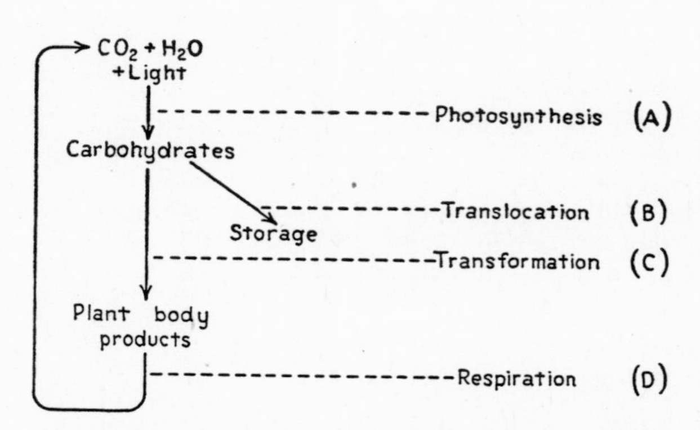

FIGURE 53.— Schematic representation of the major processes in plant metabolism (*right*) and the products they control (*left*).

Chapter 20

PHOTOSYNTHESIS

In the following discussion the term "photosynthesis" will be used in its broadest sense, meaning the total dry weight increase of the plant as a result of transformation of light energy into chemical energy which is harvested largely as carbohydrates. When we talk about photosynthesis *sensu stricto,* we usually mean the photosynthetic CO_2 reduction leading to carbohydrate formation, but we should recognize that there are other photosynthetic processes going on in the plant, such as nitrate reduction, or amino-acid synthesis (Gorham 1950). Therefore, in a physiological sense, photosynthesis should be considered the sum total of all energy storing processes, best measured as total dry weight increase. This value, also called yield, is one of the most important in all plant production, and does not come under any other general heading in Plant Physiology.

Efficiency of Light Utilization:— The actual process of photosynthetic sugar production will not be discussed since the experiments in the Earhart Laboratory have not shed any new light on this rather strictly biochemical problem. Besides, the basic process of photosynthesis is apparently the same in angiosperms, ferns, mosses, and algae, and with the greater simplicity of algal cells and their cultural convenience they seem to be the best material with which to study the biochemistry of photosynthesis. The study of *Chlorella* has also produced a better understanding of the physiology of algal photosynthesis, showing that in mass *Chlorella* cultures over 10 per cent of incident light energy can be converted into chemical energy of plant cell products. This high efficiency greatly exceeds that of higher plants in the field, where 2 per cent efficiency has hardly been attainable (Wassink 1948). This high photosynthetic efficiency (under ideal growing conditions) has led to the belief that algae are the best plant material for transformation of light energy into food products. As will be shown in this chapter, proper control over the growing conditions of angiosperms can produce the same efficiency. It is my conviction that, when as much energy and thought is put into research on the photosynthetic efficiency of higher plants as has been spent on such work in algae, we will come up with similarly satisfactory yields. And with our knowledge of the mass growing of higher plants, I believe that the future food production of the world will remain largely based on higher plants. It seems likely that, if some plants or groups of plants had a so much greater photosynthetic efficiency, evolution would have favored them and they might have overtaken all other plant groups with lower photosynthetic potential.

Work on algae, using the gas exchange method, has shown rather consistently that they can maximally transform about 30 per cent of the absorbed light energy into chemical energy. The few data available for higher plants (GABRIELSEN 1947) also indicate a potential photosynthetic efficiency of over 10 per cent. If in nature we find then so much lower efficiencies, this must be attributed to processes preceding or succeeding the photosynthetic CO_2 reduction. Thus we come to the conclusion that the *physiology* of photosynthesis is of paramount importance in the study of the yield of plants, and that we should study in the first place the processes *accompanying* photosynthetic CO_2 reduction (since the latter reaction does not seem to be limiting), if we want to find means of increasing the yield of plants.

A schematic representation of the dry weight production system of the higher plant is given in FIGURE 53. In this scheme process A has about a 30 per cent efficiency, but processes $A + B + C - D$ average less than 2 per cent under ordinary growing conditions. Therefore, there are processes both preceding and succeeding the actual photosynthetic process which must be responsible for the relatively low photosynthetic activity of the plant as a whole.

Methods:— The approaches used in the Earhart Laboratory to study photosynthesis as a whole are mainly in three directions: (*1*) Study of process A (photosynthesis *sensu stricto*) as far as duration, intensity and color of the light affect dry weight production; (2) Study of the effects of temperature, wind and other external conditions, both before, during and after light exposure, on the production and utilization of photosynthates by the plant; (3) Study of the conditions attending the utilization of carbohydrates by the plant (processes B and C), by supplying these carbohydrates through a sugar spray on the leaves, thus obviating the necessity of light for carbohydrate photosynthesis.

Two methods are mainly used to measure photosynthesis: (*1*) CO_2 analysis of the air passing over plants, and (2) total dry weight production which may approximate, but never exceed, actual photosynthesis as long as no organic carbon sources are available to the plant. The CO_2 analysis has the advantage of being an instantaneous method, the rates of CO_2 exchange between plant and surrounding air becoming steady within 5-10 minutes of a change in condition. With a time-lag of ± 2 minutes in the CO_2 recorder (*see* Chapter 2) this allows a close check on the rate of photosynthesis. The disadvantages of this method are that we have no guarantee that all CO_2 taken up enters into the photosynthetic process, since we know a number of non-photosynthetic processes requiring a supply of CO_2. In succulents, *e.g.*, large amounts of CO_2 can be taken up and transformed into organic acids in the absence of light. Besides, we have to integrate the CO_2 taken up and given off over a considerable time, at least 24 hours, before we can arrive at a value for the net photosynthesis of a plant.

To measure net photosynthesis, total dry matter production is an excellent method. Actually, we should not use dry weight increase, but increase in total chemical energy as measured by combustion. But since the increase in dry matter of a plant is more than 80 per cent carbohydrates and up to 10 per cent protein, both with approximately equal caloric value, and about 5 per cent inorganic matter, we can take one gram of dry weight

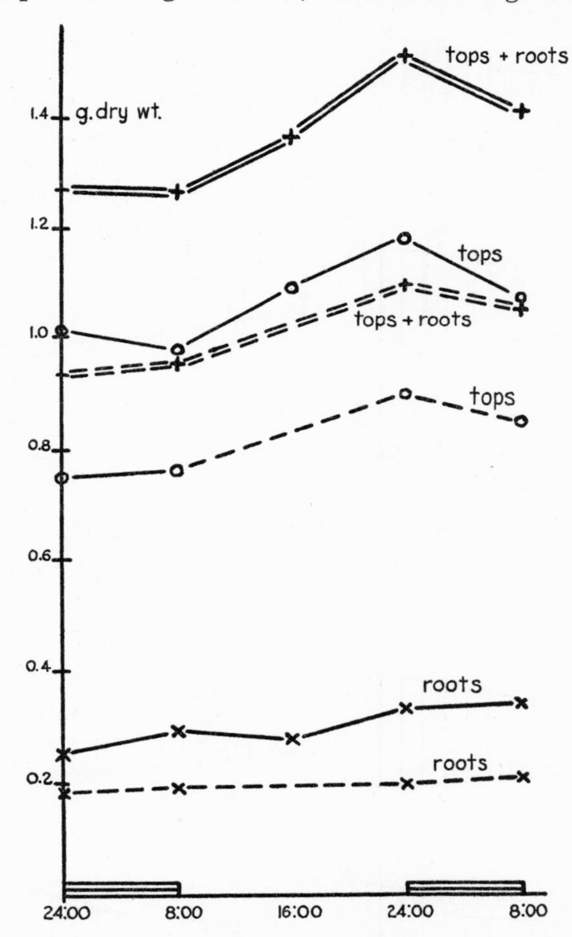

FIGURE 54.— Dry weight (*ordinate:* in grams) of roots, tops, and whole plants of Extra Early tomatoes as a function of time (*abscissa*), including two dark periods of 8 hours between midnight and 08:00. *Broken lines:* experiment 1; *solid lines:* experiment 2.

increase in a plant to be equivalent to 3500 calories. A disadvantage of the dry matter production method is that it requires sacrifice of the plants, and can be arrived at only as the differential weight between two or more groups of plants, each with their own errors. This limits the method to photosynthetic periods of more than one day, the optimal length

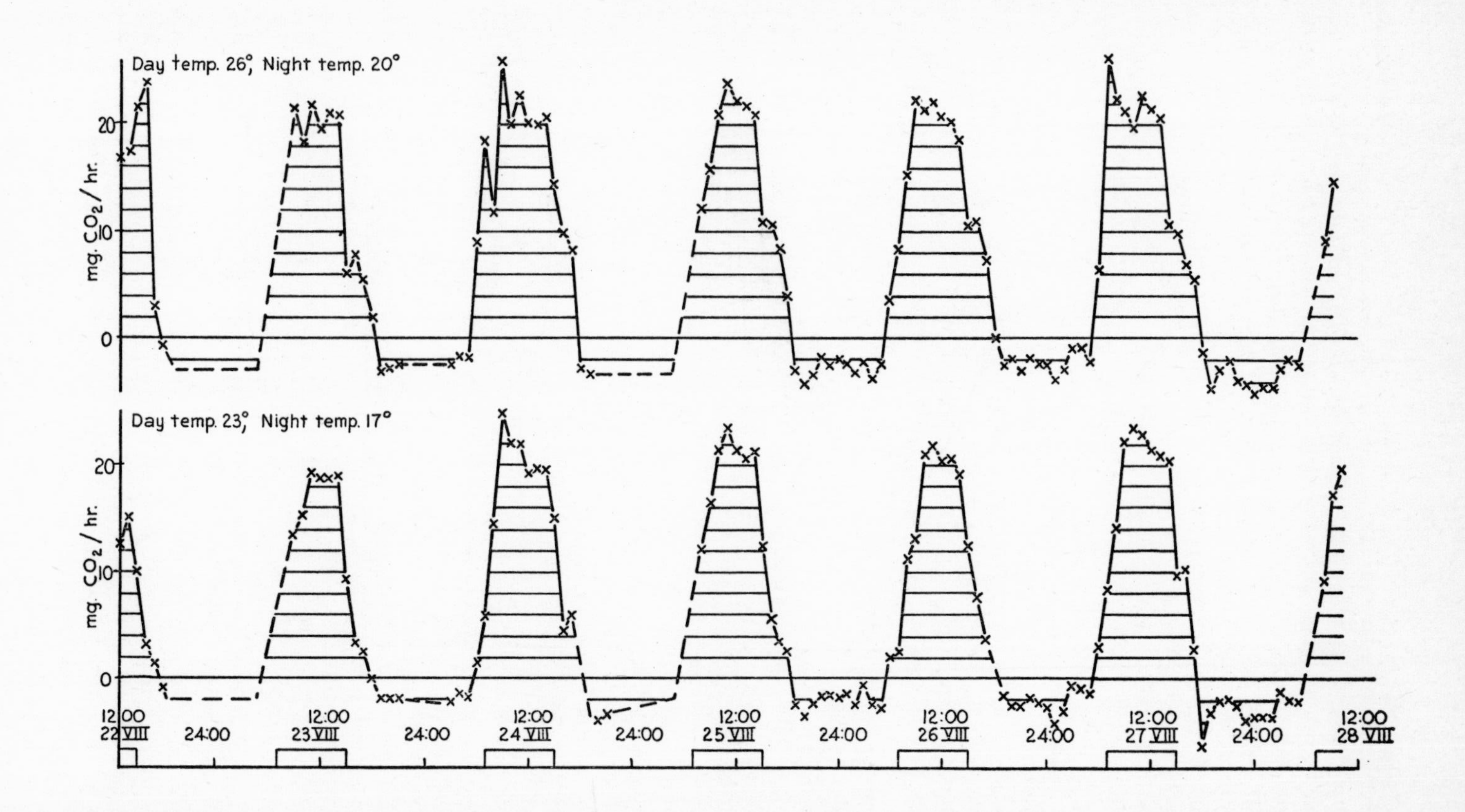

Day temp. 26°, Night temp. 20°
Day temp. 23°, Night temp. 17°
mg. CO_2 / hr.
0
10
20
12:00 22 VIII
24:00
12:00 23 VIII
12:00 24 VIII
12:00 25 VIII
12:00 26 VIII
12:00 27 VIII
12:00 28 VIII

depending upon the uniformity of the plants. A great advantage of the method is that the growing conditions can be varied easily, which is more difficult in the enclosed containers for CO_2 analysis. The data of FIGURE 54 show the limitation of the dry weight method: 200 plant samples of young tomatoes were taken at 8-hour intervals for plants exposed from 08:00-24:00 to 1000 ft.-c. of light, with an 8-hour dark period before and afterwards. Whereas the tops increased in weight in the light, the roots gained weight even in darkness, indicating that translocation of photosynthates from leaves to roots took place in darkness too.

CO_2 Analysis:— Among the results obtained with CO_2 analysis can be mentioned: some plants, such as tomatoes, respire during night only a small fraction of the photosynthates produced during day; this fraction depends of course on the degree of light saturation during day and the temperature during night, but in warm nights (20°C) after photosynthesis at half saturation, CO_2 loss by respiration during night was only 16 per cent of all CO_2 taken up during day. This can be read from FIGURE 55, in which the CO_2 exchange over a 6-day period of tomato plants weighing 2.06 grams on 22 VIII and 3.10 g. on 28 VIII is shown. Under normal field conditions young tomatoes probably lose less than 10 per cent of their photosynthates in respiration. The rest, 90 per cent, goes into the building of the tomato plant and fruit growth. Thus we can calculate that in the field, even after exceptionally hot nights, 80 per cent or more of the carbohydrates formed during day remain in the plant. Therefore, excessive respiration cannot be the process which limits tomato production in hot weather.

In other plants, such as old strawberries, with a much larger proportion of non-photosynthetically active tissue, respiration during night may almost equal photosynthesis during day (*see* FIGURE 56). This may account for the much slower growth of strawberry than of tomato plants. It also may be the reason why strawberries and other perennial plants have to be replanted every few years. In replanting, the young vigorous shoots are used, and the old tissues which only respire are removed. In this way a favorable ratio between photosynthesis and respiration is restored.

Unless the rate of air movement within a photosynthetic chamber is increased beyond what the injection of the outside air produces, photosynthesis is likely to be limited by the CO_2 gradient air-leaf. By operating a fan in the chamber, thoroughly mixing the air and decreasing the thickness of the stationary air-layer around the leaves through which CO_2 diffuses, the rate of photosynthesis is increased (*see* FIGURE 57). There-

FIGURE 55 (*opposite*).— Net CO_2 exchange in milligrams of CO_2 absorbed or released per hour for a 6-day period, for two sets of tomato plants, original dry weight 2.06 g.; final dry weight 3.16 g. for upper curve, 3.11 g. for lower. *Upper curve:* plants grown at 26°C during day, 20°C during night. *Lower curve:* similar plants grown at 23°C during day, 17°C during night. Period of higher temperature marked on *abscissa.*

fore, to get representative measurements of photosynthesis by the CO_2 analysis method, it is essential that the air movement past the photosynthesizing surfaces is carefully adjusted.

BÜNNING has during the past years published a series of papers showing the existence in many plants of an endogenous 24-hour cycle which he considers to be the basis of many other periodic phenomena such as photoperiodism. According to him, the plant passes through a photophil and a skotophil phase in the course of 24 hours, when light either enhances or inhibits physiological processes. HIGHKIN and HANSON (1954) had shown

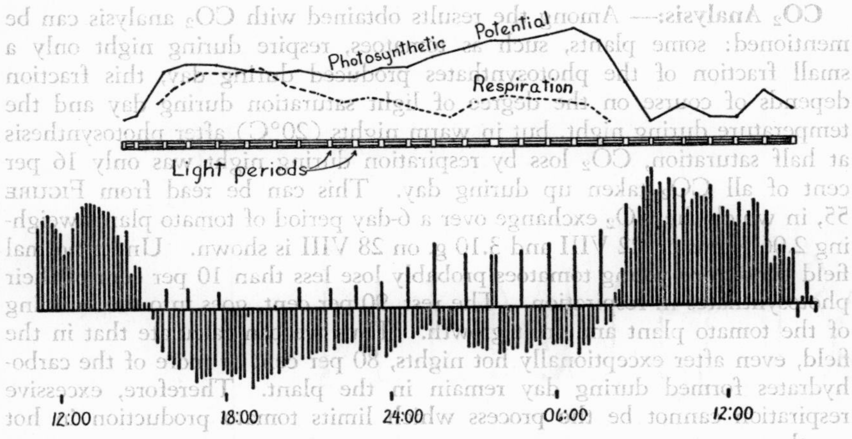

FIGURE 56.— Vertical lines in lower curve indicate quantity of CO_2 taken up (*above abscissa*) or released (*below abscissa*) by a Tennessee Beauty strawberry plant over a 30-hour period in natural daylight. From 14:00 o'clock on, supplementary light of 2000 ft.-c. for 10 min. once an hour (indicated on *upper abscissa*). Above this the rate of respiration and photosynthetic potential of the same plants is given as an average of 3 days.

that in tomatoes light during the skotophil phase retarded growth and decreased total weight. To see whether photosynthesis is also inhibited when light strikes a plant during its skotophil phase, tomato and strawberry plants were grown in a greenhouse under natural light conditions, and once each hour they were subjected for 10 minutes to artificial light of 2000 ft.-c. intensity. FIGURE 56 shows the CO_2 evolved or absorbed over a 24-hour period by a Tennessee Beauty strawberry plant. The Marshall variety showed the same behavior. Whereas during day the extra light had little effect on photosynthesis, because the plants were subjected already to near-saturating light intensities from the sun (ranging from 2000-6000 ft.-c.), during night the 2000 ft.-c. greatly changed the CO_2 balance. When net photosynthesis is calculated by subtracting the values for respiration just prior to and after the light exposure, the upper curve is obtained, which shows maximal effectiveness of light at dusk (17:00-18:00, December) and before sunrise (06:00-07:00) with a minimum between 20:00 and 23:00. Respiration shows a similar trend: in the evening it was high, decreasing gradually, with a second increase towards morning. Future work will have to show whether the Bünning cycle generally decreases potential photosynthesis and actual respiration during the skotophil phase. Further examples of the significance of the Bünning cycle will be given later in this chapter.

Dry Weight:— Much work has been carried out in the Earhart Labortory on photosynthesis of plants by measuring their increase in dry weight

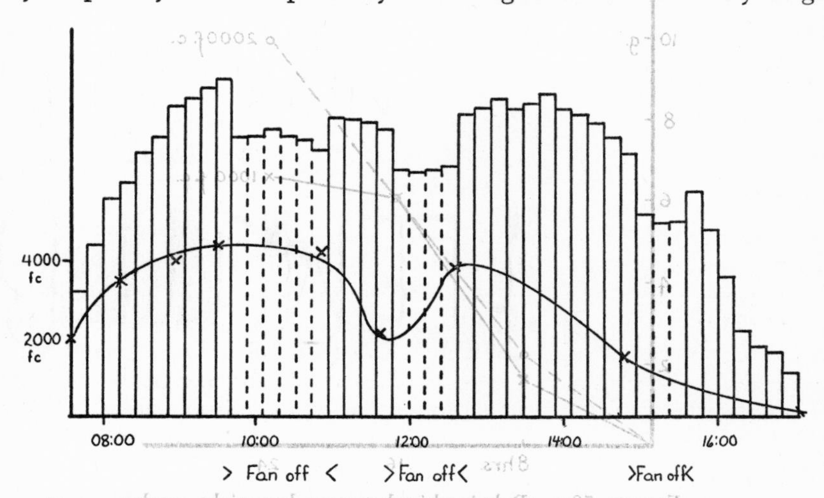

FIGURE 57.— Vertical columns indicate rate of CO_2 uptake by a tomato plant during a day in natural light during December (intensity indicated with crosses). During 3 periods, marked below the abscissa, the fan which circulated the air within the photosynthetic chamber was turned off, in which case the air renewal (2 l./minute) had to supply the necessary turbulence.

after 1-7 days of exposure to light. For this work large numbers of plants were grown so that groups of plants of equal weight and size could be selected. By using young plants, which have only a single layer of leaves and in which no older leaves are shaded by younger ones, the relationships between light intensity and dry weight production were particularly clear-cut. Usually tomato plants were used, grown 20 per 10 × 10 cm. plastic dish (*see* Chapter 6). Each group of plants consisted of 6-10 dishes, with 120-200 young plants per treatment. The uniformity of the plants could be increased to such an extent that differences in weight of only 2 per cent were significant. Around each dish of tomato plants an aluminum shield was placed (*see* FIGURE 17) which confined the leaves to an exactly outlined surface area, which made it possible to measure the total amount of incident light per group of tomato plants.

In the experiments to be described the effect of a measured amount of light on growth and dry weight production was determined. Either the dark or the light treatments were kept constant in one experiment, enabling us to assess the effectiveness in dry weight production of the processes A and B + C from FIGURE 53.

Intensity and Duration of Light:— To start with, experiments concerning the light process will be described. This work was carried out by Dr. S. DUNN, with a grant from the General Electric Company. In one set of experiments tomato plants were placed on a series of 6 turntables

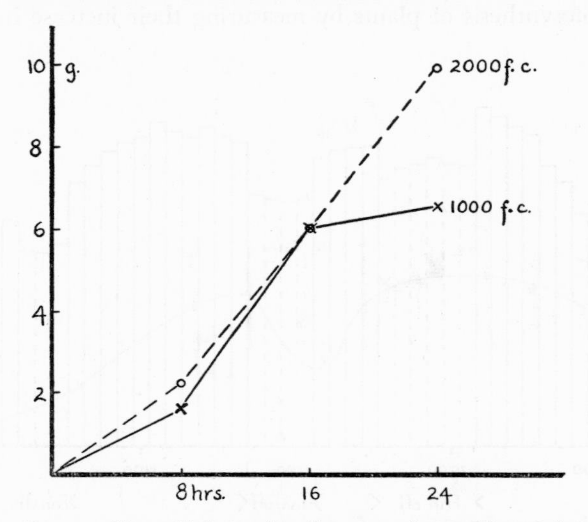

FIGURE 58.— Relationship between dry-weight production (*ordinate*), light intensity, and photoperiod (*abscissa:* in hours of light per 24-hour cycle), over a 5-day growing period of young tomato plants.

which were lined up under a bank of fluorescent lights. These lights were placed at an angle so that the plants on the turntable at one end received about 2000 ft.-c., at the other end about 600 ft.-c. By rotating the turntables at a rate of 1 revolution per 5-10 seconds, all plants on each table received exactly the same total amount of radiation. After 6 days exposure at a 16-hour photoperiod the increase in dry weight was determined, by subtracting the dry weight of the control plants harvested at the start of the light treatment from the plants kept 6 days in the light. FIGURE 63 shows a few results which give a perfect example of Blackman curves. These plants were, therefore, saturated with white light at 1270 ft.-c.; at lower intensities the dry weight production was strictly proportional to the amount of light received; at higher intensities the photosynthetic process was completely saturated, and another process was limiting dry weight production. Dr. S. DUNN has obtained scores of similar "Blackman" curves in the Earhart Laboratory, all with the pronounced inflection at saturation (DUNN and WENT 1957).

To find whether the saturation is a function of total amount of light received per 24 hours or of light intensity, plants were exposed for 8, 16 and 24 hours daily to 1000 and 2000 ft.-c. As FIGURE 58 shows, dry weight production in 5 days was more than twice as high in 16 as in 8-hour photoperiods, with practically no difference for the two intensities. Therefore, it is not the total amount of light but the light intensity which limits photosynthesis: dry weight production of tomato plants exposed 8 hours daily to 1000 ft.-c. can be doubled by doubling the length of exposure, but not by doubling the intensity. When the exposure time is further lengthened, only the 2000 ft.-c. intensity shows the expected proportionality, but at the lower intensity no increase in dry weight production is found. When an 8-hour photoperiod in daylight was supplemented with artificial light, a 1000 ft.-c. intensity doubled dry weight production both when 8 or 16 hours supplementary light was supplied (*see* TABLE 15). At 450 and 200 ft.-c. supplementary light, dry weight production was in-

TABLE 15: *Increase in five days in dry weight in grams per square of 20 tomato plants, initial weight 1.80 gr.:—*

DAYLIGHT AT 4000-6000 FT.-C.	SUPPLEMENTARY LIGHT	DARKNESS	INTENSITY OF SUPPLEMENTARY LIGHT IN FT.-C.			
			0	200	450	1000
8 hrs.	8 hrs.	8 hrs.	1.73	2.21	2.47	3.55
8 hrs.	16 hrs.	0 hrs.	1.73	1.89	2.22	3.48

creased proportional to the intensity, but again with no difference between 8 and 16 hours' duration. This shows that the tomato plant can utilize light efficiently only for 16 hours daily, and that light during BÜNNING's skotophil phase is little effective as far as photosynthesis is concerned. It also shows that equal amounts of dry weight are formed in daylight and in 1000 ft.-c. artificial light, again indicating that young tomato plants are saturated with light around 1000 ft.-c.

In similar experiments it was found that the lack of strict proportionality between length of photoperiod and dry weight production as shown in FIGURE 58 is reproducible, and that at different intensities (80, 180, 400 and 780 ft.-c.) no dry weight increase and an actual net weight decrease occurs at a 4-hour photoperiod, whereas beyond that good proportionality between both light intensity and photoperiod and wet and dry weight increase occurs (FIGURE 59). The decrease in weight, which occurs when tomato plants are subjected to short photoperiods and low light intensities, compared with similar plants left in darkness, is very interesting from an ecological point of view. Leaves, which are so strongly shaded by other plants, or by the younger leaves on the same plant, that they remain below the compensation point are apparently catabolizing under the influence of this weak light, which provides the basis for self-pruning of the non-effective leaves. In this case respiration is obviously increased by low light intensities.

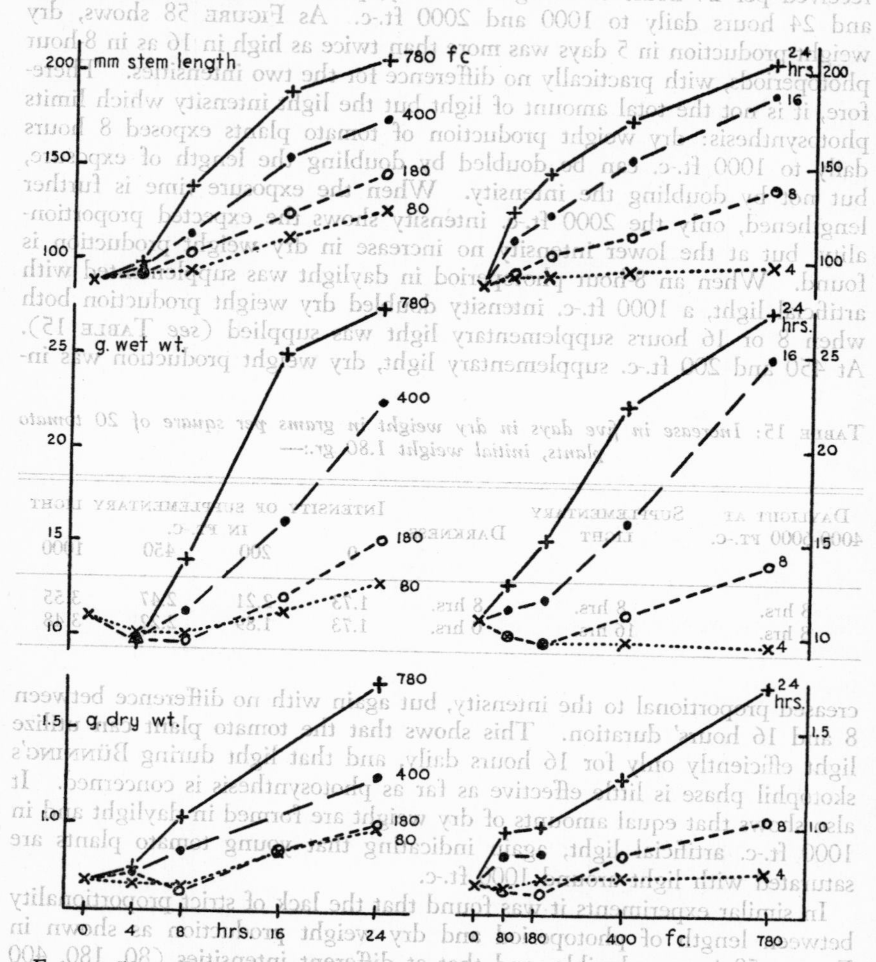

FIGURE 59.— Relationship between stem length, wet weight and dry weight (*ordinate*) of tomato plants grown for 5 days at 4, 8, 16 and 24-hour photoperiods, and 80, 180, 400 and 780 ft.-c. (*abscissa*).

Physiological Condition of Leaves:— The next experiments deal with the physiological factors indirectly influencing the light utilization of the plant, and affecting dry weight production. It had been suggested by several investigators that photosynthesis decreases as the leaf cells become saturated with photosynthates. This was also suggested by the sugar determinations in tomato leaves during the course of a day (*see* FIGURE 60), where after an initial lag period of 1-2 hours sucrose formation progressed rapidly up to a maximum, beyond which no more sugar accumulation occurred. In the following experiment, groups of tomato plants were exposed for 3 days to darkness or different light intensities. They were then all placed for 2 × 16 hours in the same near-saturating light intensity (700 ft.-c.). The plants coming from 350 or 700 ft.-c. formed the most dry weight in 700 ft.-c. intensity, those coming from darkness or strong

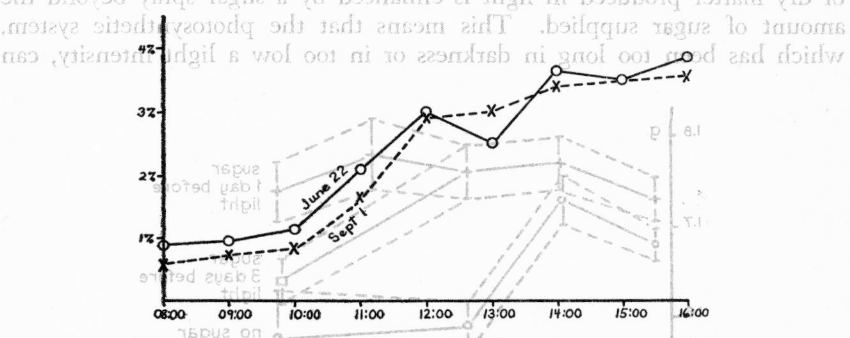

FIGURE 60.— Sucrose content (*ordinate:* in per cent of dry weight) of tomato leaves, exposed from 08:00 to 16:00 to full sunlight at 26°C, after a 16-hour nyctoperiod at 18°. Data from WENT and ENGELSBERG (1946).

light photosynthesized less in 700 ft.-c. This indicates that a certain optimal level of carbohydrates inside the cell exists, within which range photosynthesis progresses best. This would explain the curve of FIGURE 60 showing that, as the sugar level is low in a tomato leaf after a 16-hour night, photosynthesis is slow until the internal sugar concentration has reached the optimal range, then proceeds maximally until the inhibiting sugar level is reached.

TABLE 16: *Effect of pretreatment with different light intensities on subsequent growth and photosynthesis in young tomato plants grown at 17°C (after 2 days in 700 ft.-c. intensity):—*

PRETREATMENT FOR 70 HOURS IN	DARKNESS	350 ft.-c.	700 ft.-c.	1200 ft.-c.
Increase in length in mm.	7.6	13.9	10.0	9.5
Increase in top dry weight in mg.	55 ± 37	141 ± 29	172 ± 39	76 ± 41

That the initial lag in photosynthesis is due to too low a sugar level in the leaf, is also suggested by experiments in which tomato plants were kept for 0, 1, 2 or 4 days in darkness before exposure to 2 × 16 hours of light. As FIGURE 61 shows, the light was most effective after one day of darkness, and least after four days of darkness. When the plants were sprayed with sucrose a day before light exposure, there was no such decrease in effectiveness of the light after several days' darkness. This means that actually a definite sugar level has to exist inside a cell to make light most effective. It is imaginable that this sugar is necessary either to establish the proper osmotic level in the protoplasm or to provide the substances accepting the CO_2.

In the previous as in other experiments it was found that the amount of dry matter produced in light is enhanced by a sugar spray beyond the amount of sugar supplied. This means that the photosynthetic system, which has been too long in darkness or in too low a light intensity, can

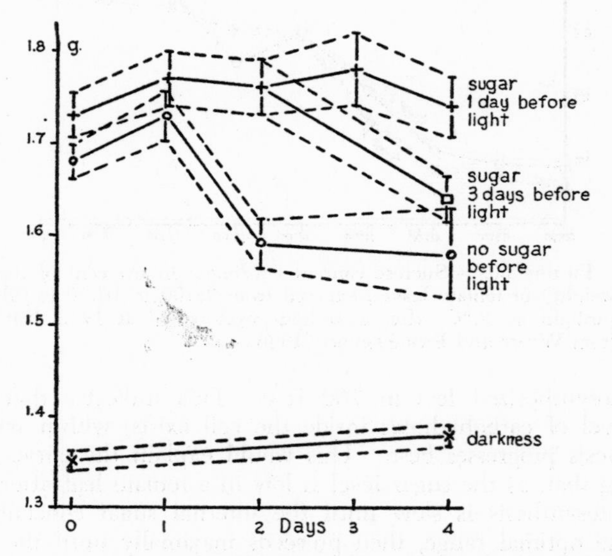

FIGURE 61.— Weight of tomato plants (*ordinate:* dry weight per square in grams) when subjected to 2 days of 32 hours of 1000 ft.-c. light after 0, 1, 2, 3, and 4 days of darkness (*abscissa*). Crosses: plants kept in darkness; circles: controls, no sugar spray; plus signs: plants sprayed with 10 per cent sugar solution 1 day before beginning of light treatment. *Vertical lines* indicate the value of twice the standard error.

be primed with sugar. Or in other words, 1 mg. of applied sugar may result in 3 mg. *more* photosynthetic carbohydrate formation. This may be the basis for the effects which are occasionally reported when sugar sprays on plants in greenhouses cause increases in production out of line with the amounts of applied sugar. One would expect sugar sprays to be particularly effective at the end of long periods of dark weather, with light intensities below 300 ft.-c.

If the photosynthetic process is so sensitive to the conditions in the cell, we can expect that it also is affected by the night conditions interposed between the light exposures. Several groups of plants were all exposed for several days to 8-hour photoperiods at 1000 ft.-c., but during the intervening nyctoperiods they were placed in 3°, 17° or 30°C. As FIGURE 62 shows, the dry weight production during the first two or three photoperiods was the same for all nyctotemperatures. This proves that respiration at the high nyctotemperature did not appreciably decrease net photosynthesis. When, therefore, dry weight production after 4 or 8 photoperiods is so much less at the high nyctotemperatures this has to be attributed to something else than excessive respiration. In line with earlier findings in tomatoes (WENT 1944*b*), we can explain the effects partly by the lack of

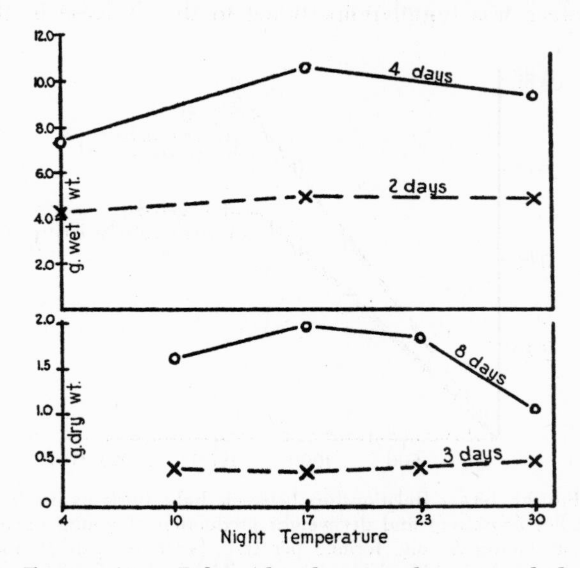

FIGURE 62.— Relationship between the wet and dry-weight production of tomato plants (*ordinate:* weight of plants per container) over different time intervals for 8-hour photoperiods at 17°C, and various night temperatures (*abscissa*).

translocation of the formed sugars out of the leaves under the influence of the high nyctotemperature. For both the high and low nyctotemperatures another explanation holds: since little growth took place, only a small amount of photosynthates was used up, leaving a higher concentration in the leaves than at the intermediate nyctotemperature. This results in another difference. The tomato plant does not store photosynthates: in no experiment did the amount of dry matter formed exceed 12 per cent of the wet weight. Plants growing slowly do not provide much new space for the photosynthates formed, and photosynthesis is soon halted by accumulation of sugars.

The degree to which photo- and nyctotemperature influence dry matter production or net photosynthesis can best be seen from FIGURE 18.

Groups of four tomato plants originally of the same size and weight, were grown for 53 days in different combinations of photo- and nyctotemperatures, all receiving an 8-hour photoperiod at 1500 ft.-c. intensity at the level of the top leaves. At the optimal temperature combinations photosynthesis was more than ten times as effective as at the lowest photo- or nyctotemperatures.

Since apparently the growth of the plant plays such an integral part in its net photosynthesis, experiments were carried out to restrict growth by decapitation and derooting. Actually, a decrease in dry matter production in tomatoes was found proportional to the decrease in their growth

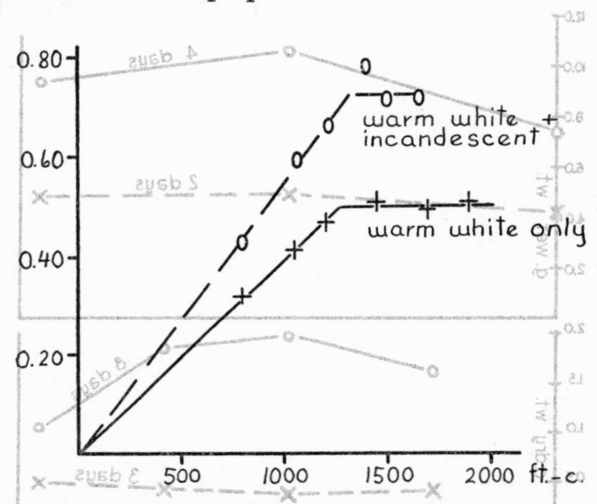

FIGURE 63.— Relationship between light intensity in foot-candles (*abscissa*) and dry-weight production of young tomato plants (*ordinate*: mg. formed per ft.-c. per 6 days of 16-hour photoperiods per 15 plants, covering 110 cm.²). Lower curve for warm-white fluorescent lamps only, upper curve when 10 per cent of the light is derived from incandescent lamps, the rest from warm-white fluorescents. Data of S. DUNN.

caused by the operations. Therefore, photosynthesis is much more intimately tied up with growth than supposed in the past. TAMYIA *et al.* (1953) have come to the same conclusion for *Chlorella.*

Wave Length:— All these facts about the physiology of photosynthesis give us materials for a better understanding of the process of photosynthesis. Facts of similar importance can be collected by studying the biophysics of light utilization by the plant. This has been carried out extensively with algae, but very little information concerning effects of wave length on photosynthesis of higher plants was available, and whenever this is discussed the curve of HOOVER (1937) for barley is reproduced.

For a 12-months' period Dr. S. DUNN has measured the effects of light intensity and light quality on dry weight production of young tomato plants in the Earhart Laboratory (DUNN and WENT 1957). The plants were grown in the standard manner in square dishes, and their dry weight production in 6 days at 16-hour photoperiods at 17°C constant temperature was measured. In all experiments each light combination was applied at six intensities, straddling the saturating intensity. The curves representing the dry weight as a function of the applied light energy all showed a sharp inflection point at the saturating light intensity (*see* FIGURE 63). Below this, there is a strict proportionality between intensity and yield, and the slope of the yield curve gives the photosynthetic efficiency. Above the

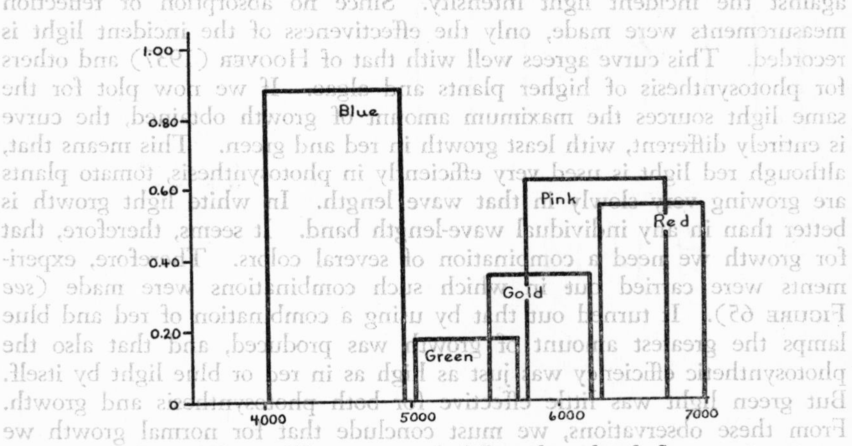

FIGURE 64.— Effectiveness of differently colored fluorescent tubes in producing dry matter in young tomato plants (*ordinate*: mg. of dry matter formed per unit of visible radiant energy, expressed as ft.-c., per 6 days at 16-hour photoperiods). The height of the columns indicates dry matter production, the width gives the approximate wavelength distribution (in Ångstroms: *abscissa*) of the lamps. Data of S. DUNN.

saturating intensity there is no further increase in yield with increased light. This maximum yield measures the amount the plant can grow in the particular light color combination. It shows that growth is saturated at a lower intensity than photosynthesis. Since we have here two completely independent processes, both affected by light, we get a typical "Blackman" curve with sharp inflection point. If growth and photosynthesis were inter-acting, a gradual change in slope would occur. In the following analysis, we will consider the slope of the photosynthetic yield curve as a measure of the efficiency of the actual photosynthetic process, whereas the maximum yield is attributed to the effects of light on growth.

To obtain sufficient intensities to reach light saturation in the growing of tomato plants, fluorescent tubes with different spectral emission were used. These were obtained from the General Electric Company, which also furnished the funds for this investigation. The "Blue" lamp had its principal emission between 4000-5000 Å. The Red lamp was between 6000-7000 Å, and other lamps had ranges in between, usually about 1000 Å wide. With gelatin filters, these spectral ranges could have been narrowed down, but only at the expense of light intensity which was not permissible in our experimental setup. FIGURE 64 shows the results obtained. The yield is plotted on the ordinate over the approximate width of the spectral emission of the lamp. It is clear that, both in blue and red light, a high efficiency of the light reaching the plants is obtained, whereas in green and yellow, photosynthesis is very much reduced when plotted against the incident light intensity. Since no absorption or reflection measurements were made, only the effectiveness of the incident light is recorded. This curve agrees well with that of HOOVER (1937) and others for photosynthesis of higher plants and algae. If we now plot for the same light sources the maximum amount of growth obtained, the curve is entirely different, with least growth in red and green. This means that, although red light is used very efficiently in photosynthesis, tomato plants are growing very slowly in that wave length. In white light growth is better than in any individual wave-length band. It seems, therefore, that for growth we need a combination of several colors. Therefore, experiments were carried out in which such combinations were made (*see* FIGURE 65). It turned out that by using a combination of red and blue lamps the greatest amount of growth was produced, and that also the photosynthetic efficiency was just as high as in red or blue light by itself. But green light was little effective for both photosynthesis and growth. From these observations, we must conclude that for normal growth we need at least two different light-requiring systems which can be separated by their wave-length requirement, each affecting growth in a different way. The results cannot be explained by the assumption that one pigment, like chlorophyll, is involved, since either red or blue light should then be effective, as in photosynthesis *sensu stricto*. Because of these differences of effectiveness of the various spectral regions, fluorescent lamps of different types have different effectiveness when plants are grown under them. Among the available lamps which were tried the so-called "warm-white" lamp was the best in practically all tests carried out, and was preferable to the "daylight" lamps. A still better combination for the growing of tomato plants was blue fluorescent lamps alternating with high intensity red fluorescent lamps. It is hoped that, in the near future, the General Electric Company will be on the market with an agricultural lamp combining the blue and red phosphors in a single tube.

Another conclusion can be drawn from FIGURE 65. The "warm-white" fluorescent lamps were less efficient than the red or blue lamps, because they emit a considerable portion of their light in the green region of the spectrum, which is only little effective in photosynthesis. This reduces the slope of the yield curve. But this should not reduce the maximum yield. It might have been expected on the basis of the yield of the combination of "red" and "blue" lamps that in "warm-white" with a lower photosynthetic efficiency light saturation would occur at 2000 ft.-c. Since this is not the case, it can be assumed that the green wave lengths have an inhibiting effect on growth, and that by filtering out the green from white light growth can be increased beyond the normal maximum in high intensity white light.

The effects of filtering the green wave lengths out of daylight have been investigated by growing tomato plants under different gelatin filters. Two neutral grey filters were used to obtain reduced light intensity without affecting the spectral composition of the light, and a pink and a light purple filter reduced the green wave lengths to different degrees. The

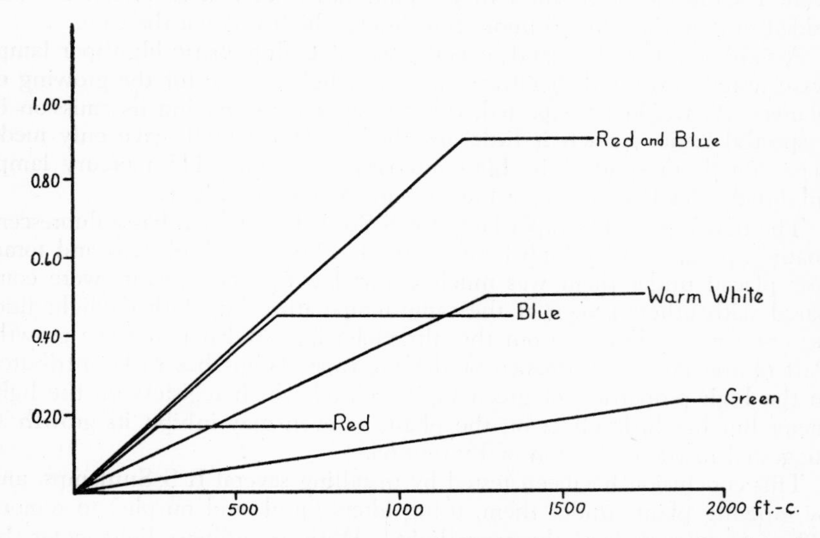

FIGURE 65.— Dry matter production (*ordinate:* mg. dry wt. produced in 6 days per square of tomato plants per ft.-c.) as a function of the incident light intensity. Colors indicate the type of fluorescent lamp used; for "Red and Blue" two of each color were used. Data of S. DUNN.

neutral grey filters were chosen to match the light absorption by the pink and purple filters. The first two to four days after tomato plants were transferred from full daylight to the reduced light under the filters, their growth rate remained the same, but within four days the plants receiving daylight minus the green wave lengths grew twice as fast as the plants under the grey filters. And in ten days the greenless-grown plants were twice as heavy. Their leaves were larger and lighter green.

In the experiments of Dr. DUNN, the effect of incandescent light alone or in combination with fluorescent light was also investigated. It had been reported (WITHROW and WITHROW 1947, and PARKER and BORTHWICK 1949) that the addition of light from incandescent bulbs increased the yield of plants grown principally in light from fluorescent tubes or carbon arcs. This beneficial effect had been found also in the Earhart Laboratory which necessitated the mixing of incandescent and fluorescent lamps in the light-banks of the artificial light rooms. In every single experiment it was found that by providing 5-10 per cent of the total visible radiation in the form of incandescent light, photosynthetic efficiency and yield were increased from 20-30 per cent, independent of the spectral distribution of the fluorescent light (*see, e.g.,* FIGURE 63). In fact, the addition of incandescent light to the red fluorescent lamps was more effective than when added to the blue lamps. No explanation for this behavior can be given. It is unlikely that the far-red and infra-red rays of the incandescent light were responsible since then they would have been more effective when added to blue than to red fluorescent light, which was not the case.

A sodium vapor lamp and several types of high-pressure Hg-vapor lamps were tested also for their effectiveness as a light source for the growing of plants. As would be expected, the Na-vapor lamp, having its emission in a spectral region which is little absorbed by chlorophyll, gave only mediocre growth in spite of its high intensity. Ordinary H5 mercury lamps inhibited growth, but gave a fair amount of photosynthesis.

The new type of Hg-vapor lamp (R S Sunlamp), which has a fluorescent coating, produces very high light intensities, but growth of peas and tomatoes placed under them was much reduced when these plants were compared with others grown at the same temperature but with daylight fluorescent lamps. Filtering out the ultraviolet light did not improve growth. Part of the poor performance of the Hg-vapor lamps has to be attributed to the high proportion of green light emitted which registers on the light meter but has little effect on the plant, or even may inhibit its growth as suggested in the discussion of FIGURE 65.

This conclusion has been tested by installing several R S Sunlamps, and by growing plants under them, using filters (pink and purple) to remove different proportions of the green light. With an ordinary light meter the plants were adjusted at two light intensities: 600 and 1000 ft.-c. under each of the filters and under unfiltered light. In 600 ft.-c. all plants grew equally well, using wet weight as a criterion. But whereas in the filtered light the plants at the 1000 ft.-c. intensity were heavier, and those under the purple filter also were taller, in the unfiltered light the plants at 1000 ft.-c. remained shorter and were considerably lighter, showing the inhibiting effect of the green rays.

In conclusion, we can say that no better combination of commercially available lamps for growing plants in artificial light was found than a mixture of fluorescent ("warm-white") and incandescent light.

Abnormal Photoperiodic Cycles:— A third variable which affects the light utilization of plants is the absolute length of photo- and nyctoperiods. As BÜNNING has shown, optimal growth and development of plants takes place in a 24-hour cycle. Any departure from this cycle decreases growth and light utilization. When tomato plants are grown in continuous light, their development is reduced because of a lack of nyctoperiod. Experiments of VERKERK (1955) have shown that a 6-hour nyctoperiod in a 24-hour cycle gives approximately optimal development in tomato plants, when they are grown entirely in artificial light.

From work described earlier in this chapter it would seem that best growth could be obtained by breaking up the light exposure into shorter periods, so that each time photosynthesis could start at a reduced sugar level in the leaves. In the following experiments tomato and Vinco pea plants were grown in interrupted light periods, yet the overall 24-hour cycle was retained. Five groups of plants were grown, each at three light intensities, 1500, 1000 and 500 ft.-c. They were all subjected to 8 hours of light per 24-hour period. In one group, the 8 hours of light were continuous, followed by a 16-hour dark period. In the other groups, the 8-hour light exposure was broken up into two 4-hour periods by 2, 4, 6 and 8-hour dark periods. In the last mentioned group, the plants were actually subjected to a 12-hour cycle of 4 hours light, 8 hours dark. The results obtained can be summarized as follows:

1) As the intervening dark period becomes longer, there is a decrease in light utilization which is most pronounced at the low intensity, and which is stronger in tomatoes than in peas.

2) At the high intensity, there is another effect in which a short interruption of the light *increases* light utilization.

The first effect is probably a result of interference with the Bünning cycle. When the second light period is delayed too much, it probably will overlap in the skotophil phase of the plant, and therefore, will be less effective. The increased effectiveness of photosynthesis after a short dark interruption is not found at the lower intensities where the plant is not light-saturated, and therefore has not accumulated a high concentration of carbohydrates in its leaves. At saturating light intensities, however, a short dark interruption was very effective in increasing light utilization.

Similar results were obtained when tomato plants were grown with 9 hours of light per 24 hours. In this case, two dark interruptions of 0, 1, 2, 3 and 5 hours a piece were given. In the latter case, the plants received 8-hour cycles of 3 hours light and 5 hours dark. Again at the high light intensities, a substantial increase in photosynthesis was obtained with 1, 2 and 3-hour interruptions (*see* FIGURE 66). In both these experiments the substantial decrease in dry matter production on the 12 and 8-hour cycle was due to interference with the Bünning cycle, as evidenced by the leaf-movements. Whereas after short dark interruptions, the leaves were in their photophil position at the beginning of each illumination, the leaf was in the skotophil position when the dark interruptions were long. This would indicate that the darkening caused the plant to shift into the skotophil phase, in which condition the plant was then caught upon its next light exposure.

In peas the situation was slightly different in that increased yields due to dark interruptions were much more pronounced than the decrease in

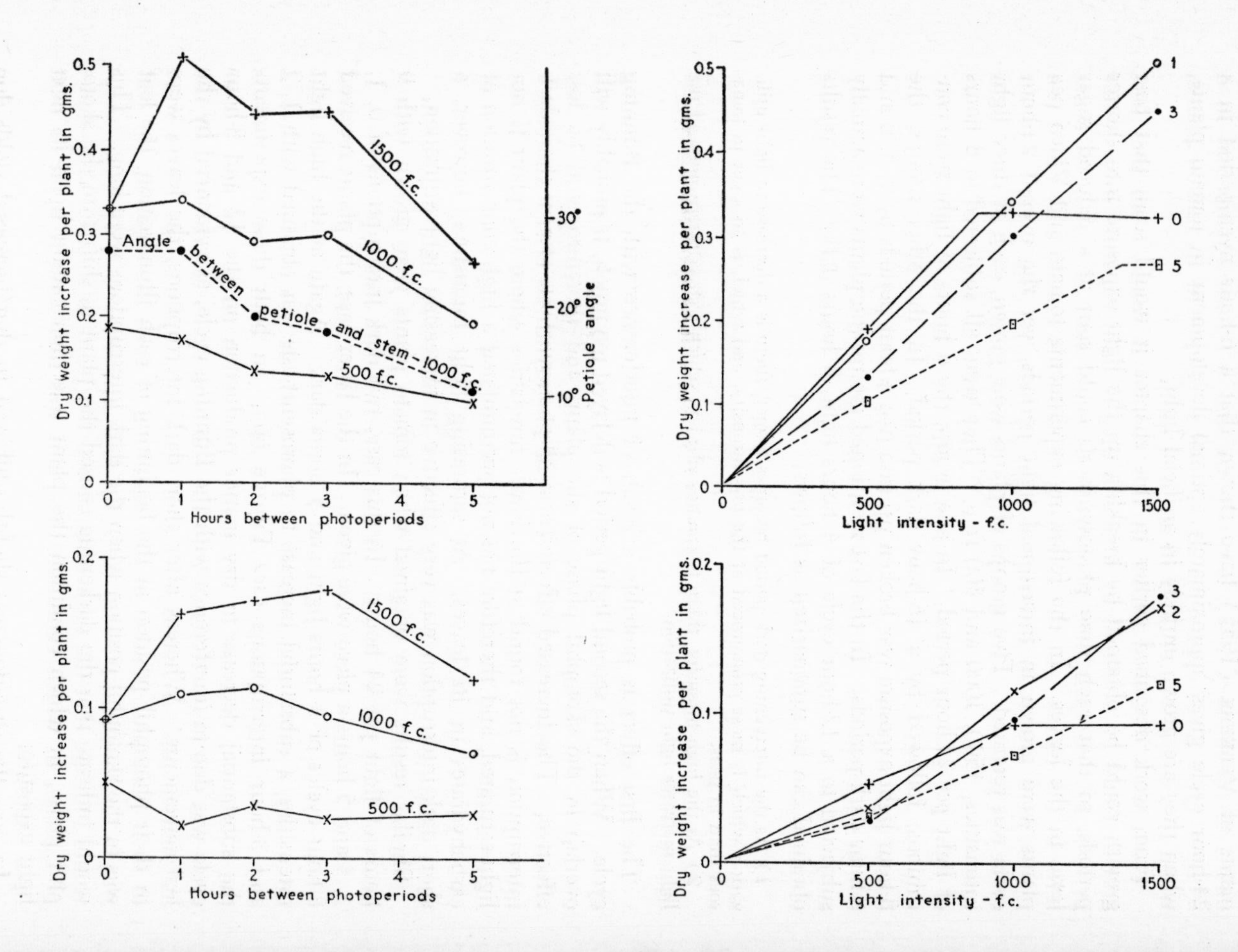
Dry weight increase per plant in gms.
Hours between photoperiods
1500 f.c.
1000 f.c.
500 f.c.
Angle between petiole and stem - 1000 f.c.
Petiole angle
30°
20°
10°
Light intensity - f.c.
1
3
0
5
2

growth at the 12 or 8-hour cycles. This may be connected with the fact that peas grow very well in continuous light and do not need a dark interruption for proper growth. Therefore, they are largely "light" plants.

Quite a number of different plants have been investigated as to their saturating light intensity in the Earhart Plant Research Laboratory. In the case of tomatoes, beets, squash, several varieties of peas and other plants, seedlings showed saturation at about 1000 ft.-c. in the artificial light rooms. After the plants had developed several leaves, plants in natural daylight started to grow better, and obviously the optimal light intensity for the plants as a whole increased. This is due to the fact that in older plants the lower leaves are shaded by the upper ones, and thus receive a substantially lower intensity. Therefore, in older plants much more light is required to saturate the lower leaves as well. In tomatoes it can be seen that the lower leaves, when they become too much shaded, die off, and thus the plant maintains a minimum light intensity level on its leaves. The more light a plant receives, the more layers of leaves it can maintain. This explains, probably, the results of BLACKMAN and WILSON (1951) and other investigators who found that in nature most plants are saturated at approximately the light intensity they are receiving. Any reduction in this light leads to a reduced yield which is probably the result of more severe self-pruning of the lower leaves. This has already been discussed in connection with FIGURE 59.

In the case of shade plants, only a slightly lower saturating intensity was found, namely 700 ft.-c. for the growth of *Cypripedium, Phalaenopsis* and of young strawberries. Therefore, it seems likely that one of the main differences between the photosynthesis of shade and sun plants is that sun plants produce many more layers of leaves, whereas shade plants have most of their leaves in one layer. Another possibility is that shade plants have a larger proportion of leaf surface to total weight of the plant than sun plants, which would mean also that they have a smaller loss of weight at night by respiration than plants with a larger proportion of non-green tissue, or their respiration rate might be exceptionally low.

As mentioned earlier, the photosynthetic efficiency of tomato plants can become as high as 10-15 per cent. That is to say, 10-15 per cent of the light incident on the plants can be harvested as chemical energy. Mrs. RACHEL MORGAN BEHNKE has also measured the photosynthetic efficiency in several other plants. The results show that, in beets, similar or slightly higher values can be obtained, whereas in *Chenopodium amaranticolor* the values were somewhat below 10 per cent. In *Bryophyllum,* however, very low values (well below 1 per cent) were found. From the very slow

FIGURE 66 (*opposite*).— Dry matter production of Extra Early tomatoes (*upper two curves*) and Vinco peas (*lower two curves*). In all cases the *ordinates* represent the dry weight increase in grams per plant during 9 days at 9 hours light per 24 hours. This light was given in three 3-hour photoperiods, with 0, 1, 2, 3, or 5 hours intervening darkperiods (*abscissa in left-hand curves*), at 3 intensities (*abscissa in right-hand curves*).

growth rates of other succulents, such as Cacti and orchids, we can conclude that the special succulent metabolism does not make for high photosynthetic efficiencies, partly because the limited amount of CO_2 which can be bound during night, and partly because of the diffusion resistance to CO_2 exchange. Plants with hygromorphic leaves all have a high photosynthetic efficiency. It seems logical to assume that maximum photosynthetic efficiency of 10-15 per cent can be achieved by most hygrophytic plants under optimal conditions of temperature, light, etc. Differences between plants would then be, not in their potential efficiency, but in the degree to which they are adapted to grow under various conditions. This also follows from the narrow range of maximal photosynthetic efficiency of different crop plants as observed in the field (WASSINK 1948).

Photosynthesis in the Tomato Plant:— As a consequence of all these observations we now arrive at the following picture. For plants grown in natural daylight, sunrise coincides approximately with the beginning of the photophil phase; photosynthesis will, therefore, not be restricted. But when the night has been long, the sucrose content of the leaf may be so low that the rate of CO_2 reduction is limited by it. It then takes one to two hours (or longer after more than 16-hour darkness or after previous days in low light intensities) for photosynthesis to reach a maximal rate. This rate (*e.g.*, shown in FIGURE 60 between 10:00 and 12:00) drops off as soon as the sucrose concentration in the photosynthesizing cells has reached an upper limit (probably 25 per cent in the cytoplasm). From then on, the photosynthetic rate equals the rate at which the sucrose is removed from the cytoplasm, either by polymerizing (presumably to a phosphor-starch which in the cold does not give a blue iodine test, but stains only light-pink and which was named transport-starch by SACHS), or by translocation. By interrupting the photoperiod with short dark periods, without interfering with the skotophil phase, the plant can utilize higher light intensities (FIGURE 66). This shows that the saturating light intensity is not inherent in the photosynthetic process itself, but is determined by the rate of removal of photosynthates.

The rate of removal of photosynthates from the leaf depends upon: (*1*) rate of translocation, and (2) rate of use elsewhere. Translocation in the tomato stem has been measured (WENT and HULL 1949, HULL 1952) and was found to occur fastest at the lower temperatures, and to be slow at temperatures above 20°C. Since most of the translocation seems to occur at night, as TSCHESNOKOV and BAZYRINA (1930) found for potatoes, it is mainly in darkness that the leaves are being freed of photosynthates. The rate of use of photosynthates depends largely upon the growth rate, since a tomato plant does not store much food. The growth rate in constant darkness falls off rapidly 30-40 hours after darkening, but can at that time be restored by sugar application to the leaves. Therefore the plant has enough stored food for about two nights' growth. Consequently, a tomato plant can photosynthesize at a maximal rate only for two days, if for some reason growth is suspended (*see* FIGURE 62). In the experiments reported, a decrease in rate of translocation (high nyctotemperatures), or a decrease of growth rate (removal of roots, low nyctotemperatures), did not immediately, but only after 2-3 days, result in a decrease in dry weight production.

The experiments of Dr. S. DUNN with colored light have also shown that the rate of the photosynthetic reaction does not limit maximal dry weight production. This rate, indicated by the slope of the yield-versus-intensity curve, is maximal in either blue or red light, and amounts to 0.12-0.13 mg. dry weight formed per 16-hour light per incident foot-candle per 110 cm.^{2} surface. From the value of 0.13 mg. dry weight formed per 16-hour light per foot-candle we can also calculate the efficiency of light transformation into chemical energy. The surface of the leaves exposed to the light is 110 cm.^{2}, the caloric value of a foot-candle/hour/cm.^{2} is 2.8×10^{-3} calories, and 1 mg. plant material formed equals 3.5 calories. Therefore we can write:

$$\frac{0.13 \times 3.5 \text{ cal.}}{16 \times 110 \times 2.8 \times 10^{-3} \text{ cal.}} \times 100 = 9.2 \text{ per cent efficiency}$$

In green light this value is only 0.02 mg./16-hour photoperiod/incident ft.-c./110 cm.^{2} In white light, which contains much — almost ineffective — green light, the photosynthetic rate is intermediate, as could be expected (*see* FIGURE 65). This is all in complete accordance with what is known about photosynthesis in algae. The most interesting part of these experiments is, however, that the photosynthetic efficiency in no way determines how much total dry weight will be formed at a saturating intensity. This is determined by the maximal rate of growth in the different colors of light. While red and blue light is equally effective in photosynthetic CO_2 reduction, red is very poor for inducing growth. In this respect green light is slightly better than red. Maximal growth is only possible when enough red *and* blue light is applied simultaneously.

When we return now to the scheme of FIGURE 53, then the previous analysis has shown that not process A, but processes B and C are the ones which limit dry weight production by photosynthesis in the field. Plants adjust their leaf surface to the average light intensity which is available and, therefore, field experiments usually show that plants are saturated with the amount of light they normally receive. At the rate of air movement, which occurs in the field or in an air-conditioned greenhouse the CO_2 gradient air-leaf is steep enough so that CO_2 is not limiting.

Processes B and C: translocation of photosynthates and transformation of them into plant substance are, therefore, the ones which we should investigate in great detail, because they are the ones which limit crop yield in the field. Besides, these processes are usually strongly influenced by external conditions and, therefore, might be controlled in a practical way.

Chapter 21

NUTRITION

Although not many experiments have been carried out on the nutrition of plants under different temperature and light conditions, there are a few results which seem worth recording. All plants in the Earhart Plant Research Laboratory are watered with the same nutrient solution, which is essentially that of HOAGLAND. The great majority of plants grow well in this mixture of nutrient elements. Some plants, among which are strawberries, oaks and orchids, show injury symptoms (brown leaf margins) when watered daily with the full concentration, but with a diluted solution no such symptoms appear and the plants grow normally. A simple way to water plants with a lower concentration is to supply them once to three times a week with the full Hoagland solution and water them on the intervening days with de-ionized water.

Nitrate Nutrition:— It is interesting to note that under specific temperature and light treatments a number of plants show symptoms which resemble certain mineral deficiencies. When, for instance, corn plants are subjected to continuous light of about 500 ft.-c. at 18°C, the young leaves do not unfold at their tips and thus a flag-like structure appears in which the leaves developed in artificial light are all attached to each other by their tips and are bent over in a fan-like fashion. This appearance of the plants resembles that of calcium deficiency. Many plants, for instance tomatoes, potatoes, and chili peppers, develop a light green or yellowish green appearance when they are grown at high night temperatures (26°C or over). The lower leaves die off prematurely and the whole syndrome is typical of nitrogen deficiency. It was actually found that by increasing the nitrate content of the nutrient solution, tomato plants could be grown at 26°C nyctotemperature with a normal green color. At low nyctotemperatures, such as 13°C, the nitrate content of the Hoagland nutrient solution could be decreased to 1/3 without the plants showing nitrogen deficiency symptoms. Therefore, it seems that the nitrogen requirement of the tomato plant is largely dependent upon the nyctotemperature to which it is subjected.

This fact is of considerable importance in connection with the interpretation of field fertilizer tests. It is known that these tests are highly variable and that for the same field and the same crop the optimal fertilizer concentration varies from year to year. Therefore, it is necessary to repeat fertilizer field tests every year. With the information on the optimal nitrogen requirement of tomato plants, it should be possible to correct these field data for any departure from the normal temperature which had occurred the year of the test and thus the results of tests in successive years would be made more comparable. In this way, it also might be possible to adjust the fertilizing program to the actual weather conditions prevailing in any particular area. In periods of high temperature a greater supply of nitrogen fertilizer would be indicated than in cool periods.

The same dependence of optimal nitrogen nutrition upon temperature was found by Dr. ULRICH (1955) in sugar beets. He grew two sugar beet varieties in a warm (26°-20°C) and a cool (20°-14°C) greenhouse and supplied each variety at each condition with a range of nitrogen concentrations. Whereas for US 22/3 optimal top and root weight was obtained at 24 p.p.m. nitrate in the cool greenhouse, the optimal concentration was 64 p.p.m. for the top and root weight in the warm greenhouse. For the variety US 35/2 both top and root weight were optimal at 64 p.p.m. in the cool greenhouse and at 128 p.p.m. in the warm greenhouse. Thus in sugar beets we find the same shift towards higher optimal nitrate concentrations at higher growing temperatures as in the tomato. It seems likely, therefore, that this phenomenon is general. For a tentative explanation, the following facts seem to be of importance:

Both in the tomato and in the chili pepper it was found that the nitrate content of leaves is directly correlated with the night temperature in which they grow. That is to say that at high nyctotemperatures the nitrate content of the leaves is very high in spite of the fact that these leaves show nitrogen deficiency symptoms which can be overcome by increasing the nitrate concentration in the nutrient solution. We can, therefore, assume that at high nyctotemperatures the rate of nitrate reduction is low. Or we might consider the possibility that nitrate reduction in the tomato plant occurs predominantly in the roots. The high nyctotemperature slows down the translocation rate of sugars towards the roots, and results in a low root weight which would thus limit nitrate uptake and reduction.

Ever since the work of KLEBS, and KRAUS and KRAYBILL, the carbon-nitrogen ratio has been considered an important factor in the flowering of different plants. Since KRAUS and KRAYBILL's work was specifically carried out with tomatoes, and since it was possible to control the fruiting development of tomatoes by temperature treatment, the possible interaction between nitrogen nutrition and temperature on the fruit development of tomato plants was investigated. To this end, San Jose Canner tomatoes were grown in the Clark greenhouses at 26°, 18° and 13°C nyctotemperatures. At each of these temperature conditions they were supplied with two or three nitrogen levels amounting to three, one, and one/third times the nitrate concentration of Hoagland's nutrient solution. At the high nyctotemperature, the plants were obviously nitrogen deficient at the two lower concentrations, whereas at the lowest nyctotemperature all plants were equally green. Whereas there was no fruit-set at the highest nyctotemperature and heavy fruit set at 18°C, fruit-set was completely independent of the nitrogen concentration in the nutrient solution. This experiment was repeated several times, always with the same results, namely that at optimal nyctotemperatures fruit-set was neither increased nor decreased by high or low nitrate supply, and that at 26°C nyctotemperature at low nitrogen level no fruit-set could be induced. These results agree with agricultural practice in which it was found that tomato production could not be decreased by high doses of nitrogen fertilizers. In 1951, Dr. H. C. MOORE repeated these experiments in the Earhart Laboratory with the same results: temperature controlled fruit-set regardless of nutrition; the largest number of perfect fruits was harvested in the solution high in nitrate.

In the chili pepper a clear-cut decrease in fruit production was obtained when the nitrogen supply was too high or too low, but this was not the case in tomatoes.

A most interesting dependence of flowering on nitrogen supply was found by Dr. G. CAMUS, working with *Baeria chrysostoma* in the Earhart Laboratory. Using the technique of Loo, he grew these plants under sterile conditions in test tubes by germinating the sterilized seeds on agar containing the necessary nutrients. In this way, it was possible to study the organic nutrition of these plants. They were grown at 20°C in short photoperiods (8 hours) at a low light intensity (200 ft.-c.). Under these conditions, the plants grew and remained vegetative for at least forty days which is in agreement with SIVORI and WENT (1944) and LEWIS and WENT (1945), who found that *Baeria* is a typical long-day plant while it is young. Among all the additions to the medium which were tried by CAMUS, the application of amino-acids in the form of casein hydrolysate was able to make the plants form flower primordia within 32 days. In this case a nutritional treatment was able to overcome a developmental block due to the environment, or in other words, amino-acids were able to produce the same effect as long-day treatment.

Other Nutrients:— Iron or magnesium deficiency results in extreme chlorosis of the newly developing leaves. These same symptoms can be produced by changes in the environment. When young tomato plants are grown in continuous light, one or two weeks later the newly expanding leaves partially fail to produce chlorophyll and remain ivory-white in spots. A somewhat different chlorosis, with yellow-colored leaves, develops when tomato plants are grown in a 4°C phototemperature. At 7° phototemperature tomatoes develop light-green leaves, but tobacco leaves are completely chlorotic, and the leaves of *Coleus, Xanthium* and a few other plants remain yellow or ivory-colored when the phototemperature is 10°C or lower. In these cases a high nyctotemperature cannot offset the effects of low phototemperature; on the contrary, it seems to accentuate the chlorosis.

At high phototemperatures (26° and 30°) potato plants show a typical edge-burn of the leaves. As soon as the plants are brought to lower temperatures, the newly developing leaves are normal again. The night temperature is ineffective in connection with this edge-burn, which resembles sodium or, in general, high-salt toxicity. Instead of developing on the mature leaves, as in the case of salt injury, high temperature edge-burn is due to collapse of marginal cells in the early stages of leaf growth.

Actual iron chlorosis can be produced in a number of plants (tomato, cosmos, sunflower, corn) by growing the plants with their roots completely submerged in a nutrient solution (WENT 1943*b*). The same chlorosis is found when plants are growing in water-logged soil. This chlorosis can be cured by spraying iron salts on the leaves, but recovery of the green color is restricted to the areas directly touched by droplets of the iron solution. Therefore, it is an iron chlorosis, but it occurs in spite of iron availability in the nutrient solution. When plants, which have first developed this root-submergence chlorosis, form new aerial roots above the solution, the chlorosis disappears even without the addition of iron or changing of the solution. In the root-fog chamber, where the roots are fully aerated, a mild degree of root-submergence chlorosis can develop in tomato plants if the spray is continuous and drips off all roots. Reducing the amount of nutrient spray to the point where no solution drips off the roots cures the chlorosis, and causes extensive root-hair development, which is absent when the solution drips off the roots.

With the excellent drainage of nutrient solution through the gravel and vermiculite media in which the roots of all plants in the Earhart Laboratory are grown, and the adequate aeration of these media, no such iron chlorosis develops in our plants (except sometimes in corn); when sand or soil was used in our metal or plastic containers a number of plants produced chlorosis (*e.g.*, strawberries).

In the previous paragraphs it was shown how the root environment changes the response of the plant to the nutrients in the root medium. The same solution, which causes chlorosis when all roots are submerged in it, causes excellent growth and produces dark-green leaves when supplied as a nutrient fog or when used to water plants grown in gravel or vermiculite.

Another difference in response between plants grown with their roots in sand or in solution was found by Dr. F. SALISBURY. He planted a series of tomatoes in crocks with their roots in nutrient solution, and a similar series in quartz sand. They were then treated with a number of nutrient solutions, either at *p*H 6.0 or *p*H 3.0. Whereas at *p*H 6 growth was good in both media, at *p*H 3 the roots died right away in solution, but in sand the roots could support the acidity of the nutrient, and the plants grew as well as at *p*H 6. This is another indication of the importance of the environment for the response of plants to different factors. And it makes one wonder whether the *p*H of the soil or soil solution really is of any importance in the growth of a plant other than by influencing the availability of nutrient elements.

Chapter 22

WATER RELATIONS

In nature, the growth of plants is largely controlled by two factors: first, temperature, and second, rainfall. Most of the work in the Earhart Plant Research Laboratory is related to the response of plants to temperature, but the equipment makes it possible to study water relations as well, particularly since the relative humidity of the air can be controlled.

Relative Humidity:— Early experiments in the Clark greenhouses (WENT 1944*a*) had already indicated that the effect of the relative humidity of the air on the growth of tomato and other plants was only relatively slight, provided the soil in which they grew was kept moist at all times. In those experiments the relative humidity was not lowered below 40 per cent.

Since in the Earhart Laboratory it was possible to reduce the relative humidity much more with the Kathabar — that is to say well below 20 per cent — several experiments were run to study the effect of the change in relative humidity on the growth of plants. A number of plants (strawberries, tomatoes, coffee, grasses, *Mimosa pudica* and several others) were divided into four groups. All the plants were grown in 1000 ft.-c. at 26°C, but they were kept during their photoperiod (P, 16 hours) or their nyctoperiod (N, 8 hours) at 80 per cent (m) or 20 per cent relative humidity (d). Their water supply was adequate at all times, since they were watered twice daily and their roots were in vermiculite. No obvious differences were found between the plants; coffee plants in Pd Nd were largest, in Pd Nm smallest. *Mimosa* and grasses had grown least in the dry atmosphere, whereas no differences at all were found in strawberries. The only significant growth differences were found in the tomatoes, as TABLE 17 shows. However, these differences existed only for stem elongation, but not for leaf color, drying of leaves, turgidity or any other observable character.

TABLE 17: *Tomato plants, 5 per square, grown under different humidity conditions (length in mm. after 7 days' growth at 26°C):—*

	PHOTOHUMIDITY	
	20%	80%
Nyctohumidity 20%	49.3 ± 1.7	51.2 ± 2.9
Nyctohumidity 80%	55.7 ± 2.2	62.2 ± 2.1

Therefore, these experiments also lead to the conclusion that relative humidity has only a minor effect on the growth of plants which have an adequate water supply.

The theory of MÜNCH concerning sugar transport in the plant requires a turgor gradient from the sugar-supplying to the sugar-utilizing cells. We can expect a greater turgor gradient between leaves and roots at night, when the leaf cells are saturated or are near saturation with water, whereas during daytime with strong transpiration the leaf turgor would be considerably reduced. Therefore, on the basis of MÜNCH's theory a high relative humidity during night should be beneficial for sugar transport and growth by providing a good turgor gradient from leaf to root. However, it was found that neither during day nor night an appreciable effect of relative humidity on the growth of plants could be found, although TABLE 17 shows that high humidity in darkness is slightly more beneficial than high humidity in light.

Many growers and botanists believe that growth of plants is better at high relative humidities of the air, and especially orchid growers and other greenhouse growers claim that the humidity of the air in their greenhouses should be kept high at all times to get best results. When the root system of plants is poor, this is definitely the case, but otherwise a high humidity only reduces the amount of watering necessary to make up transpiration losses, but does not otherwise affect the plants. Actually, it usually is not high humidity, but the factors associated with this high humidity which are of importance. In nature, we find that a high relative humidity means a relatively even temperature from day to night. This works in two ways. In the first place, water vapor in the atmosphere absorbs much of the heat radiation from the sun so that at a high humidity less radiation reaches the surface of the earth during day, and there is less sky radiation during night. This causes a small temperature difference between day and night. When the air has a low relative humidity, the earth's surface heats up much more during day and cools more during night resulting in a large temperature fluctuation throughout 24 hours. In the second place, clouds form when the relative humidity is high, which prevents further heating of the earth's surface. Therefore, a high relative humidity acts as a thermo-regulator and consequently we find relatively small temperature differences from day to night in a moist climate. Therefore, relative humidity can exert an effect on plant growth by way of temperature. It actually was found that the smoke tree (*Dalea spinosa*) and guayule (*Parthenium argentatum*) are sturdy and are quite hairy when grown at low night temperatures, whereas they have weak, almost trailing, stems and have fewer hairs, which gives them a greenish look, when grown at high night temperatures. This desert habit which is found at lower night temperatures will develop whether the relative humidity is low or high. The reason why greenhouse growers believe that high humidities are better for the growing of plants probably lies in this same direction. When a greenhouse is kept moist, the temperature in it will be reduced through evaporative cooling and, thus, it is again temperature rather than the relative humidity which is of importance.

Transpiration:— For the study of transpiration, several new methods have been developed in the Earhart Plant Research Laboratory. The older methods, such as described in MAXIMOV's The Plant in Relation to Water (1929), are either inaccurate, cumbersome, or not suitable for our purposes, since we have to measure water vapor exchange under a wide variety of external conditions. And, if possible, the methods should be automatic and self-recording.

The simplest measure for transpiration is the rapid-weighing method, using leaves or branches cut off the plant immediately prior to the first weighing. It has been pointed out by many investigators that this use of detached leaves or branches for transpiration measurements is attended by several errors. Even if the measurements are carried out over short intervals of time, the sudden release of negative tension in the vessels may cause a temporary increase in transpiration rate which is an artifact due to the cutting. Besides, no continuous record of the transpiration rate can be obtained in this way, since the leaf or branch is destroyed after the weighings.

Measurements of the weight loss by transpiration of whole plants are difficult because the large amount of dead weight of container and soil which has to be contended with. To overcome these difficulties in the Earhart Laboratory plants are grown in plastic cups in a light-weight medium such as vermiculite or sponge rok. When the plant is well established in the container, then its weight may equal that of container plus root medium. By using small plants, container plus plant do not weigh more than 200 grams and, therefore, can easily be weighed on an analytical balance. If the root medium is porous enough, the plants do not become root-bound in the small containers and grow normally.

To prevent water loss from the container, its surface is sealed with pliofilm which is attached to plant stem and cup with scotch tape. The drainage holes are also closed with scotch tape. An even simpler method for sealing the container was developed by Dr. E. EICHENBERGER. He simply slips a plastic bag over the plant container and seals this around the base of the stem.

Since most of these plants are weighed when their size is such that they cannot be introduced into an analytical balance case, a special box has been constructed with glass sides, on top of which the analytical balance is placed. Instead of one of the pans, a long arm extends through the bottom of the balance case into the box. In this way, cup plus plant can be suspended in this box from the analytical balance and the slightest change in weight can be recorded. Even relatively small plants transpire at such a rate that the balance is never at rest. Therefore, the best method of following their weight decrease is with a "chain-o-matic" balance. After some practice, it is possible to follow the transpiration rate of the plant with continuous movement of the balancing chain. As an example, an experiment with a tomato plant can be shown. This was kept for 15-minute periods at different temperatures all at 60 per cent humidity in light or darkness. Its transpiration rate expressed in mg./minute is shown in TABLE 18. These transpiration measurements are very reproducible and the rate of water loss is constant over considerable lengths of time, provided the external conditions were kept constant. In the greenhouse the same plant lost 60-70 mg./minute.

For less precise weighing, ordinary triple-beam balances are installed on top of the same box described in the previous paragraph. By re-weighing the different containers with plants, each with the same balance, it is not necessary to calibrate the balance.

Plants grown in the same way can also be used for long-time transpiration studies when they are placed on self-recording devices.

Dr. W. C. ASHBY (*see* Chapter 23) has developed another method of measuring transpiration rates over short intervals of time. A tomato or other plant is placed in a closed plastic container through which an air stream of constant humidity is passed at a constant rate. The transpiration

TABLE 18: *Loss of weight due to transpiration (in mg./min.) of a tomato plant when transferred to different conditions. Top weight of plant* ± *10 grams:—*

TEMPERATURE	10°	17°	23°	30°
In light (500 ft.-c.)	4.3	7.3	10.7	16.8
In darkness		2.8	3.8	

will adjust itself to the conditions inside the plastic container and with an Aminco humidity sensing element, located inside the plastic container, the relative humidity is measured. To get a good average reading of the humidity inside the whole container, a fan circulates the air inside the plastic container. To measure the transpiration rate the air intake and outlet of the plastic container are closed simultaneously and for the next few minutes the change in relative humidity is measured with the humidity sensing element. By checking this method with regular weighings, it was established that in this way it is possible to get a fairly accurate and almost instantaneuos measure of the transpiration rate.

Still another device has been constructed to measure water used by the plant in transpiration. Its root system after being washed free of vermiculite is sealed into a small container which is filled to the top with water. Alternatively, a cut branch without roots is used for this work. This branch is sealed in a similar container. This container is then attached to a recording potometer of which six have been constructed. The potometer operates by replenishing the amount of water used by the transpiring plant or branch. Each time that the pressure inside the system has been reduced a certain amount a small automatic pump delivers a known amount of liquid into the system. The time necessary for the plant to use this amount of water is then recorded, by passing the electrical impulse for starting of the pump motor through an Esterline-Angus recorder. When a cut-off tomato branch is attached to such a potometer its rate of water loss will gradually decrease, apparently through increasing resistance in its water supply system.

PLATE XXIV shows the experimental setup in which both transpiration and water uptake, and also photosynthesis of individual tomato plants, are measured. Each plant is placed in a plastic container through which an airstream is passed at a constant rate. The air intake at left is connected through a needle valve and a flow meter with the compressed air supply. The air outlet is connected with the CO_2 analyzer in the control room. In the wall of the plastic container the humidity sensing element is connected with the meter on the lower shelf which measures the resistance in the sensing element.

The same setup can be located in other rooms at different temperatures or light intensities, and there can be connected with the same CO_2 recorder and recorder for the potometer.

Some measurements of the transpiration rate have already been carried out in the wind tunnel. On several occasions it was found that wind up to 5 m./sec. did not change the transpiration rate of tomato plants at 20°C and in a light intensity of 1000 ft.-c. In most other plants, however, such a wind increases transpiration, and especially winds up to 20 m./sec. cause strong transpiration. Engr. A. SORIANO (1953*a*) studied adaptation effects of wind. He grew sets of plants, all at 1000 ft.-c., in no wind, and in winds of 5 and 20 m./sec. He found that tomato plants would not grow in the strong wind, but plants of *Nicotiana glauca* and *Larrea divaricata* grew fairly well in all conditions. Whereas the transpiration rate of the *Nicotiana* plants was equally increased in all three sets of plants, in *Larrea* the plants which had been subjected for several weeks to the high wind velocity increased their transpiration only little when transferred from quiet air to strong wind.

Dr. K. VERKERK also studied the behavior of tomato plants in the wind tunnel.

Rain:— In the chapter on germination the effect of rain on the appearance of seedlings has been discussed. However, rain not only affects germination, but also the later development of the plants. This was found by Engr. SORIANO and Dr. EICHENBERGER for a number of desert plants. *Erucastrum,* or *Anastatica,* grows almost twice as tall when the germination occurs with artificial rain as when the seedbed is moistened by letting the water rise up by capillarity. Subsequent watering was the same in both groups.

Some experiments with *Baeria chrysostoma* are presented here in greater detail. A total of 120 cups were sown each with about 100 6-year-old seeds. Then they received over a 10-hour period either 5 mm. (4.5-5.5),

15 mm. (13-17) or 50 mm. (48-60) of precipitation, all at 25°C, whereas the controls were soaked from below and kept for the first 10 hours at 25°C also. The cups were then placed in 10°, 17° or 23°, left there for two or four days, and after four days were placed in 17° or 23°C at 8, 16 or 24-hour photoperiods.

Taking all temperature treatments together, after 70 hours without precipitation 11.2 ± 1.4, with 5 mm. 17.8 ± 1.8, with 15 mm. 20.7 ± 1.8 and with 50 mm. rain 24.2 ± 2.2 seeds had germinated, and after one week without rain 27.7 ± 3.6, and with 50 mm. 47.3 ± 2.8 seedlings were visible. In TABLE 19 a certain number of data pertaining to these plants are presented. Because of the dense stand of plants and the irregularity of germination there was a great variability between the plants. Only the six largest plants in each treatment were measured and TABLE 19 gives the averages. It can be seen that not only the stems of the plants without rain are shortest, but that also their flowerbuds are least developed. The first 5

TABLE 19: *Effect of temperature and precipitation treatments prior to and during germination of Baeria chrysostoma, when after 4 days subjected to 24-hour photoperiods at 17°C. Columns 3-6: length of stem between cotyledonary node and tip; last 4 columns: length of flower bud. All figures averages of 5-6 largest plants in each treatment:—*

PRECIPITATION IN MM.		0	5	15	50	0	5	15	50
FIRST 2 DAYS	SECOND 2 DAYS	SHOOT LENGTH IN MM.				FLOWERBUD LENGTH IN MM.			
10°	10°	8.5	19.8	16.5	21.2	0.7	1.1	1.5	1.6
17°	17°	17.5	24.1	25.8	23.5	1.8	2.0	2.2	2.6
23°	17°	16.2	19.5	15.6	21.6	1.7	2.0	2.4	1.5
23°	20°	8.8	10.8	11.5	16.3	0.8	1.2	1.2	1.7
23°	23°	6.6	10.0	17.2	13.8	0.4	0.5	1.0	1.2
Average length		11.5	16.8	17.3	19.3	1.1	1.4	1.7	1.7

mm. of rain causes about 50 per cent increase in shoot length, tenfold this amount of rain gives another increase of only 20 per cent. The average flowerbud length increased from 1.1 to 1.7 mm. with increasing rain. This increase in size is not only due to more rapid development, but also to an increased number of florets per flowerhead, particularly of discflowers. On the average 40 per cent more discflowers was present after 50 mm. of rain, with a range of 22-62 per cent. These counts were made by Dr. G. CAMUS on plants 29 days after sowing. The absolute increase in florets due to rain was 18.9 ± 4.9.

It is clear from the examples given, that rain treatments before germination have a strong effect on subsequent development of the plant. This is another example of the induction of the germinating seed, and is comparable with vernalization, in which a temperature treatment influences later development. These effects are quantitative rather than qualitative, but make it clear that induction of the germinating seed is of very common occurrence, and that vernalization is only *one* of a number of inductive phenomena in the plant in a very early stage of development. Because of the practical significance of these inductive effects of rain much more work should be carried out on this phenomenon. This may not only explain differences in crop yield from year to year, but may also provide a tool in the control of crop production, by pre-treatment of seed before sowing with leaching or other methods.

Chapter 23

METHODS FOR DETERMINING WATER LOSS

by W. C. Ashby

University of Chicago, Chicago, Illinois

Aminco Humidity Sensing Elements:— Two methods have been developed to measure water loss by plants. One gives an immediate measurement of changes in relative humidity which may be a function of transpiration by a plant. The other records changes in weight of the plant-substrate system. Sealing off of the substrate from evaporative losses limits weight changes to transpirational losses from the plant under usual environmental conditions.

Immediate measurements of relative humidity were made with electric hygrometer sensing elements. These elements and the electric hygrometer indicator are described in the catalogue of the manufacturer, The American Instrument Co., Inc., Silver Spring, Maryland. The physical measurement from which relative humidity can be derived is the conductivity of a gelatin film containing lithium salts. The conductivity varies with moisture content of the gelatin which is exposed to the atmosphere as a thin coating on a coil of fine wire.

For transpiration studies, the top of a plant and the hygrometer sensing element were placed within a plastic bell jar (Plate XXIV). This bell jar was 15 × 15 × 30 cm., or a volume of 7 liters. Air passed through the bell jar, otherwise sealed, by means of plastic tubes on two opposite sides of the bell jar. The fan shown mixed the air quickly, so that any change in humidity resulting from transpiration by the plant would be rapidly sensed by the element. At any given time the plastic tubes were closed off by pinch clamps. The rate of enrichment of the enclosed air space by water vapor then served as an index of the transpiration rate by the plant. By varying a condition such as temperature, its influence on transpiration could thus be determined.

Inherent in this system is the operation at a rising humidity level for a given temperature with an actively transpiring plant. Relatively stable conditions can be obtained under controlled temperature and light conditions. In a greenhouse, where there is an alternation of shade and sun, the change to a sunny condition results in a marked rise in temperature, and a consequent marked drop in relative humidity. These changes may affect rather greatly the water relations of the plant. A similar type of change, in reverse, occurs when shade is suddenly cast by a beam or a cloud.

Conversion to relative humidity values was done graphically, using measurements of conductivity of the gelatin film and of temperature. At a constant temperature the electric hygrometer sensing elements gave read-

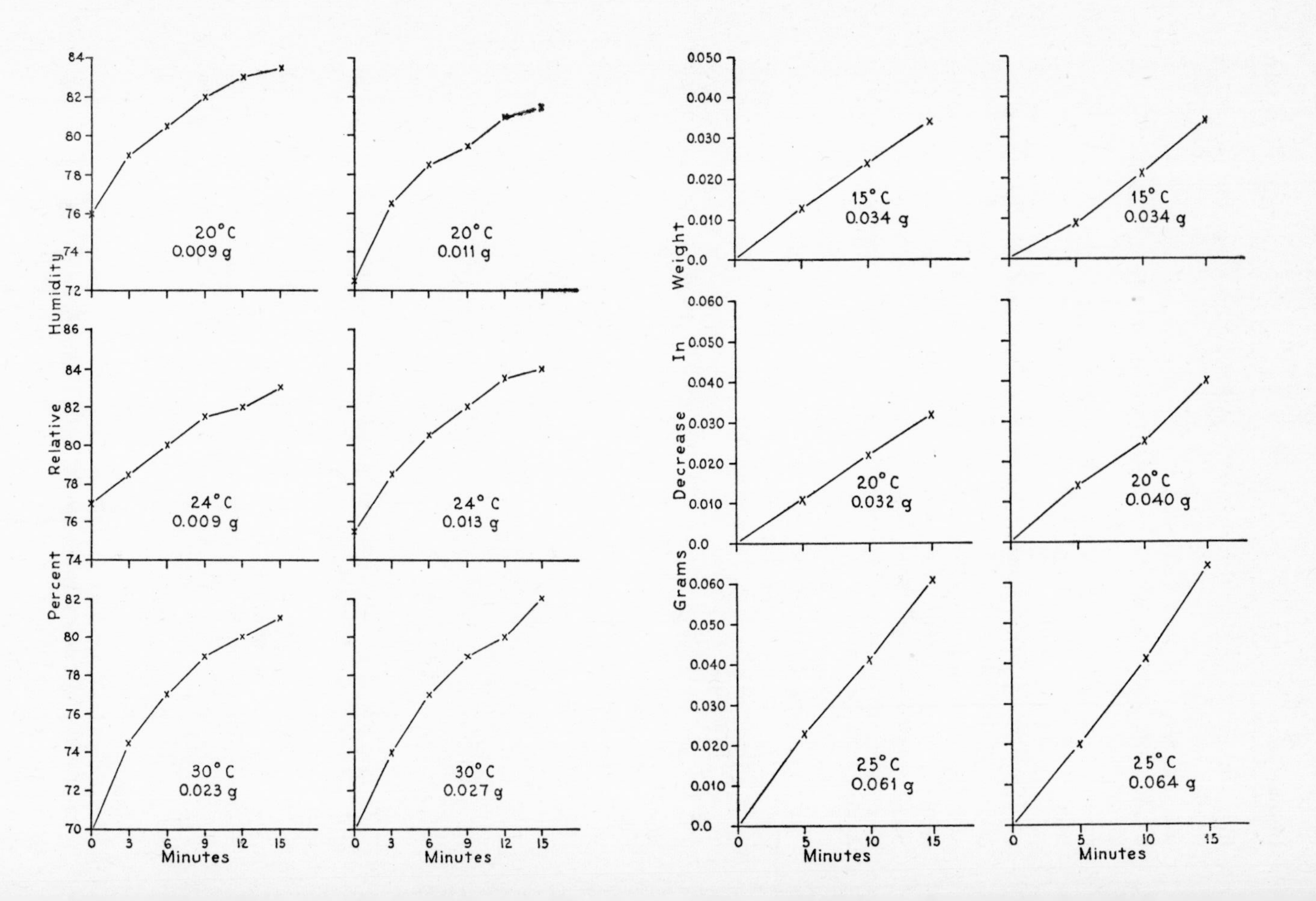
Percent Relative Humidity
20°C 0.009 g
20°C 0.011 g
24°C 0.009 g
24°C 0.013 g
30°C 0.023 g
30°C 0.027 g
Minutes
Grams Decrease In Weight
15°C 0.034 g
15°C 0.034 g
20°C 0.032 g
20°C 0.040 g
25°C 0.061 g
25°C 0.064 g
Minutes

ings within 2% of that determined by a dew-point apparatus. Since the relative humidity changes tended to be large, this closeness of measurement was sufficient. When temperature was not constant, the computation of the relative humidity values in terms of the meter reading for temperature, as well as of the conductivity reading, put a lot of reliance on the temperature determinations. A large change in the temperature estimations resulted from a small change in the meter reading. For instance, a drift in the meter zero resulted in an apparent change in temperature appreciably affecting the relative humidity values. The thermisters contained in the sensing elements had, in instances, variations from the values obtained with mercury thermometers of up to four degrees Fahrenheit. During work in artificial light with the plastic bell jars, the temperature varied somewhat. Some increase resulted from radiation into the enclosed air space. Over a period of time there was heat transfer from the fan motor, which became very hot.

Analytical Balance:— In these determinations a chain-o-matic analytical balance was used. By deft manipulation of the balance weights a momentary reading of the continuously decreasing plant weight could be obtained. The tomato seedlings used were grown in a small amount of vermiculite in a small plastic drinking cup. They were watered with nutrient solution prior to the test periods. The plant-substrate-container system weighed on the order of 150 grams. For water loss determinations the top of the cup was covered with a sheet of rubber dental dam to prevent evaporative losses from the vermiculite.

The balance was mounted on a movable table. For water loss determinations the table was moved to the appropriate temperature and light conditions. The plants, placed on the table, were allowed to come to equilibrium for about ten minutes before the first weighing. Then at intervals the plants were placed on the pan of the balance and the momentary weights determined. About a minute was required for each weighing, from picking up the plant to replacing it. The movement of the plant resulted in some bending and wind movement past the leaves. Between weighings the door of the balance was raised, to permit air circulation into it for equalization of temperature and humidity with that of the room. Even so, the temperature inside the balance was about 1°C higher than the room air.

This method gave quite satisfactory results within any one condition. The moving from one constant-temperature room to another, however, did not permit evaluation of temperature alone as an environmental factor af-

---

FIGURE 67 (*opposite, bottom*).— Water loss of a tomato plant as measured by rise in relative humidity under plastic bell jar. Experiments of ASHBY.

FIGURE 68 (*opposite, top*).— Decrease in weight of a transpiring tomato plant as determined with an analytical balance. Transpiration determined at three different temperatures: 15°, 20° and 25°C. Experiments of ASHBY.

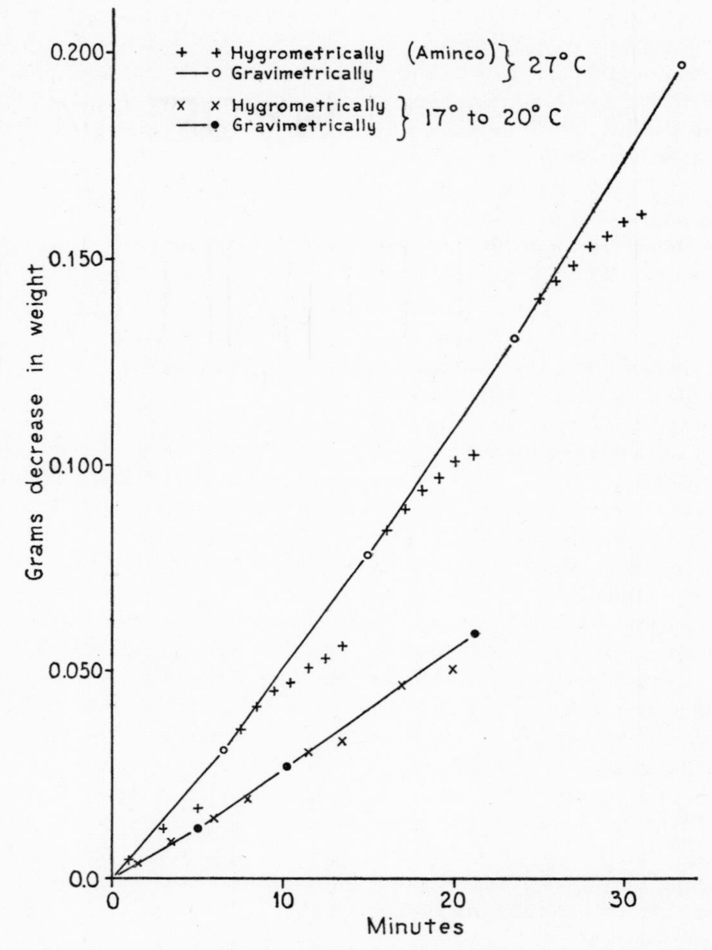

FIGURE 69.— Comparison of water loss of a tomato plant at two temperatures (17-20° and 27°C), as measured with the Aminco humidity sensing element (*crosses and plus signs*), or with an analytical balance (*circles and dots*). Experiments of ASHBY.

fecting water loss. The reason was that the vapor pressure deficits varied between certain rooms. For instance, on 23 November, 1953, the following values were determined from the Aminco sensing element. Readings from a hygrothermograph at plant level agreed quite closely:

	Temperature	Humidity	v.p.d.
Room 4 G	17°	68%	4.6
Room 9 G	27°	55%	11.5

Results and Discussion:— The results for these two methods can be summarized rather briefly:

1) Much more water loss was measured using the analytical balance weighing method than the Aminco element under the plastic bell jar.
2) Loss measured using the analytical balance tended to be linear with time. That under the plastic bell jar became successively less with time.

Figure 67 shows water loss determined hygrometrically for one plant at three different temperatures. The actual temperatures differed from room temperatures because of the plastic bell jar. In Figure 68 the water loss determined gravimetrically, on another day, is shown. The plants used for the two days were at the four-leaf stage. The first one had a dry weight of 0.063 grams, the second of 0.040 grams. Figure 69 gives similar data from a series of determinations made simultaneously by the two methods. That is, the plant was alternately in the plastic bell jar, where humidity changes were noted, and on the analytical balance for the weight determinations. Combining the two methods in this manner introduces technique difficulties which may have affected the results somewhat. One plant, with a dry weight of 0.068 grams, was used for both determinations. Unfortunately, in each instance the plants selected showed some Isotox or other damage to the leaves. The third plant showed no visible damage to the four remaining leaves after the lowest one had been removed.

Some of the reasons for greater water loss shown in Figures 67 and 68 using the analytical balance may be:

1) All the plastic bell jar determinations started at a relative humidity of from 70 to 77 per cent. Room humidities for the analytical balance work ranged from 55 to 68 per cent.
2) Moving the plants back and forth from the balance to the table may have increased water vapor dispersal from the leaves.
3) Water vapor could have leaked from or condensed on the walls of the plastic bell jar, thus resulting in a lessened net amount of water vapor which would be sensed by the Aminco element.
4) The successive decreases in water loss over time under the plastic bell jar resulted in an appreciably lessened loss.
5) Two different plants were used.

It will be noted in Figure 69 at 17° to 20°C and 68 per cent R.H. that the discrepancy in total amount lost using the two methods is small. At 27°C and 55 per cent R.H., a 2½-fold increase in v.p.d., a rather substantial difference, shows up. This could in large part be due to the higher relative humidity for that portion of time the plant was under the plastic bell jar. The weight loss measured by the analytical balance includes the weight loss under the plastic bell jar, and in addition that at the lower room humidities during the period of weighing on the analytical balance.

In the experiments which FIGURE 69 represents, temperatures were higher under the plastic bell jar than outside. Thus for Room 4 G (14°C) the room temperature at the light level used was 17°, under the plastic bell jar it ranged upwards from 19° to 21°C during the experiments. The air temperature in Room 9 G (26°C) was 27°, that under the bell jar ranged from 26° to 28°C. As noted earlier, the thermisters in the Aminco element did not seem to be particularly accurate. The effect of the higher temperatures under the bell jar would be to increase the v.p.d. Presumably this increased water loss, and makes less understandable the smaller loss under the bell jar.

Chapter 24

SMOG AND PERIODICITY

Smog has been mentioned very often in the description of the Earhart Plant Research Laboratory and of the experiments performed in it. Since it has become such an important subject in all metropolitan areas, a short chapter will be devoted to it. Smog is a form of air pollution which differs from the previously known types in that it is characterized by a light blue haze with an acrid odor which in extreme conditions becomes highly irritating to the eyes and causes damage to plants. This damage is quite different from known air pollutants such as SO_2 and HF. Whereas in the Los Angeles area complaints about smog in connection with decreased visibility and eye irritation had occurred since 1942, it was not until 1948 and 1949, just at the time that the Earhart Laboratory was under construction, that it became established that damage to crop plants was caused by this smog. One of the first research projects undertaken in the Earhart Laboratory was a study of this smog, because the unique facilities of this laboratory allowed an efficient investigation of the effects of air pollutants injected into the air circulating in the gas rooms. In this research the Los Angeles County Air Pollution Control District, the University of California and Caltech collaborated.

Effects on Plants:— In the field, it had been found that spinach, endive, alfalfa, beets and barley were particularly sensitive to smog and showed typical injury symptoms after each smog attack. It was decided that these five plants were to be used as indicator plants in a search for the phytotoxic constituents of smog. To this end, these plants were grown in a laboratory room of which the air was passed through a carbon filter which removed its phytotoxic constituents. Therefore, whereas the plants grown in the regular greenhouses showed injury symptoms after each period of smog, those in the filtered air were uninjured and their leaves were perfectly spotless and healthy. In one of the gas rooms these plants were then subjected to purified air into which one of the suspected smog constituents was injected so that a concentration of one part per million or less was reached. Since during a smog period none of the smog constituents surpasses in concentration one part per million, no substance which did not cause damage at the test concentration could be the source of smog damage. After having tested a number of organic acids, aldehydes, ketones, chlorinated compounds and hydrocarbons, none of which produced the typical smog damage symptoms, ozonized hydrocarbons were tested. To this end, a stream of hydrocarbon vapor was mixed with a stream of ozone and its reaction product was released into the smog test room. When hexene or gasoline vapors were mixed with ozone the typical silvering of the lower surface of the spinach, endive and beet leaves occurred in concentrations of the ozonides of well below one part per million. The alfalfa and barley leaves showed the typical smog spotting. Therefore, these experiments proved without doubt that the phytotoxic constituents in smog consisted of peroxides and ozonides of hydrocarbons (HAAGEN-SMIT *et al.* 1951). Later, HAAGEN-SMIT *et al.* (1953) showed that in the atmosphere the oxidation of gasoline vapors and other hydrocarbons occurs under the influence of light through catalysis with nitrogen oxides and that ozone is produced in this reaction.

Work on the effects of smog on plants was continued for several years in the Earhart Plant Research Laboratory, largely to establish the conditions under which smog damage occurred and to identify the basic physiological processes which were affected by this smog. It was soon found (KORITZ and WENT 1952; HULL, WENT and YAMADA 1954) that in addition to the silvering of the lower surface of leaves, also invisible damage was caused by smog in that the growth rate of a number of plants was decreased when they were subjected to smog. The growth rate of tomato plants for instance was only half normal on the day following exposure to smog. Complete recovery occurred afterwards and the normal growth rate was resumed after one to two days. The same effect on growth was found for *Avena* coleoptiles and in this case a further analysis was made of the way the smog affects growth. It was found that smog reduced their growth rate even in the presence of excess auxin and that, therefore, not auxin but factors with which auxin react are reduced in concentration. The regular *Avena* test is affected in the same way in that the curvature produced by a given amount of laterally applied indoleacetic acid is reduced and that particularly the maximum angle produced with an excess of auxin is reduced. This reduction in the sensitivity of the *Avena* coleoptiles to auxin could also be produced by subjecting coleoptiles to artificial smog made by oxidized hydrocarbons.

The leaf injury produced by smog is due to a loss of semi-permeability of the mesophyll cells in the neighborhood of the stomata. The very first visible effect of smog is an oilyness of the lower surface of the affected leaf. This is due to leaking of cell sap into the intercellular spaces, which thus become injected with liquid and do not reflect light any more at the air-water interphase. At lower concentrations, when no visible symptoms are produced, there is first a decreased permeability which is measurable in terms of a decreased rate of transpiration. This effect is reversible and only persists as long as the smog continues and shortly afterwards. This effect on transpiration is not mediated by the stomata since they do not close under the influence of smog.

The opening of the stomata seems to have an important bearing on the degree of injury produced by smog. Smog applied in darkness is much less effective than the same concentration applied in light. When plants have been recently watered injury is much more severe than when the plants were not watered for one or more days. No effects of nutrition were found on the sensitivity of plants to smog. As mentioned in connection with the smog filter (*see* Chapter 3), it is possible to remove all toxic air pollutants from the air if this is filtered through a carbon filter. Whereas before installation of the carbon filters we had frequent and severe smog damage to susceptible plants growing in the Earhart Laboratory, after their installation plants could be grown without any trace of smog injury. The few times that injury symptoms were observed it could be established that air had bypassed the smog filters. Since the presence of the electrostatic precipitator did not help at all in removal of smog from the laboratory air, it must be concluded that physiological effects of smog are due to gaseous components and not to the particulate matter which causes the blueish haze.

This complete lack of discolored spots or dead tips on leaves of plants grown under optimal conditions in the Earhart Laboratory contrasts with the appearance of plants grown in the field or in ordinary greenhouses. This is in part due to: (*1*) the lack of insects or other pests which produce leaf injury, (*2*) absence of diseases resulting in leaf spots, (*3*) no viruses producing mottling or other discoloration, and (*4*) adequate nutrition. Yet, a major factor in the healthy appearance of the plants is the absence of smog. Thus, we come to the conclusion that all sorts of minor blemishes on leaves, which are so common in plants, are entirely avoidable and often are due to unsuspected air pollution. Dead leaf tips on grasses, or slight spotting on other leaves may be due to a large number of reasons and, therefore, have no diagnostic value; yet, they are definitely abnormal, and since they are avoidable, they should not be tolerated in critical experiments. They also should be watched as the first symptoms of impending future increases in air pollution. For in my experience the leaf-damaging type of air pollution only increases, and never decreases in the course of the years. With few exceptions (Amsterdam, Madrid, Rome) I saw plants damaged by smog in all metropolitan areas where a million or more people have congregated (Los Angeles, San Francisco, Washington, New York, Philadelphia, Baltimore, London, Manchester, Paris, Copenhagen, Cologne, São Paulo, Bogotá, Sydney, Melbourne).

Daily Fluctuations in Sensitivity of Avena Test:— After installation of the smog filters in the general air intake for the whole laboratory, not only smog damage was eliminated, but certain other phenomena were not observed any more. In previous work, it had been found that there is a daily and seasonal variability in the *Avena* test for auxin. Extensive work by Kögl, Haagen-Smit and van Hulssen (1936) had shown that these fluctuations, which were found even in basement darkrooms in which temperature, humidity and light were kept constant, were not due to variations in any of the commonly measured physical and chemical factors of the environment such as atmospheric pressure, cosmic radiation, ionization of the air or static electricity. In later work in Pasadena during the years 1935-1939, it had been found that these fluctuations were in some way connected with air pollution (HULL and WENT 1954). When the *Avena* test was carried out in the Earhart Laboratory, then the fluctuations were not present any more when carbon-filtered air passed through the test room, whereas with non-filtered air the daily change in response to auxin was very marked. By subjecting the *Avena* plants to artificial smog their sensitivity was reduced just as with the natural air pollutants (HULL and WENT 1954). Since the *Avena* test can be evaluated quantitatively, this test can give us an objective measure for that fraction of air pollutants which lower the *Avena* test sensitivity. It is, therefore, obvious that the periodical change in sensitivity of the *Avena* test has its basis in the daily and seasonal fluctuations in air pollution and that this air pollution occurs also in places where it had not been suspected (such as in Utrecht, Holland, in the years 1930-1935: KÖGL *et al.* 1936).

Not only the fluctuations in the *Avena* test disappeared in the Earhart Laboratory after installation of the carbon filters, but also the pea test became reproducible from day to day. Therefore, we must conclude that in all biological testing of auxin the material should be grown and treated in rooms in which the air is filtered through carbon filters, which will insure removal of those air pollutants which give rise to fluctuations in sensitivity.

Other Daily Periodicities:— When Dr. O. M. VAN ANDEL investigated the bleeding of plants grown in the Earhart Laboratory, she found that the daily fluctuations in the rate of bleeding, which are so typical for the bleeding process, were very much reduced. Yet, a certain amount of daily fluctuation persisted so that some autonomical periodic process is involved in the rate of bleeding. This is greatly enhanced by the presence of air pollutants.

A number of other periodic phenomena occur in plants which do not have their basis in periodic changes in air pollutants. Such periodicities are autonomous. As examples it can be mentioned that photo- and thermoperiodicity of plants are not changed in the filtered air of the Earhart Laboratory.

Both of these phenomena occur to the same extent since carbon filters have been installed as before their installation. Since, basically, these two periodicities are based on the Bünning cycle, we will have to see to what extent the Bünning cycle is observed in our experiments. The first clear-cut case that an innate 24-hour periodicity exists in plants grown in the Earhart Laboratory is seen in the experiments presented in FIGURE 66. There it is shown that, unless periods of light and of darkness alternate with a general 24-hour period, growth is reduced and apparent photosynthesis is also decreased. This phenomenon has been studied in greater detail by Dr. W. S. HILLMAN in the past year. As a convenient test response he used the lack of chlorophyl formation which occurs in tomatoes when they are grown in continuous light. Many other characters are affected by the continuous illumination, such as leaf size, growth in length, etc., but the appearance of bleached areas on the young leaves of permanently illuminated plants is most easily recognized. When tomato plants are given a few hours of darkness within a 24-hour cycle their appearance is perfectly normal. When, however, the dark periods are applied in a 12, 16, or 48-hour cycle the bleached areas appear just as well.

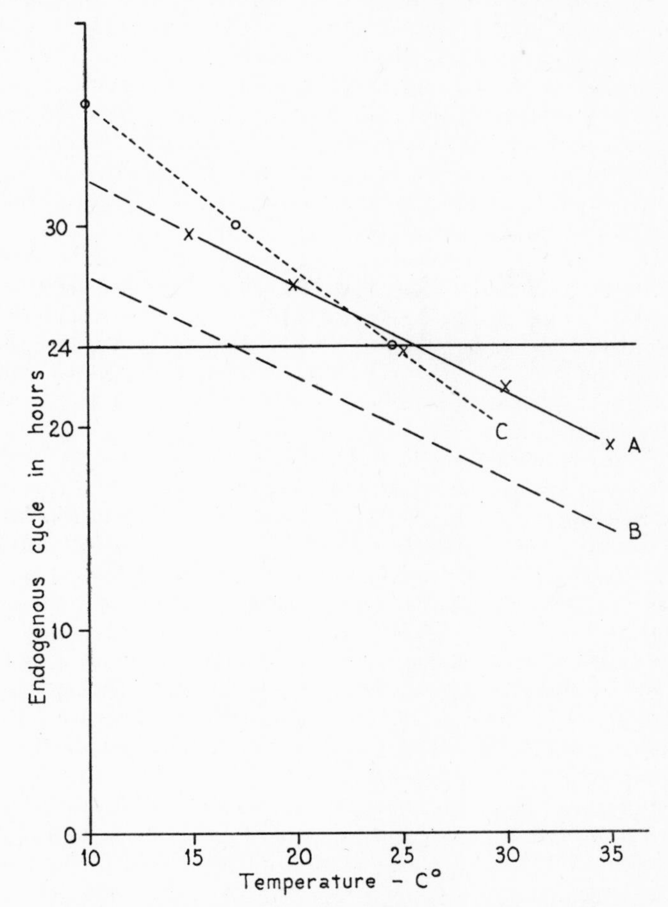

FIGURE 70.— LINE A: Relationship between temperature (*abscissa:* in degree Celsius) and length of the endogenous nyctinastic rhythm (*ordinate:* in hours) of *Phaseolus pulvini,* according to BÜNNING (1931). LINE B: Hypothetical similar relationship for a cool-climate plant, with an optimal temperature of 17°. LINE C: Length of endogenous Bünning cycle as determined for effectiveness of supplementary light in the flowering of soybeans (data of HAMNER and NANDA).

In another series of experiments, Dr. HILLMAN produced a 24-hour cycle in the plants by a temperature fluctuation instead of a light-dark alternation. When, during each 24 hours continuously illuminated tomato plants were subjected for 8 hours to a decreased or increased temperature, again no abnormal white spots appeared on leaves, and the plants were perfectly normal. From this, it can be concluded that the Bünning cycle of an autonomous 24-hour rhythm in the plant can be synchronized with either periodic changes in light or with periodic temperature changes.

In previous chapters it has been mentioned that warm-climate plants such as *Saintpaulia* will die at low temperatures, whereas cool-climate plants such as *Bellis perennis* die at the higher temperatures which are optimal for the warm-climate plants. Whereas one would, in the first place, think of a disturbance of the metabolism caused by abnormal temperatures, another explanation might be based on a disturbance in the 24-hour Bünning cycle of the plants. To test this explanation a number of preliminary experiments have been carried out in the Earhart Laboratory.

The Bünning Cycle:— The basis for these experiments is found in FIGURE 70. In this figure the data of BÜNNING (1931) on the temperature dependence of the autonomous nyctinastic period of *Phaseolus* leaves is shown in line A. This period is 24 hours at 26°C, a normal temperature for the young bean plants used in the experiments. At 10°C this period should be approximately 32 hours. Therefore, it was tried to grow a number of plants which have a high optimal temperature (young tomato plants, *Begonia semperflorens* and *Saintpaulia*), at 10°C, both in a 24 and in a 32-hour cycle. In each case the plants received light during one third of the cycle and darkness during the rest of the time. The results are highly suggestive. *Saintpaulia* plants became chlorotic in a 24-hour cycle, but developed healthy green leaves in the 32-hour cycle. Tomato plants, originally growing faster in the 24-hour cycle, started to lag, and after one week were overtaken by the plants in the 32-hour cycle, which became sturdy and dark-green. The *Begonias* died in the 24-hour cycle, whereas they grew slowly in the 32-hour cycle. These results suggest that warm-climate plants have become adapted to a 24-hour endogenous cycle at a high temperature, and would be able to grow, though slowly, at a lower temperature, provided the light-dark cycle were sufficiently lengthened. According to FIGURE 70 a plant with an optimal temperature of 26°C should require a 32-hour cycle at 10°C, and this seems to be actually the case, as described in the previous paragraph. According to the same figure, cool-climate plants such as peas and *Baeria* might survive at 26°C in a 20-hour cycle. A 15-hour cycle was tried at 26°C, but growth was as poor as in a 24-hour cycle at that temperature. This was to be expected, if conformity with the Bünning cycle determines whether or not a plant can grow at a particular temperature.

Work carried out by Dr. K. C. HAMNER and Mr. K. NANDA in the Earhart Laboratory supports the existence of an endogenous 24-hour rhythm in the photoperiodic response of soybean plants. This rhythm is lengthened to 28 hours when the plants are grown at 17°C (*see* FIGURE 70).

Chapter 25

BIOCHEMISTRY

by Arthur W. Galston

Yale University, New Haven, Connecticut

Most experiments involving the application of auxins and other growth regulating chemicals to higher plants have been conducted either in environments in which no temperature control was possible, or in controlled rooms maintained under only one given temperature regime. Where the experiment involves excised plant organs or parts which are independent of light, some studies of the temperature relations have been made. For example, using seeds, Leopold and Guernsey (1953) have investigated the effect of temperature on auxin-induced flowering responses, and using excised portions of etiolated pea epicotyls, Galston and Hand (1949) have studied the effect of adenine on growth as a function of temperature.

In the Earhart Plant Research Laboratory, with its multiplicity of illuminated and temperature-controlled chambers, it is possible to conduct similar experiments on intact, photosynthesizing and vigorously growing higher plants, to study the effect of temperature on the response to a given chemical substance. The experiments described below indicate that temperature may indeed be critical for response to a given chemical to be manifest, and emphasize the desirability of conducting similar experiments with other substances.

Auxins:— Despite more than twenty-five years of intensive research on auxins, we still have no clear concept of whether any intact plants are limited in their normal growth because of a deficiency in auxin. There are, of course, numerous data showing that auxins applied to intact plants can increase tillering (Leopold 1949), and retention of fruit (Gardner, Marth and Batjer 1939), can cause parthenogenetic development of ovaries (Gustafson 1936), especially at lower nyctotemperatures (Osborne and Went 1953), and can differentially kill or injure growing plants. We know of no experiments, however, which have clearly demonstrated an enhancing effect of auxin upon the normal vegetative growth of any plant.

We decided to attack this problem by growing a representative plant under a variety of temperature regimes. Within each treatment, some of the plants could be sprayed with water, some with auxin and some with antiauxin. If any growth differences appeared as a result of these treatments, they might be used to indicate whether the plants are operating at auxin levels below or above the optimum for their maximal growth.

The experiments were performed in conjunction with Dr. Katerina

ZARUDNAYA, who was already studying the effect of environmental treatment on sex expression in various genotypes of *Zea mays*. She had available various normal genotypes of corn, as well as certain silkless strains. These latter genotypes, obtained through the courtesy of Drs. E. G. ANDERSON and E. PATTERSON, produce female flowers devoid of silks, but capable of producing viable grains if properly pollinated.

Grains of all genotypes were germinated in vermiculite in plastic trays in a room having a day temperature of 30°C and a night temperature of 23°C. After nine days, the seedlings were transplanted into individual plastic containers containing equal volumes of vermiculite and gravel, and distributed among the various temperature treatments. Fifteen plants on a single truck were used for each of the treatments, and there were four treatments in each of three temperature regimes: (*1*) an unsprayed control, (2) sprayed daily with water, (3) sprayed daily with the auxin indoleacetic acid (IAA), 2×10^{-4}M, *p*H adjusted to 7.0, and (*4*) sprayed daily with 2,3,5-tri-iodobenzoic acid (TIBA), 2×10^{-4}M, *p*H adjusted to 7.0. TIBA is known (GALSTON 1947) to act as an auxin antagonist when applied in great molar excess to a system containing auxin, though it may act as an auxin synergist at lower concentrations (THIMANN and BONNER 1948). The temperature regimes used were: (*a*) phototemperature 20°C, nyctotemperature 14°C, (*b*) 23°-17°, and (*c*) 26°-20°.

The spray treatments were started when the plants were three weeks old and continued daily until the conclusion of the experiment 7 weeks later. They were performed in the last hour of the phototemperature treatment, with the aid of a compressed air-driven atomizer. The spray was carefully applied in a sealed chamber until all surfaces of the plant were covered with fine droplets. The plant was permitted to stand until the spray had partially dried and was then returned to the greenhouse. In all cases, the experimental plants were exposed to natural illumination and natural daylength, which varied between about 9½ and 13½ hours per day.

The most reliable growth measurement was the distance from the ground line to the height of the highest ligule. A reasonably successful attempt was made to utilize leaf length as a criterion of the effectiveness of the auxin sprays, but this seemed far more variable than "stem" height and so was not used as much.

The following general results became apparent after the first few weeks of the first experiment: (*1*) the normal plants were unaffected in their growth by any of the sprays, (2) the silkless plants grown in either of the higher temperature treatments were similarly unaffected, but (3) silkless plants grown under the 20°-14°C temperature regime were markedly enhanced in their overall growth by the IAA spray. PLATE XXIII demonstrates the difference in growth between the water- and the auxin-sprayed plants after 6 weeks of treatment, and TABLE 20 gives some of the results for the high and low temperature treatments. Although there is some overlap in the growth data, the growth differences are so marked as to require no detailed statistical justification.

Another interesting result of this experiment which is also noted in TABLE 20 was the marked effect produced by IAA and TIBA on the number and growth pattern of the prop roots produced. At the low temperature IAA increased the number of prop roots in both genotypes, at the high temperature only in the normals. Contrariwise, TIBA decreased the number of prop roots in both genotypes at the high temperatures, but only in the silkless type at low temperatures. Thus, in general, where IAA had a marked effect, TIBA did not, and *vice versa.* Another marked effect of TIBA is noted in the aberrant behavior of the prop roots (PLATE XXV), which normally grow down, but which, in the TIBA-treated plants, grow horizontally, or even upward.

TABLE 20: *Growth of normal and silkless corn plants at various temperatures and under various spray régimes. Unsprayed controls and intermediate temperature treatment are omitted, for brevity. Plants 10 weeks old at harvest:—*

TEMPERATURE RÉGIME	KIND OF PLANTS	SPRAY	AVERAGE HEIGHT (cm.) TO HIGHEST LIGULE	AVERAGE NUMBER OF PROP ROOTS PER PLANT
20° day 14° night	Normal	H_2O	36.9	9.3
		IAA	37.5	20.5
		TIBA	35.3	10.6
	Silkless	H_2O	48.3	15.7
		IAA	72.5	20.3
		TIBA	51.7	9.0
26° day 20° night	Normal	H_2O	52.0	11.0
		IAA	60.0	17.7
		TIBA	53.0	9.8
	Silkless	H_2O	88.0	17.7
		IAA	91.0	16.0
		TIBA	72.0	11.3

One may conclude from this experiment and from three others which gave essentially the same results that with certain genotypes and under certain climatic conditions, the growth of plants may be limited by their auxin supply. Under such conditions, considerable increase in growth and yield may possibly result from the judicious application of auxin-type sprays.

Adenine:— Peas are well known as a cool weather crop, and their failure to grow or produce well in warmer environments prevents their being grown in certain regions and at certain times of the year. The same general situation holds for numerous other economically important plants.

Several years ago, we found (GALSTON and HAND 1949) that the thermal inactivation of the growth mechanism of etiolated pea epicotyl sections could be largely prevented by the addition to the medium of small quantities of adenine or related compounds. When the facilities of the Earhart Laboratory became available, we decided to conduct a similar experiment with intact green pea plants, to see whether peas treated with adenine could be made to grow successfully in warmer-than-usual environments.

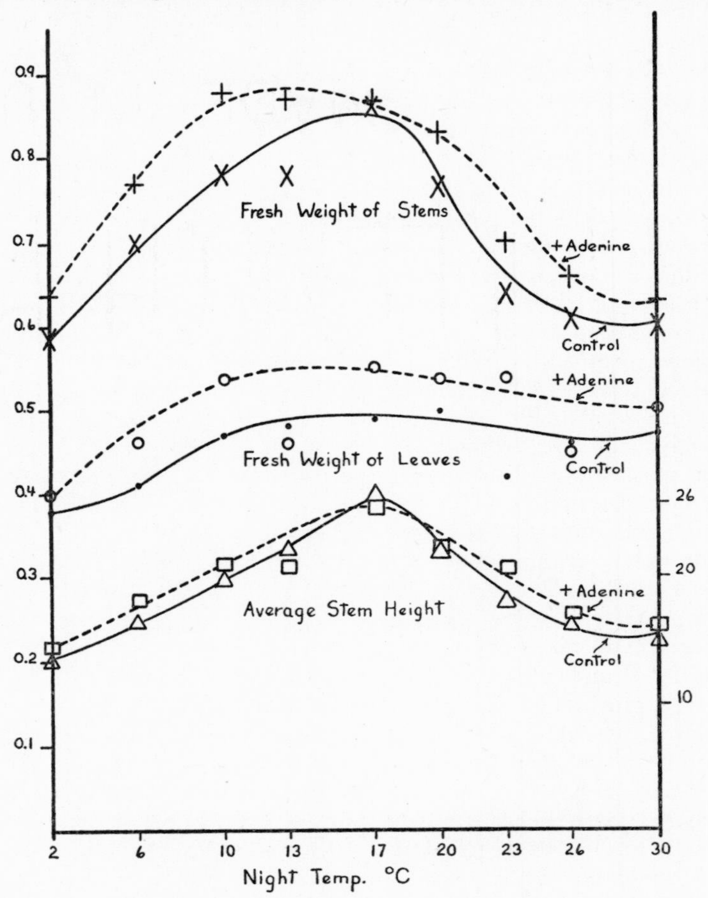

Figure 71.— Stem elongation (*right ordinate:* in cm.) and fresh weight (*left ordinate*: in g./plant) of Alaska peas as a function of nyctotemperature (*abscissa:* in degree Celsius). In each case the points for the adenine-treated plants are connected by broken lines, those for the controls by drawn lines. Adenine sulfate conc. 10 mg./l. Data of A. W. Galston.

Alaska pea seeds were soaked in tap water for four hours, then planted in a 1:1 gravel:vermiculite mixture in plastic containers. All plants were kept under the 23°-17°C temperature for one week, and were then transferred to differential night temperatures from 16:00 to 08:00, all being kept in the natural light greenhouse at 23°C from 08:00 to 16:00. The night temperatures used were (in °C): 2, 6, 10, 13, 17, 20, 23, 26 and 30. At each temperature, there were four different spray treatments:

a) H_2O
b) 1 mg./l. adenine sulfate
c) 10 mg./l. adenine sulfate
d) 100 mg./l. adenine sulfate

After two weeks of such treatment, during which time growth data were being taken, the plants were harvested, separated into their various organs, and fresh and dry weight determinations made.

The results plotted in FIGURE 71 show that the plants made optimal growth in length at a night temperature of 17°C, growth being inhibited about 35 per cent by a 10°C deviation in temperature, either upward or downward. Although adenine was without effect in the region of the optimum, it appeared to promote stem elongation slightly both at the higher and the lower temperatures. With regard to stem weight (FIGURE 71) a somewhat similar situation prevails, except that there appears to be a somewhat broader temperature optimum centered about 13°C. Data on average fresh weight of roots per plant show a very broad temperature optimum for growth centered about the surprisingly low value of 10°C and no marked effect of adenine.

The most striking effects of the adenine sprays were noted on leaves, both their size and fresh weight being enhanced at all concentrations of adenine, and under all temperature conditions (FIGURE 71). This is in accord with previous reports (D. BONNER and HAAGEN-SMIT 1939; D. BONNER and J. BONNER 1940) that adenine applications enhance leaf growth. As with roots, there is an amazingly flat temperature optimum for growth, no large effect being produced by temperature variation between 10°C and 23°C. With stems, on the other hand, a deviation of only 3 degrees from the optimum at 17°C produces greatly depressed elongation. In view of recent findings in the Earhart Laboratory that day temperatures are more important than night temperatures in controlling the growth of peas (Chapter 7) it would be interesting to repeat these experiments with an altered phototemperature.

On the basis of these experiments, especially those involving auxin, there seems little doubt that the response of plants to growth-regulatory chemicals depends to a large extent on the temperature conditions of growth. Differential responses at the different temperatures emphasize the need for temperature control in such experiments and also the fact that different experimenters obtaining divergent results in what they believe to be similar experiments may possibly resolve the disparity by working under accurately controlled temperatures.

Chapter 26

CONCLUSIONS

Significance of Phytotrons:— In the previous chapters the various aspects of the Earhart Plant Research Laboratory, and a number of results obtained in it were described and discussed. In this last chapter I should like to review the significance of "phytotrons" for future botanical work. The designation phytotron is now generally used for a comprehensive set of air-conditioned growing rooms for plants, and was for the first time applied to the Earhart Laboratory when the complexity of its control room suggested a comparison with that of a large cyclotron or synchrotron. It seems unnecessary to extend the name phytotron to a single controlled temperature plant growing chamber, which is more properly designated as an air-conditioned greenhouse or an air-conditioned light room or CEF (controlled environment facility).

Seventeen years ago there were already a number of isolated attempts to control the physical environment for mature plants. Many artificially lighted rooms and cabinets had been devised and constructed, and many greenhouses were operated with a certain degree of temperature control. However, few of these have been sufficiently effective to be duplicated or have led to a full-scale use of control over the environment. Although theoretically air-conditioned greenhouses or temperature-controlled rooms were ideal for a study of plants, in practice they were rather discounted. The situation is perhaps best characterized by the comments of reviewers for the American Journal of Botany, who were unanimous in their appraisal of my paper describing the first air-conditioned greenhouses at Caltech (WENT 1943*a*): It was unnecessary to publish another description of controlled-temperature greenhouses, since in previous years so many others had been described. The fact that I had more requests for reprints of this 1943 paper than for any other paper I ever published (with the exception of the description of the Earhart Laboratory: WENT 1950) attests to the judgment of the editor (Dr. R. E. CLELAND), who accepted it in spite of the recommendation of the four reviewers.

A phytotron differs from an ordinary range of greenhouses mainly in two respects: (*a*) the physical control over the aerial environment is positive and more or less complete, and (*b*) a whole range of conditions is available simultaneously, allowing comparison between different environments. What can it accomplish and how can it aid in botanical research in general?

In the "exact" sciences, as chemists and physicists are wont to designate their own branches of science, it is axiomatic that experiments have to be carried out under exactly defined and rigidly controlled conditions to insure reproducibility — the cornerstone of all science. I am convinced that this is the reason why there is good general agreement among physicists and chemists on most of the fundamental problems involving the inanimate world. In defiance of this obvious prerequisite for all experimentation, botanists, agriculturists, biochemists and other investigators have acquiesced in the use of plant material grown under non-controlled or poorly controlled conditions. In addition, they often have carried out their experiments under insufficiently known and therefore non-reproducible conditions. The reason for the existence of so many conflicting theories and hypotheses in the botanical sciences (to mention only a few: theories of translocation of organic substances in plants, theories of photoperiodism or bud inhibition, the concept of xeromorphy, or the main biochemical pathway of respiration) obviously lies in conflicting experimental evidence, attributable to unknown or unappreciated variables in the experimental material or the experimental conditions. Since it is practically impossible to select the significant facts from such conflicting evidence, the resulting confusion cannot be resolved, and only data collected under one set of conditions by one or a few investigators could be used for theoretical evaluation. A good example of such a theoretical analysis is VAN DE SANDE BAKHUYZEN's analysis of the growth and flowering of wheat (1934), or his theory of flower formation in long and short-day plants (1950, 1952). Yet, such complete theoretical evaluations of experimental facts are rare in botany, and in many instances the non-reproducible experimental conditions in the growing of plants prevented the enunciation of universally accepted generalizations. Therefore, inadequate experimental techniques prevented the development of a "Theoretical Botany," comparable to a generally accepted "Theoretical Physics."

The lack of control of the environment in experiments involving plants in no way invalidates all research carried out in the past with plants under uncontrolled conditions. In many cases the observed responses far exceeded the fluctuations attributable to environmental variables. Or we were dealing with processes or reactions which are not, or only slightly, influenced by the environment (such as gene segregation, all-or-none responses, or certain aspects of morphology and taxonomy). In a limited number of cases botanists were already working under properly controlled conditions (*e.g.*, using seedlings as experimental material), where reproducibility of results and their significance were usually sufficient to draw binding conclusions. But in a large number of cases conclusions remained tentative, or results were outright contradictory. In such cases no degree of statistical treatment of the experimental results could circumvent — or substitute for — proper control over the environment. The great development of statistics and its extensive use in the botanical sciences may to some extent have blinded us to the simple truth that there is no substitute for a properly executed experiment, and that a proper experiment is one in which all variables are known and controlled. Under certain conditions statistical treatment can warn us against overconfidence in results; it can sometimes tell where the main sources of error lie, but elimination of excessive variability and especially increase in reproducibility can only come from improved experimentation. Air-conditioned greenhouses and temperature-controlled artificial light rooms are the most powerful tools at present at our disposal to improve experimental conditions and to minimize the experimental error.

Before considering the full possibilities of a phytotron such as the Earhart Plant Research Laboratory, let us first consider the significance of single air-conditioned rooms or greenhouses, where plants can be grown and tested under known and reproducible environmental conditions. In experiments we have to distinguish between variability and reproducibility. The former indicates the reliability of the results of an individual experiment, and can be expressed in terms of standard error or standard deviation or least significant difference. Reproducibility cannot be calculated from a single experiment; it involves the quantitative comparison between different experiments.

As shown in Chapter 15 (variability of experimental material), the variability is at least halved, when plant material is grown in greenhouses with positive temperature control provided by simple air-conditioning. A further reduction in variability, again of the order of 50 per cent, is possible with the use of artificial light. Additional improvements can be achieved by control of air pollution, rate of air movement over the plants, uniform nutrition by eliminating soil, etc. But not only is the variability of the plant material in response to treatments reduced two to five-fold; even more important: the reproducibility of the experimental results is increased manyfold. Regardless of the time of year, the response of the plants is similar, and many troublesome fluctuations, such as occur in the *Avena* test or in the pea test for auxin, or in the growth rate of plants in general, do not occur in the Earhart Plant Research Laboratory. This means that the experiments do not have to be repeated many times, because under the well-defined conditions they are reproducible (compare TABLE 12).

For these reasons the installation of air-conditioning in laboratories, test rooms, artificial light rooms and greenhouses is not only desirable, but essential, because the effectiveness of research is increased manyfold. Only when one is reasonably certain that the environment has no effect on the experimental results, such as on Mendelian ratios, or where the measured response greatly exceeds the environmental variability, such as in certain morphogenetic problems, is control over the environment immaterial. But in all other cases, whether the concern is with nutritional, hormonal, biochemical, transpirational, photosynthetic or other problems, experimentation without air-conditioning is wasteful. Therefore, no botanical research facilities should be built anymore without a considerable degree of environmental control. The argument that the required machinery is too expensive is invalid, because with the decreased variability and increased reproducibility, only a fraction of the usual number of plants is sufficient to obtain quantitative results of equal significance. Therefore, when air-conditioners are installed, the size of the contemplated experimental rooms or greenhouses can be reduced to approximately half which may pay for the cost of machinery. In addition, all experiments will gain in significance because of increased reproducibility which makes the research worker more efficient. And last but not least: in many countries the summers are so warm that greenhouses without air-conditioning cannot be used; therefore, installation of air-conditioning makes the greenhouses themselves usable for 12 months instead of the usual 6-8 per year, and they can be used when the light conditions are most favorable. Since the Clark and the Earhart greenhouses have proven that the air-conditioning of research greenhouses is entirely feasible, and that all technical difficulties can be overcome, it seems difficult to find any arguments to justify the construction of the conventional style of research greenhouses, and only conservatism, and lack of experience among greenhouse builders, or absence of electricity, can be an excuse for their continued construction.

TABLE 21: *Construction costs of the Earhart Plant Research Laboratory, indicating the proportion between general construction and special feature costs. Included are the original $407,000.00 gift from the Earhart Foundation, and later appropriations of over $15,000.00:—*

	GENERAL CONSTRUCTION	SPECIAL FEATURES
Concrete, framework and finishing	$133,636.60	
Roofing	7,311.00	
Metal floors		$ 11,874.00
Fumigation entrance and sterilizer		4,495.00
Power and general lighting	30,700.30	14,000.00
Fluorescent light panels		16,374.00
Motor generator		2,000.00
Control panels and time clocks		3,000.00
Recorders for temperature and CO_2		3,500.00
Refrigeration and air conditioning		118,475.50
Water treatment		13,168.00
Plumbing	2,707.00	
Smog filters		3,285.00
Wind and fog equipment		1,400.00
Automatic sprinklers	6,096.00	
Plans and supervision	20,000.00	6,000.00
Insurance, legal fees, etc.	3,500.00	
Furniture, trucks, etc.	3,900.00	7,000.00
Miscellaneous	5,000.00	5,000.00
Total	$212,850.90	$209,571.50

Cost of Earhart Plant Research Laboratory:— To give an idea of the actual costs involved in the erection and operation of air-conditioned greenhouses, the following data are pertinent. As TABLE 21 shows, total construction costs, including the equipment of the Earhart Plant Research Laboratory, amounted to $407,000; when this is divided over the 15,000 square feet of total floor space in the building, it amounts to $27 per square foot. If one considers that in 1949 ordinary house construction in the U.S.A. amounted anywhere from $10 to $16 per square foot, the construction costs of a phytotron with its complicated machinery is only slightly higher than of any laboratory, and about twice the cost of home construction. A breakdown of TABLE 21 actually shows that the special features of the Earhart Laboratory (air-conditioning, metal greenhouse floors, extra electrical work, de-ionizer and special equipment) account for about half the total costs of the building.

As far as the operating costs are concerned, they should be considered in connection with the number of research workers using them. At the present time the Earhart Plant Research Laboratory accommodates about 12 full-time research workers and visitors, with 3 assistants, 3 graduate students and several persons using the facilities for part-time activities. The yearly operating costs, including utilities, salaries of the operating staff, and maintenance, is approximately $60,000. Therefore, the costs per year per research worker amount to about $4,000, if Institute overhead, supplies and apparatus are included. Since research administrators usually count on a cost of research facilities to about equal the salary of a research worker, the operating cost of the Earhart Laboratory is perhaps even slightly below the average for other laboratories, which has been achieved by a very tight and efficient organization, and at the expense of office facilities.

The above analysis has shown that even if the Earhart Laboratory did nothing more than provide reproducible growing conditions for plants, its construction and operation would have been fully justified from a standpoint of research efficiency. However, reproducibility and decreased variability are only by-products of the Clark and Earhart Laboratories. Their main function is to provide facilities by which the effect of the different climatic variables on plants can be assessed. In spite of the fact that the Earhart Plant Research Laboratory has been functioning only for 6 years, a considerable amount of information has already been gathered on the subject of climatic responses of plants, largely because of the spade-work carried out in the Clark greenhouses in the ten years before the Earhart Laboratory started functioning, and because of the experience of Dr. EVERSOLE in the years before that.

For a study of plant climatology the Earhart Laboratory is so eminently suited because it provides the whole spectrum of biological temperatures in combination with light control. If only part of the rooms and greenhouses had been constructed, the phytotron would not have been able to fulfill its functions, and, therefore, I am most grateful to the Earhart Foundation that it increased its original gift from $200,000 to $407,000 when it had become clear that, due to the sharply increased building costs during and after the war, the original plans could not be realized for the originally anticipated sum.

Because of the great cost of a phytotron, in which all environmental factors for plant growth can be varied independently, and also because an extensive technical staff is required to operate it, in most cases it seems advisable that phytotrons should be conceived as coöperative ventures, satisfying simultaneously the needs of a considerable number of research workers. This divides the construction and operating costs over a large number of users, as exemplified in the Earhart Plant Research Laboratory. In an agricultural experiment station, for instance, there may be groups in agriculture, horticulture, plant nutrition, plant breeding, pathology and climatology who all have a need for a whole range of environmental conditions. And a large botanical institute with physiologists, experimental morphologists, ecologists, geneticists, taxonomists and biochemists will find untold and as yet unsuspected uses for a phytotron. Especially a number of botanical disciplines which have been largely descriptive because of the difficulties involved in experimentation, such as Ecology, Morphology, Anatomy and Evolution will find new and fertile fields opening up in a phytotron. The previous chapters have already indicated the type of problems which can be attacked in a phytotron in the fields of plant physiology, plant climatology and ecology, but without doubt other applications are possible.

Practical Significance:— Not only in the field of pure research, but in numerous other directions will a phytotron prove itself indispensable. In future all testing of herbicides, pre-emergence killers, fungicides and insecticides should not only be carried out under controlled and reproducible conditions, but also over a whole range of temperature and light conditions, since their effectiveness is so often strongly influenced by external conditions. Once a compound has been tested over the whole spectrum of climates where it is to be used, it can safely be recommended, since it will be known whether under the prevailing light and temperature conditions it can be expected to produce results.

Other possible future applications of a phytotron lie in the fields of agriculture and horticulture. When a new plant or crop variety with superior qualities in one or another respect (high yield, disease resistance, taste, keeping qualities, flower color, chemical composition, etc.) has been produced, a simple test in a phytotron can indicate the range of climates over which it is likely to grow well and produce satisfactorily. This will reduce the number of expensive field tests in which it has to be included. An example of this possible use has been described in Chapter 13 on Miscellaneous Wild Plants. *Veratrum viride* had never been grown under cultivation, and had been completely refractory in any field tests. After establishing its climatic requirements in the Earhart Laboratory it was possible to suggest locations where it could be expected to grow properly as far as its climatic requirements were concerned. When it was tried out in these locations, it grew well as predicted on the basis of laboratory experience.

Since most of our cultivated plants come from a specialized climate (semi-arid and sub-tropical), it would seem logical that in future a great number of plants from the rich floras of other climates will come under cultivation. But particularly the introduction of plants of new and unfamiliar climates will pose special problems and can be expected to give only a small percentage of success, unless phytotron trials of their climatic response have preceded the field trials. This has been pointed out by Dr. Hellmers in Chapter 14, and he has illustrated this in connection with the introduction of plants for erosion control in southern California.

Instead of selecting the optimal climate for a particular plant, or selecting plants to be cultivated in a particular climate, as was described in the previous paragraphs, there are two other possible approaches to climatic adaptation of plants. In the first place it may be possible to change the climate sufficiently in a particular locality to grow a plant which previously could not be grown there. The most obvious instance of this is provided by greenhouses. This is an expensive method of climatic control, and can be used only in case of plants of great economic value, such as flowers, luxury fruit, etc. But since it was pointed out in previous chapters that in most plants only one or another climatic variable really controls or limits their growth, it may be possible to change only that single climatic character, without changing the others. This is actually being done in the case of photoperiodic response, where whole fields are illuminated for limited periods during the night, or where blocks of plants are shaded during part of the day.

Genetical and Physiological Problems:— Instead of changing the climate we can imagine the possibility of changing the plant's response to climate. This would involve a breeding program as at present practiced in the selection of other characters. This presupposes that the response to individual climatic factors depends on individual genetic units, which statement will probably go unchallenged. But it also requires methods for selection of these characters, and these methods are at present not available. Therefore, we can look forward with much interest to the results of the investigations of Dr. H. R. Highkin, who presently is investigating the genetic basis of the temperature response of the pea plant in the Earhart Plant Research Laboratory. There are two possibilities which can be envisaged: either the complex climatic response, which is usually expressed as "yield," depends on a series of polygenes, or each climatic response character depends on a few major genes, which, because of their multiplicity for temperature, light, photoperiod and other factors, may seem to make the impression of a polygenic series. The results of Prof. N. Barber on vernalization and photoperiodic response in peas, obtained in the Earhart Laboratory, can be explained on the basis of one or two major genes. But the complex temperature relationships in the various tomato varieties indicate rather a polygenic set-up. In this connection it should be recalled that grafting experiments in peas indicated that qualitative responses in peas (acacia-leaf, stipuleless, dwarf and slender) depended on well-analyzed simple or double Mendelian gene differences, whereas the much smaller quantitative differences between pea varieties were dependent on another genetic mechanism, such as on polygenes (WENT 1943*c*).

From the purely physiological work described in the previous chapters it also will have become evident, that the controlled growing and testing conditions of the Earhart Plant Research Laboratory can contribute very significantly to the study of physiological processes in general. Although in many cases simple air-conditioned rooms will suffice for such studies (for instance, temperature, humidity, light and pure-air controlled rooms for the *Avena* and pea tests), there are many other processes in which various temperatures and light conditions should be compared, and again here the availability of a wide range of temperatures and photoperiods is helpful in research. Yet it seems to me that the wide range of growing conditions has other and important advantages. As indicated in previous chapters, all plants differ more or less in their optimal climatic requirements. For many experiments it is important to use plant material grown under optimal conditions. These seldom are available in ordinary greenhouses, and, therefore, physiological experiments are often carried out with poorly growing plants. It probably is no exaggeration that in most Botanical Institutions the poorest plants are found in the greenhouses occupied by physiologists and biochemists. This trend can definitely be counteracted by phytotrons, where for each plant the optimal growing conditions can be supplied. In the Earhart Laboratory we can grow orchids, or tomatoes, or potatoes which are as good as or better than any grown by practical growers, which makes the results obtained acceptable to them. The statement, so often made by practical growers, that greenhouse experiments cannot possibly contribute to the knowledge of the field response of plants, has become invalidated. Most greenhouses have been constructed to keep conditions deliberately different from those in the field, and, therefore, the plant responses also differ. But when the conditions in the greenhouses reflect those in the field, the plant responses are also similar. By using air-conditioned greenhouses, the field conditions can be maintained for any length of time which makes them so much superior to field testing.

General Problems:— In general, soil characters can be modified by soil amendments, nutritional deficiencies can be corrected with fertilizers, lack of moisture can be overcome by irrigation, diseases and pests can be controlled with fungicides and insecticides. But usually climate is not under control as yet. Therefore, before deciding which crop or which variety to grow in a certain area, we should know *in the first place* whether the climate is optimal or at least suitable for such plants, because if it is not, no amount of water or fertilizer or disease control can counteract this. Therefore, a climatic survey should never be omitted in an agricultural appraisal of a particular locality. Based on purely theoretical grounds the recommendation could be made that it should have precedence over all other surveys. There are, however, at present very great difficulties in the implementation of such a recommendation: in the first place, we have insufficient information about which particular climatic factors should be surveyed. And in the second place, we have very little information about the climatic response of even our major crop plants. Therefore, preliminary to making the recommendation that full climatological surveys be made of all parts of the world, I should like to recommend that very high priority be given to an extensive and intensive survey of the climatic requirements of all crop plants. I hope that the information contained in this book will make it clear that such surveys are possible because of the effectiveness of phytotrons and are practical because several examples have shown that phytotron information is applicable to field problems.

There is also another reason, why physiological research is often not fully appreciated by the agriculturist or the practical grower. The field response of plants depends on the interaction of so many independent variables, that in many instances laboratory tests could not be used in the evaluation of cultural practices, new varieties, nutritional treatments or disease-control measures. These all require repeated field testing, statistical treatment and careful interpretation of results before they can be presented to the practical grower, who is not interested in the individual factors, but only in the composite response of his plants in the field. Although not enough comparisons have been made as yet between the phytotron behavior of plants and their field response, there are enough indications that a partial substitution of phytotron testing for preliminary field testing is possible. The field behavior of plants is the response to the interaction of a large number of independent variables. In most physiological research the effect of a single variable, like light intensity or photoperiod, has been tested under otherwise similar conditions. In the field, however, we have to deal with a large number of more or less independent variables, which often invalidate the conclusions of the physiologist which were based on only a single variable. In a phytotron it is possible to measure the interaction between a number of independent variables. Thus we get a much closer correspondence between theoretical expectation and field behavior. As an example, the response of strawberries can be mentioned. In greenhouse experiments it had been clearly established that most strawberries were short-day plants. This, however, was true only under high temperature conditions, as prevailing in ordinary greenhouses. In the Earhart Laboratory it was shown that at low temperatures the strawberry plant is photoperiodically indifferent, which explains their behavior in cold climates, where they will flower without ever being subjected to short days during their growing period. To indicate the complexity in response which is analyzable in a phytotron, FIGURES 36, 37, 38 and 39 have been included. They show the relationships between morphological and physiological responses on the one hand, and their change with time of two pea varieties to light intensity, photoperiod and temperature on the other hand. This really means a seven-dimensional interrelationship or seven-dimensional correlation in these peas. By adding further dimensions, such as recording of the flowering behavior, dry weight production, and the differentiation between day and night temperature or different nutritional treatments, which are perfectly feasible in a phytotron like the Earhart Plant Research Laboratory, three or four more dimensions could have been added. It is most likely that within the framework of these ten to eleven dimensions every field response could have been predicted or explained. Thus, the complexity and impossibility of analytical treatment of a field experiment becomes explainable on the basis of the known response of the particular plant to the individual environmental variables.

It is not only in field tests that the botanist is faced with multidimensional relationships. Every experiment, involving living organisms, deals with the influence of perhaps only one variable on a multidimensional system. By this is meant not only the physical four-dimensionality of the living organism, in which time is an essential dimension to describe it, but there may be primary and secondary responses to the variables applied. When for instance a young tomato plant is subjected to different temperatures, these will cause different growth rates, which in turn will result in plants with different responses to temperature. Or we must consider that temperature not only affects the growth process, but simultaneously it changes the rate of translocation, of respiration, of mineral uptake, etc. Also the possibility exists that temperature or light conditions the plant so that later it responds differently to further treatments.

These examples are given to stress that in any biological experimentation we are continuously dealing with multidimensional interrelations which cannot be expressed in simple two-dimensional correlation diagrams, but require multidimensional graphing and thinking. It is hoped that with the frequent three- and multidimensional presentations in this book the complexity of the plant response has been done justice, and that at the same time it has alerted the botanist to the fact that he is continuously dealing with systems, which, even under the most perfect experimental conditions, are highly complex, and which become essentially un-analyzable under less well-controlled experimental conditions. The degree of variability in experimental results is a good index of the degree of complexity of the problem under investigation and is a measure of the number of uncontrolled conditions. Where a statistical analysis is required to sort out results, it can be safely concluded that we are on the verge of, and perhaps already beyond the point, where the complexity of the system under investigation precludes not only experimental solution but also theoretical penetration. A phytotron may reduce the complexity of response sufficiently to approach problems which formerly were submerged in a morass of statistics.

When for each experimental treatment a large number of plants has to be used to cope with the variability of the response, it becomes difficult and often impossible to observe the individual plant closely, and one has to be satisfied by taking average measurements, which may obscure details in response. When only a few plants are needed and used per treatment, as is possible with genetically uniform material in the Earhart Plant Research Laboratory, the characteristics and the development of the individual plant can be followed much closer than is possible in mass experiments, also because the experimenter has more time available due to the simpler handling of fewer plants. This closer contact with the individual plant cannot fail to be beneficial to the development of botany, which is the science of plants and not of averages.

The trend in botany, to become more and more detached from the living plant, is counteracted by the organization of the Earhart Plant Research Laboratory. The apparatus and machinery required for the experiments have mostly been separated from the growing rooms, and are largely installed in the basement, whereas the first floor is largely reserved for the growing and handling of plants. Anyone carrying out an experiment in the Earhart Laboratory is continuously in the closest contact with thousands of other living plants, all being tested for their responses, and naturally one gets an appreciation of the general validity of the response obtained with one's own experimental plants.

The essentially international nature of scientific research is strongly emphasized in the Earhart Plant Research Laboratory. Investigators from every continent have used or are using its facilities, and to the extent that space permits, qualified persons are welcomed as guest investigators to carry out experiments for which the air-conditioned facilities are essential. Unfortunately, we are unable to offer financial assistance to such investigators, but a grant from the National Science Foundation provides for the cost of space used in the growing rooms and greenhouses by visiting scientists.

In this way the Earhart Plant Research Laboratory is becoming an important place, where modern techniques are harnessed to further the development of botany, and to help international understanding.

BIBLIOGRAPHY

ALLARD, H. A. & M. W. EVANS, 1941: Growth and flowering of some tame and wild grasses in response to different photoperiods (Jour. Agr. Res. 62: 193-228).

ANDEL, O. M. VAN, 1957: Diurnal periodicity of exudation in relation to temperature and light (Amer. Jour. Bot., *in press*).

ASHBY, W. C. & H. HELLMERS, 1955: Temperature requirements for germination in relation to wild-land seeding (Jour. Range Management 8: 80-83).

BAILEY, I. W. & T. KERR, 1935: The visible structure of the secondary wall and its significance in physical and chemical investigations of tracheary cells and fibers (Jour. Arnold Arb. 15: 273-300; repr. *in* Contributions to Plant Anatomy, Chron. Bot. 15: 72-90, 1954).

BANDURSKI, R. S., F. M. SCOTT, M. PFLUG & F. W. WENT, 1953: The effect of temperature on the color and anatomy of tomato leaves (Amer. Jour. Bot. 40: 41-46).

BARTON, L. V., 1945: Respiration and germination studies of seeds in moist storage (Ann. N.Y. Acad. Sci. 46: 185-208).

BENDIX, S. & F. W. WENT, 1956: Some effects of temperature and photoperiod on the growth of tomato seedlings (Bot. Gazette 117: 326-335).

BENNETT, J. P., 1949: Temperature and bud rest period (California Agric. 3(11): 9, 12).

BLAAUW, A. H., 1941: On the relation between flower-formation and temperature (Bulbous irises) (Proc. Ned. Akad. Wetensch. 44: 513-520, 684-689).

BLAAUW, A. H., I. LUYTEN & A. H. HARTSEMA, 1930: Verschuiving der periodiciteit (Shifting of periodicity. Adaptation and export to the Southern Hemisphere) (Hyacinth and tulip) (Verh. Kon. Ned. Akad. Wetensch. Amsterdam 26(7): 1-105).

BLACKMAN, G. E. & G. L. WILSON, 1951: Physiological and ecological studies in the analysis of plant environment (Ann. Bot. 15: 373-408).

BONNER, D. M. & J. BONNER, 1940: On the influence of various growth factors on the growth of green plants (Amer. Jour. Bot. 27: 38-42).

BONNER, D. M. & A. J. HAAGEN-SMIT, 1939: Leaf growth factors, II. The activity of pure substances in leaf growth (Proc. Nat. Acad. Sci. 25: 184).

BONNER, J., 1943: Effects of application of thiamine to *Cosmos* (Bot. Gazette 104: 475-479).

BONNER, J., 1947: Flower bud initiation and flower opening in *Camellia* (Proc. Amer. Soc. Hort. Sci. 50: 401-408).

BONNER, J. & J. ENGLISH, JR., 1938: A chemical and physiological study of traumatin, a plant wound hormone (Plant Physiol. 13: 331-348).

BONNER, J. & J. LIVERMAN, 1953: Hormonal control of flower initiation *in* Growth and differentiation in plants (Monograph, Am. Soc. Plant Physiol. 1953: 283-303).

BÜNNING, E., 1931: Untersuchungen über die autonomen tagesperiodischen Bewegungen der Primärblätter von *Phaseolus multiflorus* (Jahrb. wiss. Bot. 75: 439-480).

CAMUS, G. C. & F. W. WENT, 1952: The thermoperiodicity of three varieties of *Nicotiana tabacum* (Amer. Jour. Bot. 39: 521-528).

CANDOLLE, A. DE, 1855: Géographie botanique raisonnée, I, 606 p. (Paris: Masson).

CAPITE, L. DE, 1955: Action of light and temperature on growth of plant tissue cultures in vitro (Amer. Jour. Bot. 42: 869-873).

CASAMAJOR, R., 1955: Factors governing the flowering of *Cymbidiums* (Cymbidium Soc. News 10(8): 12).

CASAMAJOR, R. & F. W. WENT, 1954: *Cypripedium* at Earhart Laboratory (Cymbidium Soc. News 9(2): 3).

CHOUARD, P., 1951: Dormances et inhibitions des graines et des bourgeons; Préparation au forçage; Thermopériodisme, 157 p. (Paris: Cours Cons. Nat. Arts et Métiers).

CLAUSEN, J., D. D. KECK & W. M. HIESEY, 1940: Experimental studies on the nature of species, I. Effect of varied environment on western North American plants, 452 p. (Carnegie Inst. Wash. Publ. 520).

CLAUSEN, J., D. D. KECK & W. M. HIESEY, 1948: Experimental studies on the nature of species, III. Environmental responses of climatic races of *Achillea*, 129 p. (Carnegie Inst. Wash. Publ. 581).

COOPER, J. P., 1950: Day-length and head formation in the rye-grasses (Jour. British Grassland Soc. 5: 105-112).

COOPER, J. P., 1951: Studies on growth and development in *Lolium*, II. Pattern of bud development of the shoot apex and its ecological significance (Jour. Ecol. 39: 228-270).

COOPER, J. P., 1954: Studies on growth and development in *Lolium*, IV. Genetic control of heading responses in local populations (Jour. Ecol. 42: 521-556).

COVILLE, F., 1920: The influence of cold in stimulating the growth of plants (Jour. Agr. Res. 20: 151-160).

CROCKER, W. & L. V. BARTON, 1953: Physiology of seeds, 267 p. (Waltham, Mass.: Chronica Botanica Co.).

DARROW, G. M. & G. F. WALDO, 1934: Responses of strawberry varieties and species to duration of the daily light period (U.S.D.A. Tech. Bull. 453).

DAUBENMIRE, R. F., 1947: Plants and environment, 424 p. (New York: Wiley).

DORLAND, R. E. & F. W. WENT, 1947: Plant growth under controlled conditions, VIII. Growth and fruiting of the chili pepper (*Capsicum annuum*) (Amer. Jour. Bot. 34: 393-401).

DUNN, S. & F. W. WENT, 1957: Influence of fluorescent light quality on growth and photosynthesis (*in press*).

EVENARI, M., 1949: Germination inhibitors (Bot. Review 15: 153-194).

EVENARI, M. & D. KOLLER, 1955: Desert agriculture — a summary of problems encountered and results achieved in Israel (Israel Scientific Press).

FRANCO, C. M., 1941: Fotoperiodismo del cafeto (Rev. Inst. Defenso Café Costa Rica 11: 219-222).

GABRIELSEN, E. K., 1947: Quantum efficiency in photosynthesis (Experientia 3: 439-442).

GALSTON, A. W., 1947: The effect of 2,3,5-triiodobenzoic acid on the growth and flowering of soybeans (Amer. Jour. Bot. 34: 356-360).

GALSTON, A. W. & M. E. HAND, 1949: Adenine as a growth factor for etiolated peas and its relation to the thermal inactivation of growth (Arch. Biochem. 22: 434-443).

GARDNER, F. E., P. C. MARTH & L. P. BATJER, 1939: Spraying with plant growth substances to prevent apple fruit dropping (Science 90: 208-209).

GARDNER, F. P. & W. E. LOOMIS, 1952: Floral induction and development in orchard grass (Plant Physiol. 28: 201-217).

GARNER, W. W., 1937: Recent work on photoperiodism (Bot. Review 3: 259-275).

GEIGER, R., 1950: Climate near the ground (Harvard U. P.).

GLEASON, C. H., 1944: How to sow mustard in burned watersheds of Southern California, 32 p. (Forest Res. Note 37: U.S. Forest Service, Calif. Forest and Range Exp. Sta.).

Gorham, P. R., 1950: Heterotrophic nutrition of seed plants with particular reference to *Lemna minor* L. (Canad. Jour. Res. 28: 356-381).

Gregory, F. G., 1948: The control of flowering in plants (Symposia Soc. Exper. Biol. 2: 75-103).

Gregory, L. E., 1954: Some factors controlling tuber formation in the potato plant (Thesis, Univ. of Calif. at Los Angeles).

Gregory, L. E., 1956: Some factors for tuberization in the potato plant (Amer. Jour. Bot. 43: 281-288).

Grobbelaar, N., 1955: Growth and nitrogen metabolism of certain legumes, with special reference to the effects of controlled environments (Thesis, Cornell University).

Gustafson, F. G., 1936: Inducement of fruit development by growth promoting chemicals (Proc. Nat. Acad. Sci. 22: 628-636).

Gustafson, F. G., 1953: Influence of photoperiod on thiamine, riboflavin and niacin content of green plants (Amer. Jour. Bot. 40: 256-259).

Haagen-Smit, A. J., 1952: Chemistry and physiology of Los Angeles smog (Ind. and Eng. Chem. 44: 1342-1346).

Haagen-Smit, A. J., E. F. Darley, M. Zaitlin, H. Hull & W. Noble, 1951: Investigation on injury to plants from air pollution in the Los Angeles area (Plant Physiol. 27: 18-34).

Hanson, A. A. & V. G. Sprague, 1953: Heading of perennial grasses under greenhouse conditions (Agron. Jour. 45: 248-251).

Hartsema, A. M. & I. Luyten, 1953: De invloed van lage temperaturen op het snelle strekken en bloeien van *Convallaria majalis,* I & II (Der Einfluss niederer Temperaturen auf die Streckungsfähigkeit von *Convallaria majalis*) (Proc. Kon. Akad. Wetensch. Amsterdam 36: 120-127, 210-216).

Hess, C., 1955: Über die Rhytmik der Schichtenbildung beim Stärkekorn (Z. Bot. 43: 181-204).

Hewitt, S. P. & O. F. Curtis, 1948: The effect of temperature on loss of dry matter and carbohydrate from leaves by respiration and translocation (Amer. Jour. Bot. 35: 746-755).

Hiesey, W. M., 1953: Growth and development of species and hybrids of *Poa* under controlled conditions (Amer. Jour. Bot. 40: 205-221).

Higgins, J. J., 1952: Instructions for making phenological observations of garden peas (Seabrook, N.J.: Johns Hopkins Univ. Lab. of Climatology).

Highkin, H. R., 1956*a*: Vernalization in peas (Plant Physiol. 31: 399-403).

Highkin, H. R., 1956*b*: Temperature-induced variability in the growth and development of pea plants (Plant Physiol. 31: iii).

Highkin, H. R. & J. B. Hanson, 1954: Possible interaction between light-dark cycles and endogenous daily rhythms on the growth of tomato plants (Plant Physiol. 29: 301-302).

Hillman, W. S., 1956: Injury of tomato plants by continuous light and unfavourable photoperiodic cycles (Amer. Jour. Bot. 43: 89-96).

Hoover, W. H., 1937: The dependence of carbon dioxide assimilation in a higher plant on wave length of radiation (Smithsonian Misc. Coll. 95(21): 1-13).

Hull, H. M., 1952: Carbohydrate translocation in tomato with particular reference to temperature effect (Amer. Jour. Bot. 39: 661-669).

Hull, H. M., F. W. Went & N. Yamada, 1954: Fluctuations in sensitivity of the Avena test due to air pollutants (Plant Physiol. 29: 182-187).

International Grassland Congress, 6th, State College, Pa., 1952, Proceedings, 2 vols., 1801 p.

Jaffe, L., 1954: On a carbon dioxide gradient in the *Fucales* egg (Thesis, California Institute Technology).

Jansen, L. L., 1953: Studies in fruit growth and in vernalization (Thesis, California Institute Technology).

Juhrèn, M., W. M. Hiesey & F. W. Went, 1953: Germination and early growth of grasses in controlled conditions (Ecology 34: 288-300).

Juhrèn, M., F. W. Went & E. Phillips, 1956: Ecology of desert plants, IV. Combined field and laboratory work on germination of annuals in the Joshua Tree National Monument, California (Ecology 37: 318-330).
Julander, O., 1945: Drought resistance in range and pasture grasses (Plant Physiol. 20: 573-599).
Kerner von Marilaun, A., 1888-1891: Pflanzenleben (Leipzig).
Klebs, G., 1918: Über die Blütenbildung von *Sempervivum* (Flora 111-112: 128-151).
Kögl, F., A. J. Haagen-Smit & C. J. van Hulssen, 1936: Über den Einfluss unbekannter äusserer Faktoren bei Versuchen mit *Avena sativa.* Mitteilung über pflanzliche Wachstumsstoffe, 19 (Z. physiol. Chemie 241: 17-33).
Koot, I. J. van & G. van Antwerpen, 1952: Belichting en suikerbespuiting van komkommers (Illumination and sugar spraying of cucumbers) (Meded. Directeur Tuinbouw 15: 427-454).
Koritz, H. G. & F. W. Went, 1952: The physiological action of smog on plants, I. Initial growth and transpiration studies (Plant Physiol. 28: 50-62).
Kramer, M. & F. W. Went, 1948: The nature of the auxin in tomato stem tips (Plant Physiol. 24: 207-221).
Kurtz, E., 1952: Studies on the metabolism of lipids in plants (Thesis, California Inst. Technology).
Lammerts, W. E., 1943: Effect of photoperiod and temperature on growth of embryo-cultured peach seedlings (Amer. Jour. Bot. 30: 707-711).
Lang, A., 1952: Physiology of flowering (Ann. Rev. Plant Physiol. 3: 265-306).
Laude, H. M., 1953: The nature of summer dormancy in perennial grasses (Bot. Gazette 114: 284-292).
Laude, H. M. & B. A. Chaugle, 1953: Effect of stage of seedling development upon heat tolerance in bromegrasses (Jour. Range Management 6: 320-324).
Laude, H. M., J. E. Shrum, Jr. & W. E. Biehler, 1952: The effect of high soil temperatures on the seedling emergence of perennial grasses (Agron. Jour. 44: 110-112).
Laurie, A. & D. C. Kiplinger, 1944: Commercial flower forcing, ed. 4 (Philadelphia).
Leopold, A. C., 1949: The control of tillering in grasses by auxin (Amer. Jour. Bot. 36: 437-440).
Leopold, A. C. & F. S. Guernsey, 1953: Modification of floral initiation with auxins and temperatures (Amer. Jour. Bot. 40: 603-607).
Lewis, H. & F. W. Went, 1945: Plant growth under controlled conditions, IV. Response of California annuals to photoperiod and temperature (Amer. Jour. Bot. 32: 1-12).
Liverman, J. L., 1952: The physiology and biochemistry of flowering (Thesis, California Inst. Technology).
Loo, S. W., 1946: Preliminary experiment on the cultivation of *Baeria chrysostoma* under sterile conditions (Amer. Jour. Bot. 33: 382-389).
McKinney, H. H., 1940: Vernalization and the growth-phase concept (Bot. Review 6: 25-47).
Marshall, L. C., H. O. Eversole, A. J. Hess & F. W. Went, 1948: Technical features of greenhouse airconditioning (Refriger. Engineering 55: 151, 269).
Mather, K., 1949: Biometrical genetics — the study of continuous variation (New York: Dover).
Maximov, N. A., 1929: The plant in relation to water (London).
Melchers, G. & A. Lang, 1948: Die Physiologie der Blütenbildung (Biol. Zentralbl. 67: 105-174).
Mitchell, K. J., 1953*a*: Influence of light and temperature on the growth of ryegrass (*Lolium* spp.), I. Pattern of vegetative development (Physiol. Plantarum 6: 21-46).
Mitchell, K. J., 1953*b*: Influence of light and temperature on the growth of ryegrass

(*Lolium* spp.), II. The control of lateral bud development (Physiol. Plantarum 6: 425-443).

Mitchell, K. J., 1954: Influence of light and temperature on the growth of ryegrass (*Lolium* spp.), III. Pattern and rate of tissue formation (Physiol. Plantarum 7: 51-65).

Murneek, A. E., R. O. Whyte *et al.*, 1948: Vernalization and photoperiodism, 196 p. (Lotsya 1: Waltham, Mass.: Chronica Botanica Co.).

Muyzenberg, E. W. B. van den, 1942: De invloed van licht en temperatuur op de periodieke ontwikkeling van de aardbei (*Fragaria grandiflora* Ehrh.) en de beteekenis daarvan voor de teelt (Influence of light and temperature on the development of the strawberry in connection with its practical application), 160 p. (Meded. Lab. Tuinbouwplantenteelt Wageningen, 37).

Nitsch, J. P., 1951: The role of plant hormones in fruit development (Thesis, California Inst. Technology).

Nitsch, J. P., E. B. Kurtz, J. L. Liverman & F. W. Went, 1952: The development of sex expression in Cucurbit flowers (Amer. Jour. Bot. 39: 32-43).

Nuttonson, M. Y., 1948: Some preliminary observations of phenological data as a tool in the study of photoperiodic and thermal requirements of various plant material *in* A. E. Murneek, R. O. Whyte *et al.*: Vernalization and photoperiodism, p. 129-143 (Lotsya 1: Waltham, Mass.: Chronica Botanica Co.).

Olmsted, C. E., 1944: Growth and development in range grasses, IV. Photoperiodic responses in twelve geographic strains of side-oats grama (Bot. Gazette 106: 46-74).

Osborne, D. J. & F. W. Went, 1953: Climatic factors influencing parthenocarpy and normal fruit set in tomatoes (Bot. Gazette 114: 312-321).

Overbeek, J. van, M. E. Conklin & A. F. Blakeslee, 1942: Cultivation in vitro of small *Datura* embryos (Amer. Jour. Bot. 29: 472-477).

Parker, M. W. & H. A. Borthwick, 1949: Growth and composition of biloxi soybean grown in a controlled environment with radiation from different carbon-arc sources (Plant Physiol. 24: 345-358).

Parker, M. W. & H. A. Borthwick, 1950: Influence of light on plant growth (Ann. Review Plant Physiol. 1: 43-58).

Peterson, M. L. & W. E. Loomis, 1949: Effects of photoperiod and temperature on growth and flowering of Kentucky bluegrass (Plant Physiol. 24: 31-43).

Pilet, P. E. & F. W. Went, 1956: Control of growth of *Lens culinaris* by temperature and light (Amer. Jour. Bot. 43: 190-198).

Purvis, O. N., 1934: An analysis of the influence of temperature during germination on the subsequent development of certain winter cereals and its relation to the effect of length of day (Ann. Bot. 48: 919-956).

Purvis, O. N., 1939: Studies in the vernalization of cereals, V. The inheritance of the spring and winter habit in hybrids of Petkus rye (Ann. Bot., N.S.3: 719-729).

Ráfols, W. de, 1953: Experiencias ecológicas sobre el "T. Kok-saghyz" (Anales Invest. Agron. 2: 1-52).

Robertson, T. B., 1923: The chemical basis of growth and senescence, 389 p. (Philadelphia: Lippincott).

Roodenburg, J. W. M., 1952: Irradiation of greenhouse plants by artificial light sources (Report 13*th* Int. Hortic. Congress, p. 947-952).

Sachs, J., 1860: Physiologische Untersuchungen über die Abhängigkeit der Keimung von der Temperatur (Jahrb. wiss. Bot. 2; repr. *in* Ges. Abh. 1: 49-83).

Sachs, J., 1872: Über den Einfluss der Lufttemperatur und des Tageslichtes auf die stündlichen und täglichen Änderungen des Längenwachsthums (Streckung) der Internodien (Arbeiten bot. Inst. Würzburg 1: 99-192).

Sachs, R., 1955: Floral initiation in the night-blooming jasmine (*Cestrum nocturnum*) (Thesis, California Inst. Technology).

Sachs, R., 1956*a*: Floral initiation in *Cestrum nocturnum*, I. A long-short-day plant (Plant Physiol. 31: 185-192).

SACHS, R., 1956*b*: Floral initiation in *Cestrum nocturnum,* II. A 24-hour versus a 16-hour photoperiod for long-day induction (Plant Physiol. 31: 429-430).

SACHS, R., 1956*c*: Floral initiation in *Cestrum nocturnum,* III. The effect of temperature upon long-day and short-day induction (Plant Physiol. 31: 430-433).

SANDE BAKHUYZEN, H. L. VAN DE, 1937: Wheat grown under constant conditions, 400 p. (Food Research Inst. Misc. Publ. 8: Stanford Univ. Press).

SANDE BAKHUYZEN, H. L. VAN DE, 1951: Flowering and flowering hormones (one single scheme for both long-day and short-day plants), II A and B. Photoperiodism in long-day plants (Proc. Kon. Akad. Wetensch. Amsterdam 54: 603-623).

SANDE BAKHUYZEN, H. L. VAN DE, 1953: Flowering and flowering hormones (one single scheme for both long-day and short-day plants), III A and B (Proc. Kon. Akad. Wetensch. Amsterdam 56: 164-184).

SCHIMPER, A. F. W., 1898: Pflanzengeographie auf physiologischer Grundlage (Jena: Fischer).

SCHOUTE, J. C., 1935: Professor MOLL's method of determining the amount of sunshine on greenhouses (Rec. Trav. Bot. Néerl. 32: 311-316).

SINCLAIR, J. D., 1954: Erosion in the San Gabriel mountains in California (Trans. Amer. Geophys. Union 35: 264-268).

SIVORI, E. & F. W. WENT, 1944: Photoperiodicity of *Baeria chrysostoma* (Bot. Gazette 105: 321-329).

SKOSS, J., 1953: The structure and chemistry of the plant cuticle in relation to environmental factors and to permeability (Thesis, Univ. of Calif. at Los Angeles).

SORIANO, A., 1953*a*: Observaciones experimentales sobre el efecto del viento en las plantas (Rev. Invest. Agric. 7: 253-275).

SORIANO, A., 1953*b*: Estudios sobre germinación, I (Rev. Invest. Agric. 7: 315-340).

STOUT, M., 1946: Relation of temperature to reproduction in sugar beets (Jour. Agric. Research 72(2): 49-68).

STRONG, J., 1939: A new radiation pyrometer (Jour. Opt. Soc. Am. 29: 520-530).

TAMIYA, H., E. HASE, K. SHIBATA, A. MITUYA, T. IWAMURA, T. NIHEI & T. SASA, 1953: Kinetics of growth of *Chlorella,* with special reference to its dependence on quantity of available light and on temperature *in* Algal Culture, p. 204-232 (Carnegie Inst. Wash. Publ. 600).

THIMANN, K. V. & W. D. BONNER, JR., 1948: The action of triiodobenzoic acid on growth (Plant Physiol. 23: 158-161).

THOMAS, M. D., 1933: Precise automatic apparatus for continuous determination of carbon dioxide in air (Industrial Engineering Chem. Anal. Ed. 5: 193).

THOMAS, M. D., R. H. HENDRICKS, T. R. COLLIER & G. R. HILL, 1943: The utilization of sulphate and sulphur dioxide for the sulphur nutrition of alfalfa (Plant Physiol. 18: 345-370).

THOMAS, M. D. & G. R. HILL, 1937: The continuous measurement of photosynthesis, respiration, and transpiration of alfalfa and wheat growing under field conditions (Plant Physiol. 12: 285-307).

THOMPSON, H. C., 1939: Vegetable crops (McGraw-Hill).

THORNTHWAITE, C. W., 1952: Temperature relations to time of maturity of vegetable crops (Seabrook, N.J.: Johns Hopkins Univ. Lab. Climatology).

TSCHESNOKOV, V. & K. BAZYRINA, 1930: Die Ableitung der Assimilate aus dem Blatt (Planta 11: 473-484).

ULRICH, A., 1952: The influence of temperature and light factors on the growth and development of sugar beets in controlled climatic environments (Agron. Jour. 44: 66-73).

ULRICH, A., 1955: Influence of night temperature and nitrogen on the growth, sucrose accumulation and leaf minerals of sugar beet plants (Plant Physiol. 30: 250-257).

VEEN, R. VAN DER, 1950: A small greenhouse with artificial lighting for studying plant growth under reproducible conditions (Philips Techn. Review 12: 1-5).

VERKERK, K., 1955: Temperature, light and the tomato (Meded. Landbouwhogeschool Wageningen 55: 176-224).

VIGLIERCHIO, D., 1955: Plant wound hormones (Thesis, California Inst. Technology).
VYVYAN, M. C. & G. F. TROWELL, 1953: A method of growing trees with their roots in a nutrient mist (Annual Rept. East Malling Research Station, p. 95-98).
WALTER, H., 1949-1951: Grundlagen der Pflanzenverbreitung, 525 p. (Stuttgart: Ulmer).
WAREING, P. F., 1954: Growth studies in woody species, VI. The locus of photoperiodic perception in relation to dormancy (Physiol. Plant. 7: 261-277).
WASSINK, E. C., 1948: De lichtfactor in de photosynthese en zijn relatie tot andere milieufactoren (Photosynthesis as a function of light in relation to other environmental factors) (Meded. Directeur Tuinbouw 11: 503-513).
WENT, F. W., 1938: Transplantation experiments with peas (Amer. Jour. Bot. 25: 44-55).
WENT, F. W., 1943*a*: Plant growth under controlled conditions, I. The air-conditioned greenhouses at the California Institute of Technology (Amer. Jour. Bot. 30: 157-163).
WENT, F. W., 1943*b*: Effect of the root system on tomato stem growth (Plant Physiol. 18: 51-65).
WENT, F. W., 1943*c*: Transplantation experiments in peas, III (Bot. Gazette 104: 460-474).
WENT, F. W., 1944*a*: Plant growth under controlled conditions, II. Thermoperiodicity in growth and fruiting of the tomato (Amer. Jour. Bot. 31: 135-140).
WENT, F. W., 1944*b*: Plant growth under controlled conditions, III. Correlation between various physiological processes and growth in the tomato plant (Amer. Jour. Bot. 31: 597-618).
WENT, F. W., 1944*c*: Morphological observations on the tomato plant (Bull. Torrey Bot. Club 71: 77-92).
WENT, F. W., 1945: Plant growth under controlled conditions, V. The relation between age, light, variety and thermoperiodicity of tomatoes (Amer. Jour. Bot. 32: 469-479).
WENT, F. W., 1946: Effects of temporary shading on vegetables (Proceedings Amer. Soc. Hort. Sci. 48: 374-380).
WENT, F. W., 1948*a*: Thermoperiodicity *in* A. E. MURNEEK, R. O. WHYTE *et al.*: Vernalization and Photoperiodism, p. 145-157 (Lotsya I: Waltham, Mass.: Chronica Botanica Co.).
WENT, F. W., 1948*b*: Ecology of desert plants, I. Observations on germination in the Joshua Tree National Monument, California (Ecology 29: 242-253).
WENT, F. W., 1949: Ecology of desert plants, II. The effect of rain and temperature on germination and growth (Ecology 30: 1-13).
WENT, F. W., 1950: The Earhart Plant Research Laboratory (Chron. Bot. 12: 91-108).
WENT, F. W., 1953*a*: The effect of temperature on plant growth (Ann. Review Plant Physiol. 4: 347-362).
WENT, F. W., 1953*b*: Gene action in relation to growth and development, I. Phenotypic variability (Proc. Nat. Acad. Sci. 39: 839-848).
WENT, F. W., 1955*a*: Air pollution (Scientific American 192: 63-72).
WENT, F. W., 1955*b*: Fog, mist, dew and other sources of water (Yearbook of Agriculture 1955: 103-109).
WENT, F. W., 1955*c*: Physiological variability in connection with experimental procedures and reproducibility (*in* Handbuch der Pflanzenphysiologie I).
WENT, F. W. & D. M. BONNER, 1943: Growth factors controlling tomato stem growth in darkness (Arch. Biochemistry 1: 439-452).
WENT, F. W. & L. COSPER, 1945: Plant growth under controlled conditions, VI. Comparison between field and air-conditioned greenhouse culture of tomatoes (Amer. Jour. Bot. 32: 643-654).
WENT, F. W. & R. ENGELSBERG, 1946: Plant growth under controlled conditions, VII. Sucrose content of the tomato plant (Arch. Biochemistry 9: 187-200).

WENT, F. W. & H. HULL, 1949: The effect of temperature upon translocation of carbohydrates in the tomato plant (Plant Physiol. 24: 505-526).

WENT, F. W., G. JUHRÈN & M. C. JUHRÈN, 1952: Fire and biotic factors affecting germination (Ecology 33: 351-364).

WENT, F. W. & P. A. MUNZ, 1949: A long term test of seed longevity (El Aliso 2: 63-75).

WENT, F. W. & M. WESTERGAARD, 1949: Ecology of desert plants, III. Development of plants in the Death Valley National Monument, California (Ecology 30: 26-38).

WHITE, P. R., 1937: Survival of isolated tomato roots at suboptimal and supraoptimal temperatures (Plant Physiol. 12: 771-776).

WHYTE, R. O., 1946: Crop production and environment, 372 p. (London: Faber and Faber).

WITHROW, A. P. & R. B. WITHROW, 1947: Plant growth with artificial sources of radiant energy (Plant Physiol. 22: 494-513).

WITHROW, R. B. & A. P. WITHROW, 1956: Generation, control, and measurement of visible and near-visible radiant energy *in* A. HOLLAENDER, ed., Radiation Biology III, p. 125-258 (McGraw-Hill).

AUTHOR INDEX

SUBJECT INDEX

PLATES

—Plate I—

— PLATE II —

PLATE I.— East façade of the Earhart Plant Research Laboratory showing aluminum roof and air intake for the gas room on top of roof.

PLATE II.— View of greenhouse roof. Conical sprays distribute roof spray water evenly over glass panes between aluminum rafters. On roof at right exhaust outlets of light panel ventilation fans.

— Plate III —

— PLATE IV —

PLATE III.— View of the greenhouse showing glass roof with water running over it, and slotted steel-channel floor. On the left can be seen a truck demonstrating the use of four expanded metal shelves.

PLATE IV.— View of the atrium at 16:00, moving time. Doors at the left open out from greenhouses, at the right from artificial light rooms. Laboratory staff can be seen moving trucks to their night conditions. The trucks shown at the left are awaiting being put in the light and darkrooms in the proper order.

PLATE V.— View of artificial light room with sliding doors and partitions between every two light panels. Purple and Green compartments lighted, Red compartment dark and door towards dark compartment open. Truck at left with *Saintpaulia* at four different levels of light intensity. Plants at 1000 and 750 ft.-c. flowering abundantly, at 400-500 ft.-c. not flowering. At right truck with strawberries.

PLATE VI.—View of the Control Room. In right background desk of superintendent, in right foreground desk of assistant superintendent, with some of the files of space-cards. At right against wall multiple temperature recorder. At left control panels. In foreground controls for air-conditioners with valves and indicators for re-circulation of air (lower-most dials), light-master control (top) and temperature regulation indicators (in between). The indicators are pressure gauges, showing the air pressure in the circuits of the pneumatic controls. In background the time-clock panel and between this and the air-conditioning panel the motor indicator panel, with indicator lights showing whether the various motors are in operation or not. The time-clock panel has indicator lights below each time-clock and below the elapsed-time counters. By connecting the time-clock plugs with the light panel plugs (on bench) the light panels are operated according to a pre-set schedule.

PLATE VII.— Two different types of trucks, one of fixed height and at left one with adjustable shelves. Also shown are different types of containers (cups, squares, crocks, and 3-gallon cans). In front the cup racks in two positions.

— Plate VI —

— Plate VII —

PLATE VIII.— Tomato plants grown with their roots in nutrient fog. Fog injected at left hand side, but entering root chamber at right. Notice at left the two tubes for nutrient solution and compressed air. Roots with numerous rootlets and covered with root hairs. Plastic window in front is kept covered at all times to prevent light from reaching roots.

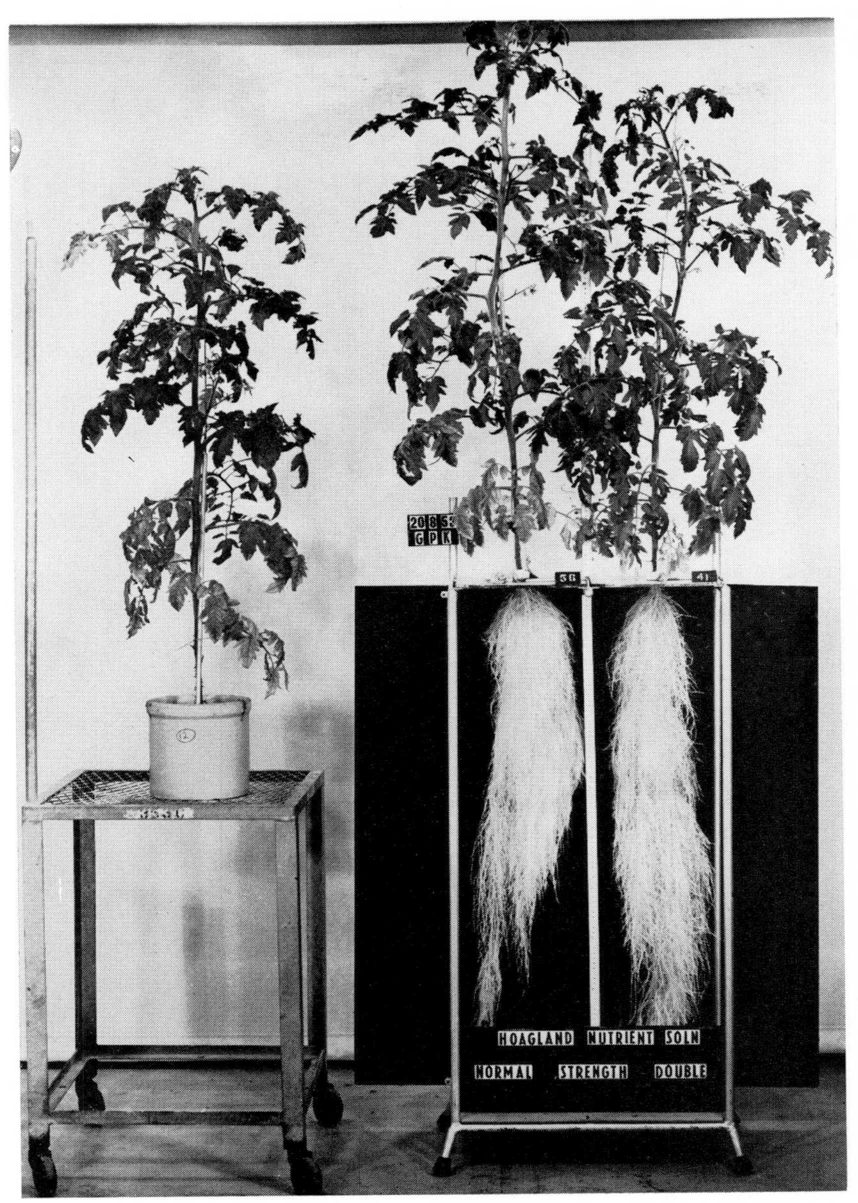

PLATE IX.—Tomato plants of same age grown in vermiculite (*left*) or with their roots in nutrient fog (two plants *on right*), using either single or double strength nutrient solution.

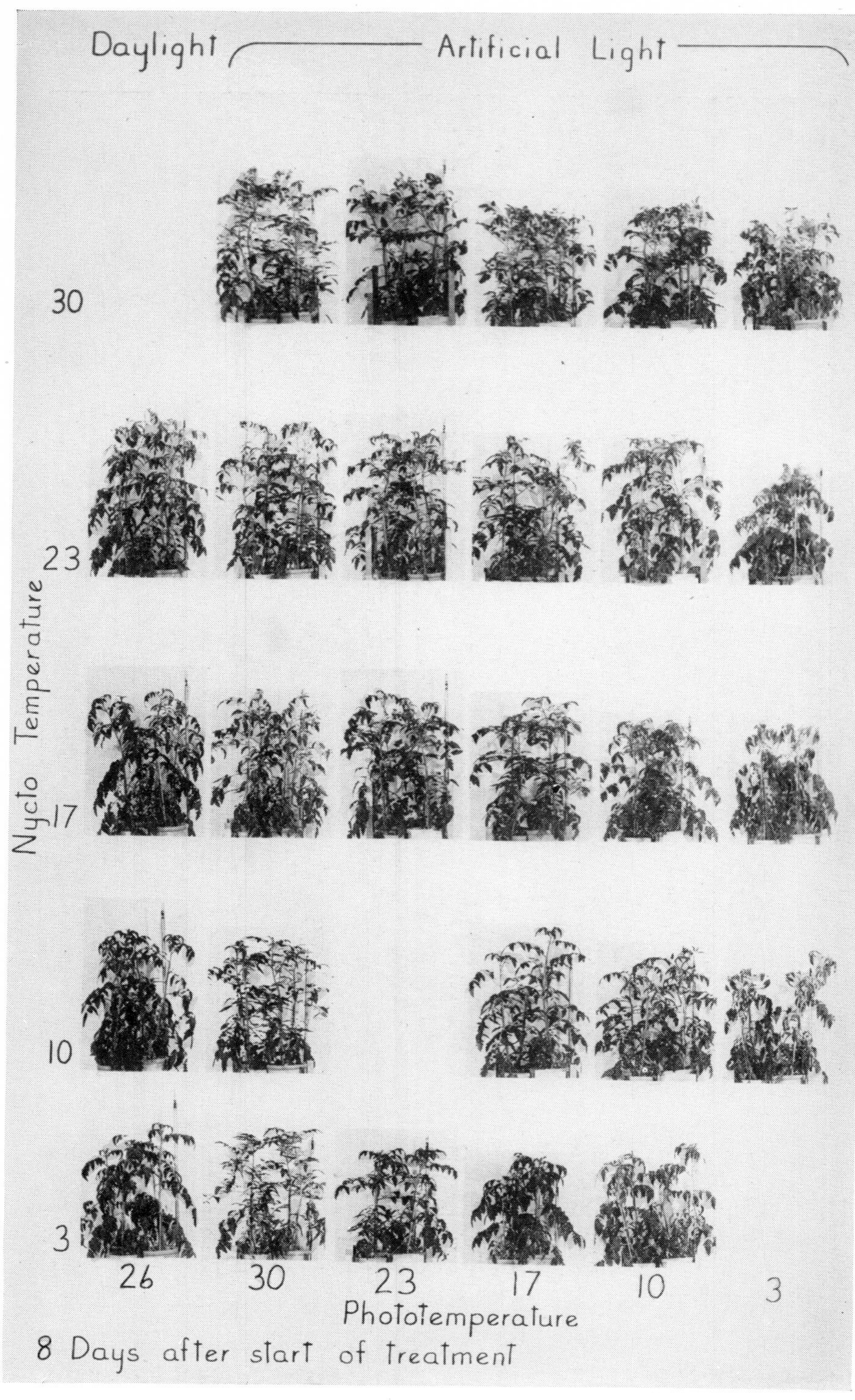

Daylight
Artificial Light
30
23
Nycto Temperature
17
10
3
26
30
23
17
10
3
Phototemperature
8 Days after start of treatment

— PLATE X*a* —

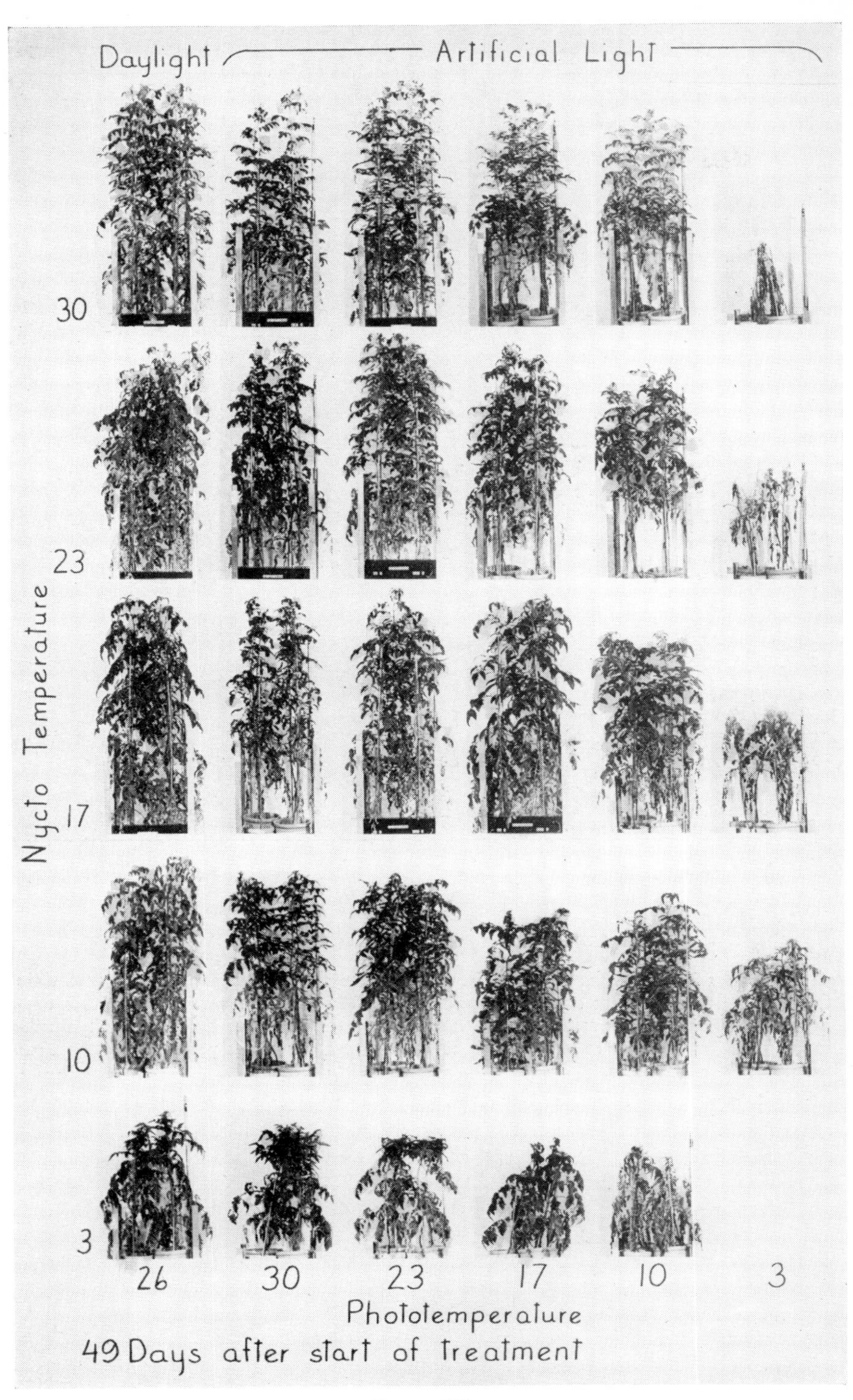
Daylight
Artificial Light
30
23
17
10
3
Nycto Temperature
26
30
23
17
10
3
Phototemperature
49 Days after start of treatment

— PLATE X*b* —

— Plate XI —

Plates X*a* & X*b*.— Photo-record pictures on same scale of tomato experiment 8 days (*a*) or 49 days (*b*) after start of temperature treatment. Plants receiving either daylight (*left hand row*), or artificial light at 1000 ft.-c. (*five rows to right*), night temperature decreasing from top to bottom. Observe how the four plants per treatment on each truck have the same size.

Plate XI.— Series of tomato plants grown in 8-hour photoperiod in artificial light at constant temperatures; from left to right at 10°, 14°, 17°, 20°, 23°, 26°, 30°C.

PLATE XII.— Kennebec potatoes grown in the coolest (*left*) to the warmest greenhouse (*right*) in natural daylight. Good potatoes formed at lowest temperature, no potatoes at highest temperature.

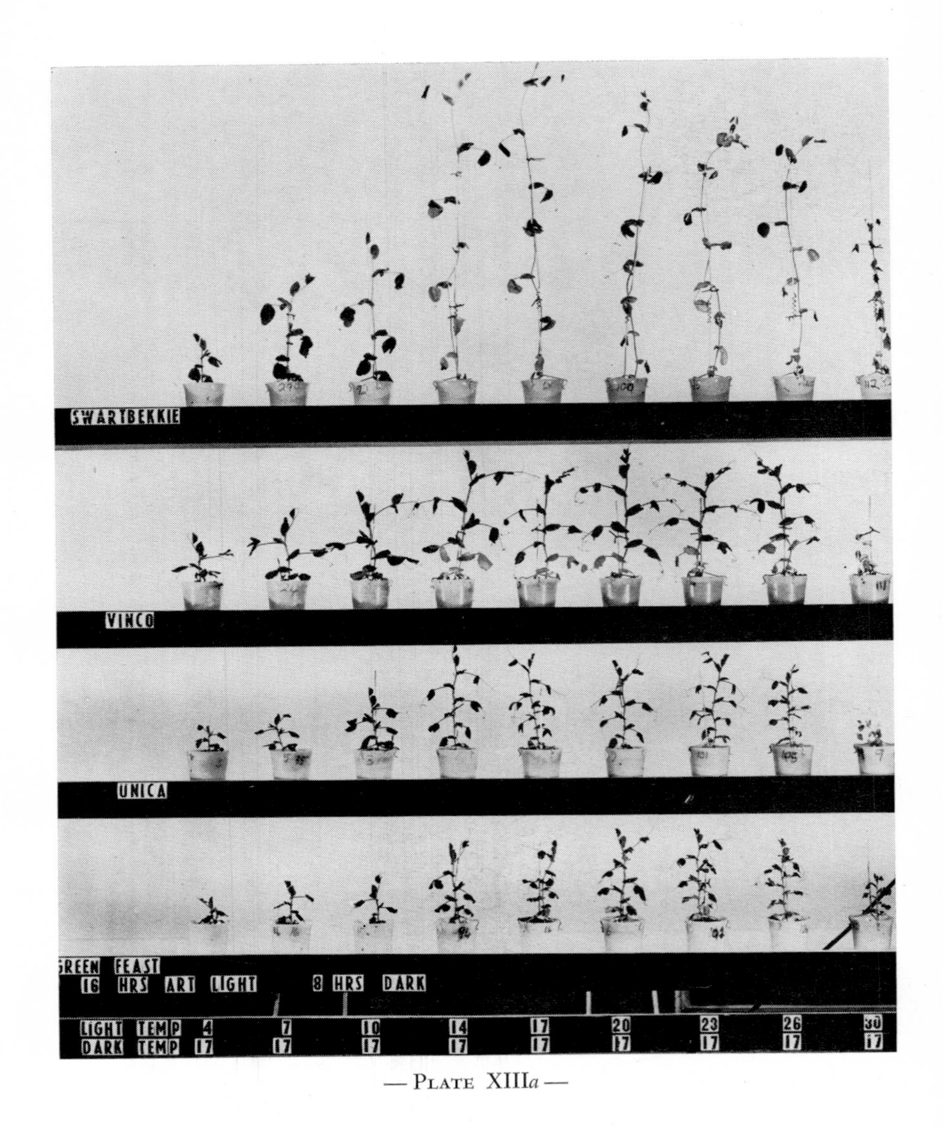

— PLATE XIII*a* —

PLATES XIII*a* & XIII*b*.— Development of four pea varieties over a range of phototemperatures from 4°-30° (*a*) and different nyctotemperatures between 4°-30° (*b*) all at 16-hour photoperiod at 1000 ft.-c. Experiment of N. GROBBELAAR.

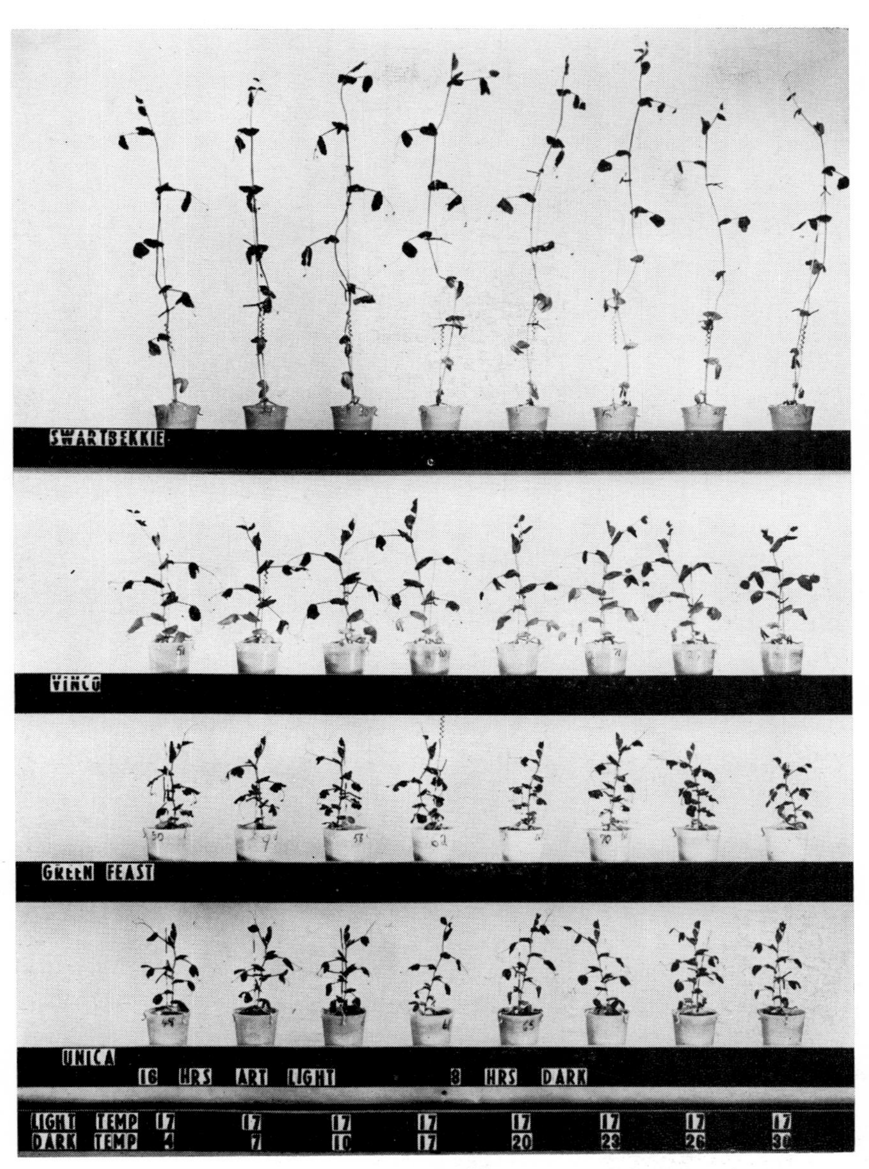
SWARTBEKKIE
VINCO
GREEN FEAST
UNICA
16 HRS ART LIGHT
8 HRS DARK
LIGHT TEMP 17 17 17 17 17 17 17 17
DARK TEMP 4 7 10 17 20 23 26 30

— Plate XIII*b* —

— Plate XIV —

— Plate XV —

Plate XIV.— Effects of light intensity (1000 ft.-c. upper row, 500 ft.-c. lower row) on flax plants grown in a 16-hour photoperiod (*right side*) and an 8-hour photoperiod (*left side*) at different photo- and nyctotemperatures. Experiment of C. R. Millikan.

Plate XV.— *Vicia faba* plants grown at different temperatures in the Purple (*left*), Blue, Yellow, Orange and Red (*right*) greenhouses. Experiment of L. Evans.

PLATE XVI.— *Saintpaulia* grown with different nyctotemperatures (increasing from 14° to 26° from bottom to top) and different phototemperatures (increasing from 14° to 26° from left to right). All plants receiving an 8-hour photoperiod at 700 ft.-c. Plants in PLATE V belong to same experiment.

PLATE XVII.— Effect of nyctotemperature (*upper row*), phototemperature (*middle row*) and photoperiod (*lower row*) on the growth, leaf development and pigmentation of *Coleus*. Lower row: all plants grown in constant 17° temperature, the photoperiods increasing from left to right: 8, 12, 16, 20 and 24 hours. At short photoperiods very little anthocyanin is formed in the leaves and this increases with increasing photoperiod up to continuous light. Optimum anthocyanin at 17° nyctotemperature and 17°-20°C phototemperature. Optimum growth at 23° phototemperature and 17° nyctotemperature with a 16-hour photoperiod. Experiment of R. SACHS.

PLATE XVIII.— 15 Month old coffee trees grown during first 9 months at 30° phototemperature and 23° nyctotemperature and afterwards in the photo- and nyctotemperatures shown in lower two rows.

PLATE XIX.— 27 Month old Bourbon coffee trees, fruit being picked from tree on the right. The trees are the same but 1 year older than those shown in PLATE XVIII. From left to right, plants were grown in 17°-12°, 20°-14°, 30°-23°, 26°-20° and 23°-17° (day and night temperature) in natural daylight. Observe supernumerary orthotropic shoots in middle plant.

PLATE XX.— Uniformity of pea plants. From a bag of Vinco pea seeds a random sample of 65 seeds was taken. The heaviest 16 were sown in white cups on the bottom row, and the intermediate weight peas are shown on the two middle shelves.

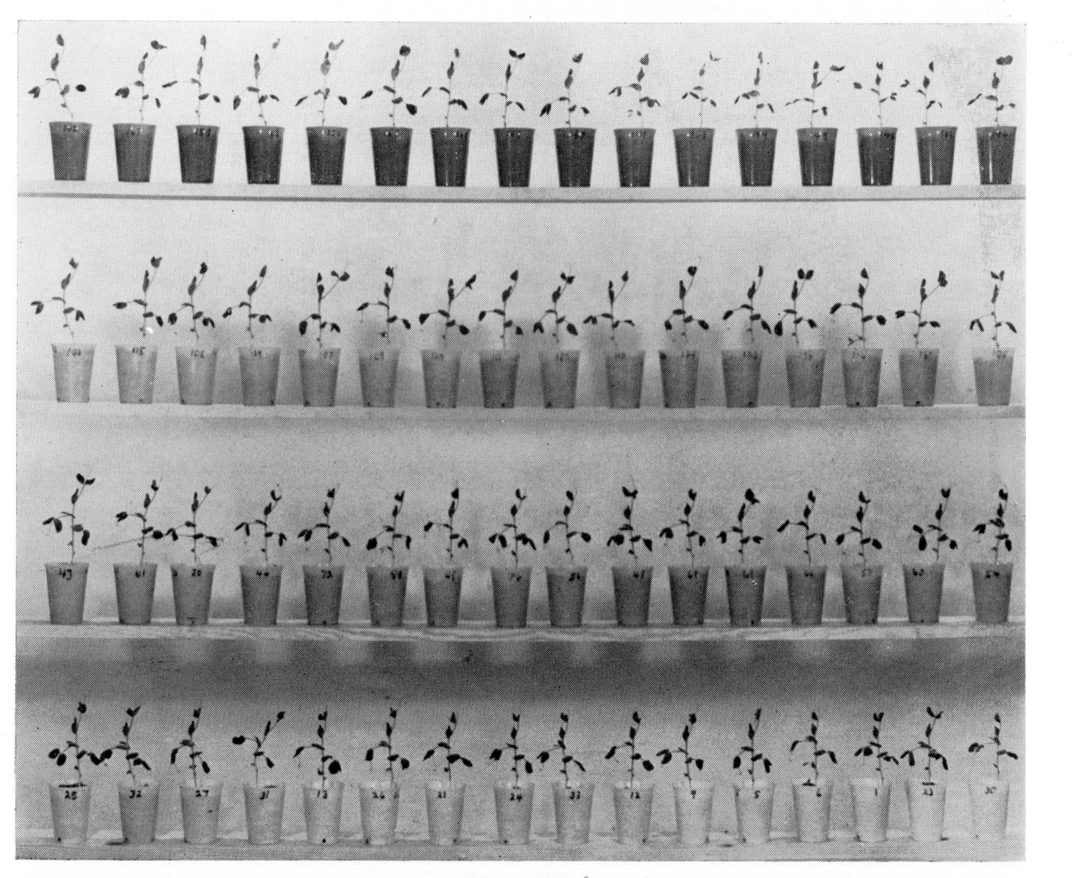

— PLATE XX —

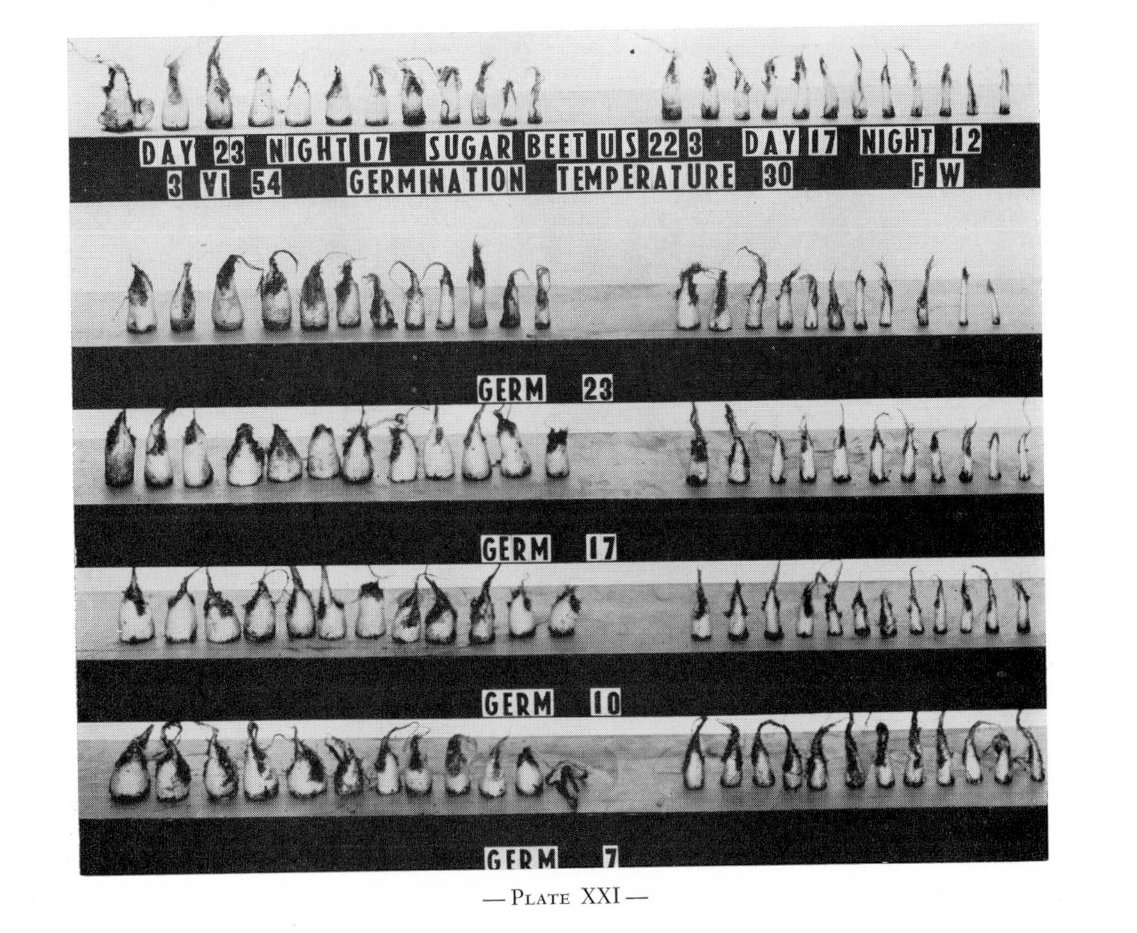
DAY 23 NIGHT 17 SUGAR BEET US 22 3 DAY 17 NIGHT 12
3 VI 54 GERMINATION TEMPERATURE 30 F W
GERM 23
GERM 17
GERM 10
GERM 7

— Plate XXI —

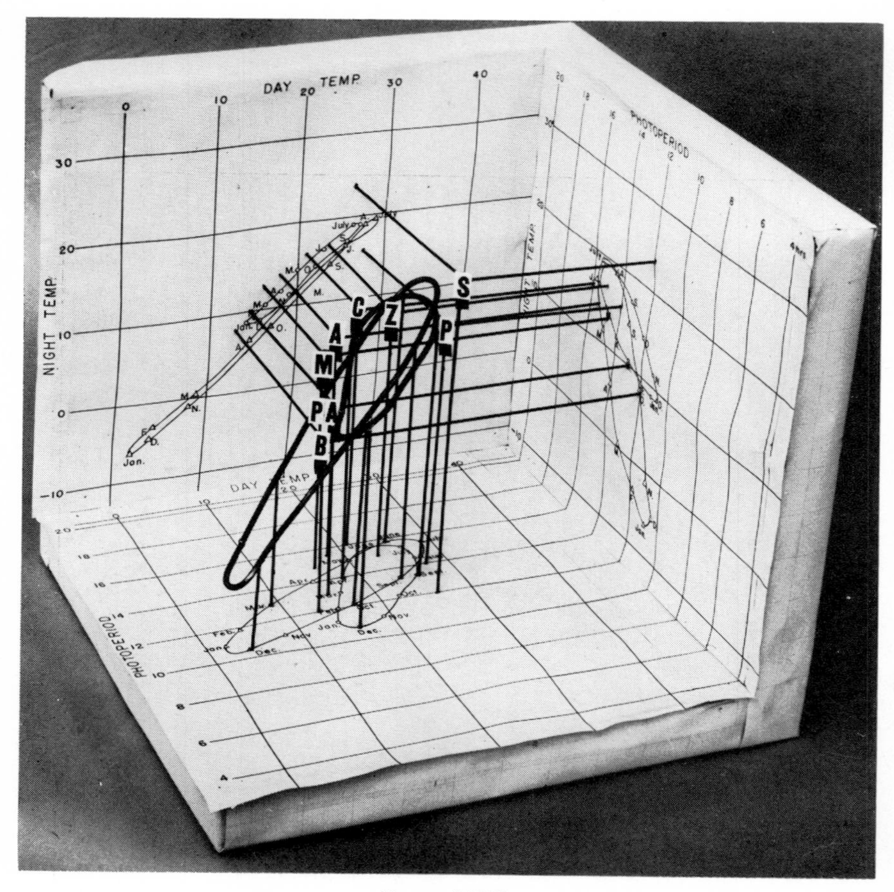

— Plate XXII —

Plate XXI.— Roots of sugar beets grown in cups in vermiculite, 12 plants/group. The beets on the left hand side grew in the intermediate greenhouse temperature; the beets to the right grew in the colder greenhouse. All beets in the upper row were germinated at 30° and in the next rows at 23°, 17°, 10° and 7°C. Notice the uniformity of the beets germinated at 17° and grown in the intermediate temperature greenhouse compared with the variability in the cold greenhouse. When germinated at 7° the plants in the cold greenhouse are more uniform than those growing in the intermediate temperature greenhouse.

Plate XXII.— Relationships between phototemperature, nyctotemperature and photoperiod and the optimal growth of a number of garden flowers. Letters denoting the optimal growing conditions for several garden plants (for explanation *see* Figure 39). Climates of Pasadena (upper ellipse) and of Denver (lower ellipse) shown in heavy black line.

PLATE XXIII.— Two groups of corn plants of same age, both grown in cool greenhouse. Plants at left sprayed daily with water, at right sprayed daily with indoleacetic acid solution. Experiment of A. W. GALSTON and K. ZARUDNAYA.

ELECTRIC HYGROMETER INDICATOR
CAT. 4-4900
MICROAMPERES
CK 100
OFF
HUMID
TEMP
ADJUST 100

— Plate XXIV —

— Plate XXV —

Plate XXIV.— Apparatus for simultaneously measuring photosynthesis and transpiration, mounted on truck with adjustable top. Top of tomato plant enclosed in plastic container through which an air stream passes (tube leading off towards right). Inside container is also small fan (*at right*) and Aminco humidity sensing element (*at left*) with leads to meter below. Experiment of W. C. Ashby.

Plate XXV.— Root behavior of corn plants growing under same conditions as those of Plate XXIII. Plant at right sprayed daily with water, plant at left with triiodobenzoic acid, 10 mg./1. Experiment of A. W. Galston and K. Zarudnaya.

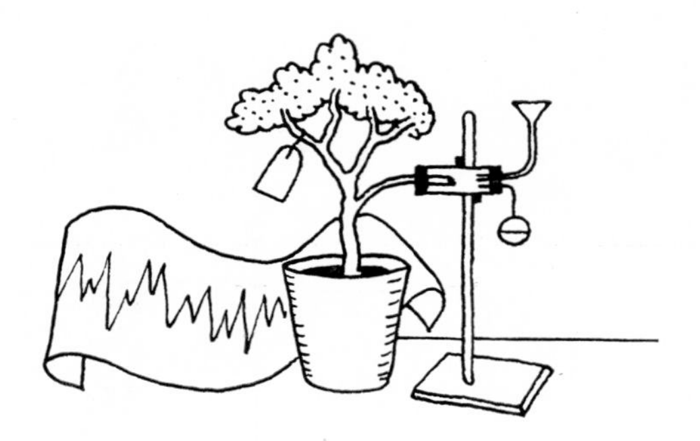